Basic Mathematics Electronic Engineers

OWAIN DAVIES

TUTORIAL GUIDES IN ELECTRONIC ENGINEERING

Series editors
Professor G.G. Bloodworth, *University of York*
Professor A.P. Dorey, *University of Lancaster*
Professor J.K. Fidler, *University of York*

This series is aimed at first- and second-year undergraduate courses. Each text is complete in itself, although linked with others in the series. Where possible, the trend towards a 'systems' approach is acknowledged, but classical fundamental areas of study have not been excluded. Worked examples feature prominently and indicate, where appropriate, a number of approaches to the same problem.

   A format providing marginal notes has been adopted to allow the authors to include ideas and material to support the main text. These notes include references to standard mainstream texts and commentary on the applicability of solution methods, aimed particularly at covering points normally found difficult. Graded problems are provided at the end of each chapter, with answers at the end of the book.

Basic Mathematics for Electronic Engineers

Models and applications

J.E. Szymanski
Department of Electronics
University of York

VNR
International

Van Nostrand Reinhold (International)

First published in 1989 by
Van Nostrand Reinhold (International) Co. Ltd
11 New Fetter Lane, London EC4P 4EE

Typeset in Times $9\frac{1}{2}$/11pt by
Colset Private Limited, Singapore
Printed and bound in Great Britain by
Richard Clay Ltd, Bungay, Suffolk

ISBN 0 278 00068 1

British Library Cataloguing in Publication Data

Szymanski, J.E.
    Basic mathematics for electronic engineers.
    1. Electronic engineering. Mathematics
    I. Title
    621.381'01'51

    ISBN 0-278-00068-1

Contents

Preface

A wide range of textbooks is already available dealing with the assorted mathematical methods required by scientists and engineers. It is obviously necessary to justify the production of this particular book and establish its relationship to some of these other texts.

Mathematics itself comprises a huge field of knowledge. In practice it is necessary to subdivide it into advanced courses on applied mathematics, pure mathematics, computational mathematics and statistics to stand a chance of fitting even a reasonable subsection of it into a normal course of learning. The sheer volume of this material is reflected in the corresponding textbooks by the fact that it is usually necessary to produce a series of associated texts on individual topics, or one very large text which attempts to cover most of the requisite mathematical methods rather more compactly, but still in adequate detail. Each approach suffers from problems: the former tends to impose an artificial set of boundaries on the subject and leaves the student in the position of needing to purchase a large number of books; the latter leads to difficulties with regard to trying to present an overview of most of the necessary mathematics in sufficient detail in a text which cannot be allowed to grow to unreasonable proportions. Despite these difficulties, good texts exist, in both of these formats, which contain many practice examples in a range of mathematical methods and which cover most of the mathematical information needed by a student of any applied science. However, nearly all such texts suffer from one critical shortcoming: they illustrate the mathematical methods in only an abstract sense or within a very narrow range of standard applications.

This book offers a fresh approach to first-year electronic engineering students in particular by presenting the mathematical tools that they will need to use together with a wide range of examples of electronic applications in which these tools are commonly used. Each individual engineering application may require different mathematical tools, but each tool can be used for a range of diverse applications – many branches of science require similar mathematical tools. To first appearances, in most subjects, the use of particular mathematical methods is governed by the specific requirements and constraints of the problem being investigated. An applied biologist finds that it is necessary to use multivariable partial differential equations to describe the sounds created by the drum-like membrane on a dragonfly's wing. A theoretical chemist finds that immense electron–electron interaction matrices are required to describe the detailed bonding between atoms within a molecule. A physicist can use vector and tensor analysis to model the quantitative features of interacting particles moving at relativistic speeds. In a more industrial environment, the fields of process control and simulation, job scheduling, resource flow management, product fault diagnosis and even risk assessment have become dependent on a considerable armoury of specialized mathematical methods. More relevantly to this book, the electronic engineer finds that without the mathematical theory of Fourier analysis the fields of spectral analysis, communication theory, signal processing and image processing will remain closed books. Without the Laplace transform, eigenvalue analysis, and the theory of three-dimensional rotations it is impossible to make meaningful headway in the fields of control system theory, industrial process control, robotics and aircraft flight simulation. Electric circuit analysis needs the techniques of coupled differential equations and network theory; solid-state electronics relies on the mathematics of diffusion, classifies the structures of solids with group theory and describes the sub-microscopic properties of charge carriers in devices in a statistical fashion; electromagnetic theory and Maxwell's equations require the tools of multivariable vector analysis; software techniques, program testing, and the growing subjects of expert systems and artificial intelligence require knowledge of numerical analysis, finite mathematics, network theory and even n-dimensional coordinate geometry!

The above topics give some indication of the diversity of the applications employing mathematical methods but in this introductory text each will receive no more than a passing mention: it will be possible only to indicate some of the power of the mathematical and theoretical techniques available to the electronic engineer. Nevertheless, the aim is to provide a generalized set of basic techniques which will be sufficient for most practical needs and which will prepare the reader to use advanced or specialized texts as necessary. A good working knowledge of the available electronic equipment and components, physical insight and the abilities to design, construct and test practical systems are traits that must be developed during any form of engineering training. However, it is also necessary to keep in sight the fact that only by being able to use mathematical methods in order to simulate and interpret the behaviour of individual components/devices and composite systems is it possible to develop those systems. Without some prior knowledge of the behaviour of a system under a range of operational conditions, which are often impractical to create in the laboratory, it is impossible to design a reliable end product.

It is common for many courses in electronic engineering to contain a large amount of mathematical material in the first year. Often it may seem that there is little point to learning all of this material because some of it seems to be 'mathematics for the sake of mathematics'. This is not so: the material is covered early in the course deliberately, in order to provide support for the remaining courses. It is usually impractical to cover these mathematical topics in detail within the more applied courses because the same mathematical tools are used again and again in different applied contexts. This book aims to teach the mathematical principles in a concise fashion, and also to illustrate a variety of applications within electronic engineering where the most basic mathematical tools are employed in a constructive fashion. In each chapter of Part One of this book there are examples of the modelling, simulation and interpretation of practical electrical and electronic systems using a range of basic mathematical techniques. A more detailed summary of the principles and methods broadly associated with each chapter is contained in the five chapters of Part Two, which together form a *Mathematical Toolkit*. This toolkit is intended to provide a reference guide to the basic set of mathematical information needed by any electronic engineer. Few detailed derivatives are given and the emphasis is strongly on applicable methods.

Because of the wide spread in mathematical backgrounds of students entering engineering courses it is left to each individual reader to tailor their usage of the material to their own specific needs. Those who are already familiar with some of the applications aspects may need to concentrate more on the contents of the Mathematical Toolkit, while those students with more mathematical experience will find that they can spend more time on the applied aspects of the methods, using the Toolkit mainly for reference. A further advantage of this approach is that each chapter of this book can be read almost independently of those which have preceded it: the order in which the material is covered can be adjusted to an individual's needs or desires, or the requirements of a specific course. For those who require more mathematical detail than can be compressed into a book of this size this text can be used in conjunction with a book giving a more general approach to the mathematical methods, such as Jeffrey (1989), while those who lack confidence in their abilities to actually perform some of the mathematical manipulations can refer to any text providing practice examples in mathematical methods for scientists or engineers.

One advantage of this approach is that the mathematical tools are shown in action, proving that they are indeed good for something after all! One potential disadvantage is that certain tools or techniques might wrongly appear to be associated only with the specific application which is used as an example: bear in mind that most mathematical methods are as multi-functional as the oscilloscope and must, as an ideal, be understood independently of the restrictions of any particular single application.

This book is based on material developed for a series of mathematical workshops given by the author to first-year students in electronic engineering at the University of York. These 1–2 hour sessions are held weekly in a laboratory environment and take the form of a 'theoretical laboratory': the kit involves calculator, pen and paper and, as in their practical laboratory, the students are given a carefully prepared application example to work through from beginning to end via a number of guided stages. These sessions have proved very successful: they provide excellent support and motivation for the associated mathematical lecture course; they establish early connections with, and give some support to, concurrent applied courses; they are held in an environment in which the student can work naturally; and, most importantly of all, they have introduced a degree of enjoyment into a subject area that is not easy to present as relevant in the early stages of a course in electronic engineering. If this book enables some others to explore this large common ground between electronic engineering and mathematics I will be most delighted.

In conclusion, I wish to thank Professors Tony Dorey, Greville Bloodworth and Kel Fidler for their editorial support, and Dominic Recaldin (VNR) for his continuing interest, throughout the growth of this text. The students at York who have acted as guinea pigs for this approach also deserve an honourable mention for their motivation and hard work. Finally, I must acknowledge the support of my wife, Irene, who has been forced to play second fiddle to a wordprocessor, if only temporarily.

Models and Applications within Electronic Engineering

PART ONE

Basic Mathematical Methods   1

☐ To motivate the use of mathematical tools in an engineering context.
☐ To illustrate the power of some of the most basic mathematical techniques.
☐ To provide examples of the applications of the differential calculus within electronic engineering.
☐ To emphasize particularly a number of practical uses of differentiation, integration and series expansions.

Introduction

This chapter offers a review of some of the concepts and methods most basic to the application of mathematics within the context of electronic engineering. As with future chapters, the information which can be considered to comprise the more abstract reference material is gathered into a separate chapter in Part Two, leaving the main chapter in Part One to concentrate on some appropriate illustrative applications and situations in which the mathematical methods may prove useful.

This introductory chapter will concentrate on reviewing some of the basic mathematical ideas of the calculus which will be used heavily later in this text. The associated mathematical details are contained in Chapter T1 of the 'Mathematical Toolkit'. Also, at the beginning of Part Two there is a useful list of common symbols and mathematical notation used throughout this book.

Applications of differentiation

The mathematical operation of differentiation has a number of obvious applications in electronic engineering. When any response of a system is plotted as a function of some input parameter, or perhaps time, differentiation of the function leads to a measure of the rate with which that system variable responds to the input. This is important because many components of electronic systems react not to a constant dc input, but to changes in the input. For example, the time-dependent voltage response of a perfect inductor of inductance L is related to the current, I_L, through it by

$$V_L = L \frac{dI_L}{dt} \tag{1.1}$$

while, similarly, the current through a capacitor satisfies

$$I_C = C \frac{dV_C}{dt} \tag{1.2}$$

Practical measurements may be available in a continuous form, as a trace on a chart recorder or oscilloscope, or in a discrete form, from a series of measurements or as the output of a digitized system. In the latter case it is necessary to either use a numerical differentiation algorithm on the raw data or fit an analytic function to the data before using the techniques of ordinary differentiation.

The time dependence of the current in a series RL circuit with a constant voltage source E is found to be represented accurately by the function

$$I_L = \frac{E}{R}\left[1 - \exp\left[-\frac{Rt}{L}\right]\right] \tag{1.3}$$

What is the voltage across the inductor at any time?

Worked Application Example 1.1

In fact, this relationship gives the response of the inductor to being connected to a constant voltage source E at time $t=0$. Example 4.3 derives this result from first principles.

Since E is a constant: it is being assumed that R and L also do not change with time.

Notice that this result is dimensionally sensible: cancellation has occurred of several terms, leaving only V_L and E, which both have units of volts. Ensuring that the dimensions of both sides of an equation are consistent is a very useful way of tracking down errors in reasoning when working with a series of equations.

Solution Equation (1.1) shows that it is necessary only to differentiate this expression and multiply by the value of the inductance. Upon differentiation, the first term of Equation (1.3) vanishes, leading to

$$\frac{dI_L}{dt} = \frac{E}{R}\left[\frac{R}{L}\exp\left[-\frac{Rt}{L}\right]\right]$$

so that

$$V_L = E\exp\left[-\frac{Rt}{L}\right] \tag{1.4}$$

The above example involves a particularly simple form of recorded experimental data. This is due solely to the fact that the circuit elements are assumed to be perfect and invariant to the conditions of their operation. As realistic effects are introduced into a system model the results tend to look less like the familiar exponential law given above.

Worked Application Example 1.2

Such a drift might be due to resistive heating in the resistor or a time dependence of the internal resistance of the voltage source: here implicitly assumed to be represented in the overall resistance R. The parameter α is known as the resistor **temperature coefficient** and determines the overall importance of the drift effects relative to the main circuit parameters Equation (1.5) is derived in Example 4.5.

A simple RC circuit with a constant capacitor and constant voltage source contains a resistor which suffers from a gradual drift in its resistance value which follows the linear law $R = R_0(1 + \alpha t)$. It can be shown that the time dependence of the voltage measured across the capacitor will be given by the expression

$$V_C - V_0 = [E - V_0][1 - [1 + \alpha t]^{-1/\alpha C R_0}] \tag{1.5}$$

where V_0 is the voltage across the capacitor at time $t = 0$. What is the expected current through the capacitor as a function of time?

Differentiation of the second r.h.s. term produces a multiplying factor of $-1/\alpha C R_0$ and reduces its power by unity But the term $(1 + \alpha t)$ is itself a function of t: the **chain rule** demands that another factor of α appear due to this.

Solution In this case the voltage relationship is less familiar, but the functional form is less complicated than it looks. Equation (1.2) indicates that it will be necessary to differentiate this to obtain the current and, as before, the first term on the r.h.s. will vanish. The second term is a power law in t, and is no more difficult to differentiate than x^n. We obtain

$$I_C = \left[\frac{E - V_0}{R_0}\right]\left[1 + \alpha t\right]^{-1/\alpha C R_0 - 1} \tag{1.6}$$

The uses of differential techniques are not confined to circuit applications: while circuits and any dynamic system are a rich source of examples, differentiation is needed to evaluate the speed and acceleration of a particle or object from a knowledge of its position as a function of time, for example.

Worked Application Example 1.3

The path of a charged particle moving in the XY plane under the influence of its initial momentum and an exponentially decaying magnetic field is given by the parametric equations

$$x = 1 + 2t + \cos(10t)\exp(-0.3t)$$
$$y = 3 + 3t + \sin(10t)\exp(-0.3t)$$

In what direction is the particle moving at time $t = \pi/4$?

Solution Differentiating each equation with respect to t gives

$$\frac{dx}{dt} = 2 - 0.3\cos(10t)\exp(-0.3t) - 10\sin(10t)\exp(-0.3t)$$

and

$$\frac{dy}{dt} = 3 - 0.3\sin(10t)\exp(-0.3t) + 10\cos(10t)\exp(-0.3t)$$

so that

$$\frac{dy}{dx} = \frac{3 - 0.3\sin(10t)\exp(-0.3t) + 10\cos(10t)\exp(-0.3t)}{2 - 0.3\cos(10t)\exp(-0.3t) - 10\sin(10t)\exp(-0.3t)}$$

and

$$\left.\frac{dy}{dx}\right|_{t=1} = \frac{-3.095}{6.217} \approx -0.5$$

Therefore at $t = 1$ the particle is moving instantaneously along a line with gradient -0.5. Examination of the sign of dx/dt shows that it is moving from left to right along this line.

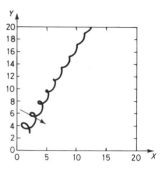

The trajectory of the charged particle as a function of time: the overall direction of motion is broadly from bottom left to top right.

In general electromagnetic applications the force, F, on a particle of charge q is related to the electric field intensity, E, and the associated **potential**, V, by

$$F = qE = -q\cdot\frac{dV}{dx} \tag{1.7}$$

if the system is considered to be restricted to one-dimensional motion in the X-direction.

At a semiconductor pn junction the detailed structure of the barrier space-charge in the region of the interface is critical in determining the properties of the electrostatic **barrier potential** at the junction and hence the overall macroscopic properties of the device under a range of applied potentials. If the potential in the region of an interface can be represented approximately by the expression

$$V = \frac{A}{1 + \exp(-kx)} \tag{1.8}$$

where A and k are material-dependent parameters, what is the force exerted upon an electron in the region of the interface? What is the maximum force that an electron can experience?

Worked Application Example 1.4

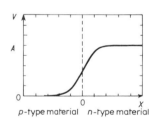

The form of the model potential barrier for a semiconductor pn junction. The barrier can be viewed as arising from diffusion of electrons from the n-type material into the p-type and a corresponding diffusion of holes in the reverse direction.

Solution The X-axis is orthogonal to the plane of the interface and the assumption is being made that we are interested only in electron motion in this direction. To obtain the force from Equation (1.7) it is necessary to differentiate Equation (1.8). This can be achieved using the ratio rule of differentiation, leading to

$$\frac{dV}{dx} = \frac{Ak\exp(-kx)}{[1 + \exp(-kx)]^2}$$

so that the force on an electron of charge $-e$ is given by

$$F = -(-e)\frac{dV}{dx} = \frac{eAk\exp(-kx)}{[1 + \exp(-kx)]^2} \tag{1.9}$$

To find the value of x for which this force is a maximum it is necessary to differentiate again to find a turning point. This is quite possible, by using the ratio formula, but first Equation (1.9) can be put in a somewhat simpler form:

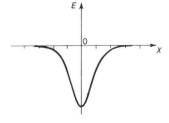

The form of the electric field for the specified potential. The field

5

drives a drift of electrons from the p-type material into the n-type and a corresponding hole drift from the n-type into the p-type. Under equilibrium conditions (no applied external potential) the total drift movement of charge carriers compensates the total movement due to diffusive effects.

$$F = \frac{eAk \exp(-kx)}{[1 + 2\exp(-kx) + \exp(-2kx)]} = \frac{eAk}{[\exp(kx) + 2 + \exp(-kx)]}$$
$$= \frac{eAk}{2[1 + \cosh(kx)]} \tag{1.10}$$

Differentiation of this gives

$$\frac{dF}{dx} = -\frac{eAk^2\sinh(kx)}{2[1 + \cosh(kx)]^2} \tag{1.11}$$

which is zero only when $x = 0$. To check that this turning point is a maximum it is sufficient either to differentiate Equation (1.11) again and establish that d^2F/dx^2 is negative, or to examine a sketch of the magnitude of the force: there is only one turning point and it is clearly a maximum.

Exercise 1.1   Differentiate Equation (1.11) to obtain the value of d^2F/dx^2 when $x = 0$.

As a final illustration of differentiation as a practical analytical tool it is well worth considering an example which, while simple in its structure, is basic to a range of electrical applications and yields a surprisingly powerful result.

Worked Application Example 1.5

Consider a circuit which consists of a constant voltage source and a load resistor, R_1. In the previous circuit examples no account has been taken of the internal resistance, R_s, of the voltage source: only single-loop circuits have been considered and it has been possible to consider any such source resistive contribution as being part of an overall circuit resistance. However, if interest is centred upon the power characteristics of the circuit the situation changes. The power dissipated in a resistance R when a constant current I is passed through it is given by I^2R, and in a practical circuit the total power dissipated will be composed of two components: one arising from the internal resistance of the source and one from the resistance of the load.

Power dissipated in the voltage source will be lost as waste heat: thus it is usually desirable to maximize the power transfer from the source to the load resistance, which is presumably where the power is intended to go! For a given set of **source characteristics**, E and R_s, what value of load resistance will produce the maximum power transfer?

These source characteristics are pre-specified and assumed constant: they are merely the individual properties of whatever particular battery or voltage source is being used. The functional form of the power dissipated in the load resistance.

Solution   Within such a circuit an application of KVL and Ohm's law leads to

$$E = IR_s + IR_1$$

where the first term of the r.h.s. is the voltage dropped across the internal resistance of the source and the second term is that dropped across the load resistance. This means that the current through both elements is

$$I = \frac{E}{R_s + R_1}$$

so that the power dissipated in the load resistance alone is given by

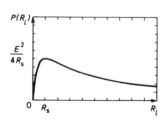

The functional form of the power dissipated in the load resistance.

$$P(R_1) = I^2R_1 = \frac{E^2 R_1}{[R_s + R_1]^2} \tag{1.12}$$

This has been written as $P(R_1)$ to emphasize that this expression defines the functional dependence of the power dissipation on R_1: for a given source R_s and E are just numbers. To find the size of load that will maximize the power dissipated in it differentiate Equation (1.12):

$$\frac{dP}{dR_l} = \frac{E^2[[R_s + R_l]^2 - 2R_l[R_s + R_l]]}{[R_s + R_l]^4}$$

$$= \frac{E^2[R_s - R_l]}{[R_s + R_l]^3} \qquad (1.13)$$

This expression is zero only when $R_l = R_s$, giving the condition for a turning point of the function. Further differentiation, or arguing from practical considerations, shows that this turning point must be a maximum.

Therefore, in a purely resistive circuit, the greatest amount of power will be dissipated in the load resistance when it is equal to the value of the internal resistance of the source. This result is known as the **maximum power transfer theorem**.

This theorem can be extended to ac sources and more general impedance matching in RLC circuits. These circumstances are considered in Chapter 5.

Differentiate Equation (1.13) in full and confirm analytically that the turning point in the above example corresponds to a maximum.

Exercise 1.2

Polynomial series approximations

Most mathematical methods are illustrated with ideal analytic examples. It is important to bear in mind that there is no set of experimental circumstances under which it will be possible to say that an output has the functional form $\sin x$ or $\exp(-kt)$: at best a series of experimental measurements of the properties of the output will be available. These measurements might be made in sequence as some system parameter is varied: in which case they can be plotted against that parameter and the graphs can be compared with the predictions of a range of analytical models. Often graphs with clear **operational regions** (possibly linear, or linear if plotted on log-linear or log-log paper) will be obtained, and it will be possible to **extrapolate** the properties of the system into a region where experimental data are not available.

Alternatively, a series of simultaneous measurements can be made of a range of properties of a system: in which case it is possible to know a great deal about one particular instantaneous state of a system, but it is harder to see how that information can be utilized to make predictions about the future behaviour of the system.

The appropriate mathematical tool for the latter case is **Taylor's theorem**. In its full form this expresses a given function $f(x)$ as an **infinite power series expansion** of the form:

$$f(x) = f(x_0) + (x - x_0)\frac{df}{dx}(x_0) + \frac{(x - x_0)^2}{2!}\frac{d^2f}{dx^2}(x_0) + \dots$$

$$+ \frac{(x - x_0)^r}{r!}\frac{d^rf}{dx^r}(x_0) + \dots \qquad (1.14)$$

around some specific point, $x = x_0$, at which information is available about the derivatives of the function. Even when only a limited amount of derivative information is known this has a number of useful practical applications as a technique for building up a finite power series approximation to the true functional form of some system property. It can be used as a technique of extrapolation, prediction or approximation, for example.

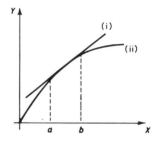

When a small-signal analysis of a device is performed a linear equivalent circuit is designed that represents an approximation to the nonlinear properties of that device in some small-signal range of validity, around some nominal operating conditions (a process sometimes known as piecewise linearization: see Sparkes, 1987). In effect, the full system is being approximated by a first-order (linear) Taylor expansion. The diagram illustrates a linear approximation (i) to a nonlinear system characteristic (ii) which will be an acceptably valid representation over some operational range [a,b]. The precise size of this range will be determined by pre-specified operational design criteria.

In a series RLC circuit the circuit elements are measured to have the values of $R = 2$ ohms, $C = 1/9$ farads and $L = 1$ henrys. Simultaneous measurements are made of

the capacitor voltage V_C: 2.270 volts
the circuit current I: 0.0834 amperes
and the inductor voltage V_L: -0.437 volts

one second after closing a switch which connected a voltage source and closed the circuit. By performing a second-order Taylor series expansion around $t = 1$ second predict the voltage dropped across the capacitor at $t = 1.5$ seconds.

Solution   Three simultaneous measurements are available to specify the state of the circuit at $t = 1$. It may happen in practice that a number of such measurements may not be independent: one of the experimental values could have been calculated from a knowledge of the others. In this particular case the circuit element relationships

$$I = C\frac{dV_C}{dt} \quad \text{and} \quad V_L = L\frac{dI}{dt} = LC\frac{d^2V_C}{dt^2} \tag{1.15}$$

show that the three measurements are not directly dependent on each other: they are connected only by derivative relationships and cannot be expressed as a **linear combination** of other measurements.

Using the known values of L and C, and the measured values of I and V_L, Equation (1.15) means that at $t = 1$

$$V_C = 2.270 \qquad \frac{dV_C}{dt} = 0.751 \quad \text{and} \quad \frac{d^2V_C}{dt^2} = -3.933$$

These values can be used within the general Taylor expansion of Equation (1.14), truncated after the quadratic term, to give

$$V_C(t) \approx 2.270 + 0.751(t - 1) - 1.967(t - 1)^2 \tag{1.16}$$

This represents an approximate polynomial fit to the time dependence of the capacitor voltage about one second after the voltage source was connected. It is the

For example, the measured voltage drops across a number of elements in a source-free loop form a set of dependent measurements: since KVL states that the measured voltages must sum to zero it is necessary only to measure all but one of the element voltages.

The possibility of experimental data being dependent (also known as **redundant** data) can lead to the impression that enough information is known about a system when, in fact, more independent measurements are required. Likewise, in theoretical circuit analysis, it is necessary when applying KVL and KCL in a multi-loop circuit to ensure that the resultant set of loop equations form an independent set: a careful choice of paths around the circuit is required to be certain that one large loop is not just composed of two or three small loops that have already been considered. Chapter 3 examines the idea of linearly dependent equations in more detail.

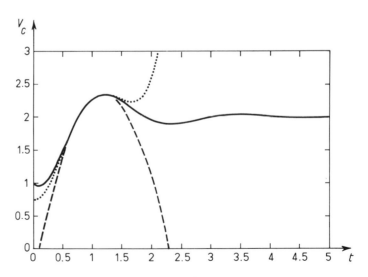

Fig. 1.1   A comparison of a particular time response of the voltage measured across a capacitor with quadratic (-------) and quartic (· · · · · ·) Taylor series expansions around $t = 1$.

simplest polynomial function which reproduces exactly the experimental measurements at $t = 1$. The predicted value of the capacitor voltage at $t = 1.5$ is $V_C(1.5) \approx 2.154$ volts.

Exercise 1.3

Differentiate Equation (1.16) twice and use the circuit relationships of Equation (1.15) to show that the quadratic function does reproduce the experimental measurements at $t = 1$.

Fig. 1.1 shows the actual value of the capacitor voltage over a period of time (solid curve): the correct value at $t = 1.5$ is in fact $V_C(1.5) = 2.242$ volts, so that the value predicted by the quadratic function (dashed curve) is about 4% too low. If more independent measurements of the behaviour of the circuit at $t = 1$ are available, it is possible to build a higher-order approximation which in general will represent the behaviour of the circuit accurately over a longer period of time.

Exercise 1.4

If, in addition to the information given in the previous example, it is known that the voltage across the inductor at $t = 1$ satisfies

$$\left. \frac{dV_L}{dt} \right|_{t=1} = 0.123 \quad \text{and} \quad \left. \frac{d^2V_L}{dt^2} \right|_{t=1} = 3.685$$

construct a fourth-order Taylor expansion and show that the predicted value of $V_C(1.5)$ from this expansion is within 1% of the correct value of 2.242 volts. The dotted curve of Fig. 1.1 illustrates how this fourth-order polynomial fit matches on to the true curve in the region of $t = 1$.

Another useful application of Taylor expansions arises when it is desired to obtain a simple polynomial approximation to an analytic function of interest. For example, in most high-level computer languages pre-defined functions are available which can be used to calculate sin, cos, exp, and most of the other common mathematical functions. In microprocessor applications these functions are not usually available, however, and it is often necessary to design a section of program code to calculate some specific desired function. It is important to keep the length and complexity of this code to a minimum: the speed of execution of the program is often the limiting factor in the design of a system, and the evaluation of a complicated function is considerably more time consuming than the basic machine operation of addition.

Most computers and calculators use algorithms based on a polynomial expansion carried out around the origin: a **Maclaurin expansion**. The common infinite series expansions given in Chapter T1 are effectively Maclaurin expansions carried out to an arbitrary number of terms. Recall that the arguments of trigonometric functions in these expansions must be measured in radians.

A microprocessor flight control system is usually connected to a number of transducers via analogue-to-digital converters and has to perform a series of calculations on the measured data to establish the current state of motion of the aircraft. Perhaps the most important single pieces of data in any avionic application are a knowledge of whether the aircraft is going up or down, and how quickly!

If two independent anemometers provide measurements of the vertical and horizontal components of the speed of the aircraft, say v and h respectively, the overall speed of the aircraft is given by $[v^2 + h^2]^{1/2}$, while the angle of ascent/descent, θ, is given by

$$\theta = \tan^{-1} \left[\frac{v}{h} \right]$$

Worked Application Example 1.7

An anemometer is a particular type of transducer which returns an electrical signal that depends on the speed of fluid (in this case air) past the anemometer.

Since $\tan^{-1}x$ is an **odd function** with respect to the origin it is guaranteed that the even derivatives will vanish.

There are easier ways to obtain this particular expansion: it is possible to expand $1/(1+x^2)$ by the binomial expansion:

$$\frac{1}{1+x^2} = 1 - x^2 + x^4 - x^6 + \dots + (-1)^r x^{2r} + \dots$$

and integrate the whole series term by term (valid for most 'well behaved' series)

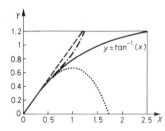

The accuracy of the fits of the first (- - - - -) third (. . . . . .) and fifth (. _ . . . _.) order polynomial approximations to the function $\tan^{-1}x$ (solid line).

Exercise 1.5

In general, when high-order derivatives of products of functions are required it is possible to use **Leibnitz's theorem** of repeated differentiation (see Chapter T1).

For most aircraft it would be hoped that this angle will never be too large in magnitude! Obtain a fifth-order polynomial expansion for $\tan^{-1}x$ which can be used by the control system.

Solution The procedure is usually tedious and repetitive, but can be used to high order if required:

$$f(x) = \tan^{-1}x \qquad \Rightarrow f(0) = 0$$
$$\frac{df}{dx} = \frac{1}{1+x^2} \qquad \Rightarrow \left.\frac{df}{dx}\right|_{x=0} = 1$$
$$\frac{d^2f}{dx^2} = \frac{-2x}{[1+x^2]^2} \qquad \Rightarrow \left.\frac{d^2f}{dx^2}\right|_{x=0} = 0$$
$$\frac{d^3f}{dx^3} = \frac{-2+6x^2}{[1+x^2]^3} \qquad \Rightarrow \left.\frac{d^3f}{dx^3}\right|_{x=0} = -2$$
$$\frac{d^4f}{dx^4} = \frac{24x(1-x^2)}{[1+x^2]^4} \qquad \Rightarrow \left.\frac{d^4f}{dx^4}\right|_{x=0} = 0$$
$$\text{and} \quad \frac{d^5f}{dx^5} = \frac{24 - 48x^2 + 120x^4}{[1+x^2]^5} \qquad \Rightarrow \left.\frac{d^5f}{dx^5}\right|_{x=0} = 24$$

so that insertion of these values into a Maclaurin expansion leads to

$$\tan^{-1}x \approx 0 + 1x + \frac{0}{2!}x^2 + \frac{-2}{3!}x^3 + \frac{0}{4!}x^4 + \frac{24}{5!}x^5$$

$$\Rightarrow \tan^{-1}x \approx x - \frac{x^3}{3} + \frac{x^5}{5}$$

is a fifth-order expansion for $\tan^{-1}x$.

One particular functional form that occurs very frequently in the analysis of the transient response (see Chapter 4) of a circuit or control system is the function $[\cos t][\exp(-t)]$: an exponentially decaying cosine response. Obtain a fifth-order Maclaurin approximation to this function.

Integration and its applications

An amazingly large number of dynamic systems are modelled around three basic properties of the system: its response to the current value of some input; its response to the rate of change of that input; and its response to the cumulative effect of the input. The first two properties are represented mathematically by the concepts of functional dependence and differentiation respectively: to evaluate the cumulative effect of some input/variable the appropriate tool is **integration**.

When a function is plotted with respect to some independent variable the integral of that function corresponds to an area under that curve if a pair of **limits** are specified. If no limits are specified a new function is obtained which reflects the **cumulative** properties of the initial function.

Many particular applications of integration can be found. Definite integrals arise with regard to the calculation of the total dissipation of power within a circuit as a function of time; for the evaluation of the total distance travelled by a charged particle as its moves through a region of variable field intensity; to evaluate the total work done by a variable force; or to sum the total charge associated with a charge distribution of variable charge density. Indefinite integrals are of use for calculating the time dependence of the voltage across a capacitor, given a knowledge of the time dependence of the current through it; or likewise the current through an inductor from a knowledge of the voltage dropped across it. Definite integrals are also of considerable use in the fields of Fourier analysis of the spectral structure of a signal and the Laplace transform approach to the dynamic properties of circuits and control systems.

The details of these topics are beyond this text, but Jeffrey (1989) contains a treatment of both methods.

The **instantaneous power**, $P(t)$, dissipated by the components in any branch of a circuit at any time t is defined by

Worked Application Example 1.8

$$P(t) = V(t) I(t) \qquad (1.17)$$

where $V(t)$ and $I(t)$ are functions which describe the time dependence of the voltage measured across the terminals of the branch and the current passing through it respectively. Hence, the total energy dissipated/generated by (or stored within) the elements in the branch over a period of time, $[t_0, t_1]$, is given by

$$E = \int_{t_0}^{t_1} V(t) I(t) \, dt \qquad (1.18)$$

If a variable load draws current from a constant 5 volts voltage source in such a fashion that the current drawn as a function of time is given by $I(t) = 2 + [\sin(3t)][\exp(-t)]$ amperes, calculate the energy dissipated by the load in the first second of operation of the circuit.

Solution   For this particular example the energy will be given by the definite integral

$$E = \int_{0}^{1} 5[2 + \sin(3t) \exp(-t)] \, dt \qquad (1.19)$$

The first term within the integrand is trivial: to take care of the remaining product term it is worth while looking at the more general indefinite integral

$$i(t) = \int \sin(at) \exp(bt) \, dt$$

where the notation $i(t)$ has been introduced as a shorthand notation for this integral. Integration by parts leads to

$$i(t) = \frac{\sin(at) \exp(bt)}{b} - \frac{a}{b} \int \cos(at) \exp(bt) \, dt$$

Setting $u = \sin(at)$ and $dv/dt = \exp(bt)$.

which involves a new integral which is every bit as difficult to evaluate as the original! However, it is possible to apply integration by parts again, but this time to the new integral:

$$i(t) = \frac{\sin(at) \exp(bt)}{b} - \frac{a}{b} \left[\frac{\cos(at) \exp(bt)}{b} + \frac{a}{b} \int \sin(at) \exp(bt) \, dt \right]$$

Now setting $u = \cos(at)$ and $dv/dt = \exp(bt)$.

But in this expression, the newest integral now has the form of the original $i(t)$ again: replacing it by $i(t)$ and gathering both of the $i(t)$ terms to the l.h.s. gives

$$i(t) \left[1 + \frac{a^2}{b^2} \right] = \frac{\sin(at) \exp(bt)}{b} - \frac{a \cos(at) \exp(bt)}{b^2}$$

$$\Rightarrow \qquad i(t) = \frac{[b \sin(at) - a \cos(at)] \exp(bt)}{a^2 + b^2} \qquad (1.20)$$

11

This entirely general result can be used to evaluate the specific integral of Equation (1.19):

$$\int_0^1 5[2 + \sin(3t) \exp(-t)] \, dt = \left[10t - 5 \exp(-t) \, \frac{\sin(3t) + 3\cos(3t)}{10} \right]_0^1$$

$$= (10 + 0.52) - (0 - 1.5) = 12.02 \text{ joules}$$

Such as circuit analysis and communication theory.

Many periodic (but non-sinusoidal) functions arise in circuit and communication applications: triangle waves, rectified sine waves, saw-tooth waves, and the ubiquitous square wave. If the signal of interest is non-periodic and of finite duration it is possible to employ the related theory of Fourier transforms.

Application areas where the mathematical theory of Fourier series is used are particularly rich in analytical integrals. The theory cannot be covered in detail here, but, in brief, the process of Fourier analysis takes a similar form to the polynomial expansions covered in the previous section, where functions or experimental data were represented by a polynomial series. In that case any function was built up as a linear combination of power terms, x^n. Fourier series are applied only to periodic functions, and the function of interest is built up instead from a linear combination of the sinusoidal functions $\sin(nx)$ and $\cos(nx)$ for all positive integral values of angular frequency, n. A series expansion in terms of these functions leads naturally to the idea of a frequency (or spectral) analysis of a signal: the numerical coefficients of the sinusoidal components $\sin(nx)$ and $\cos(nx)$ govern the amount of a signal of frequency $f = n/2\pi$ that is contained in the original, perhaps extremely complicated, periodic signal.

The appropriate weighting coefficients for the sinusoidal signals of a certain frequency are given by the **Fourier integrals** (see Jeffrey, 1989):

If the function has any other period it can be scaled to a period of 2π by an appropriate change of variable.

It is possible to work with Fourier series in a more elegant form using complex numbers.

$$\left.\begin{array}{ll} a_n = \dfrac{1}{\pi} \displaystyle\int_{-\pi}^{\pi} f(x) \cos(nx) \, dx & n = 0,1,2,3,\ldots \\[4mm] \text{and} \quad b_n = \dfrac{1}{\pi} \displaystyle\int_{-\pi}^{\pi} f(x) \sin(nx) \, dx & n = 1,2,3,\ldots \end{array}\right\} \qquad (1.21)$$

if $f(x)$ is a periodic function with period 2π. In terms of these numerical coefficients the Fourier series of a function is given by

$$f(x) = \frac{a_0}{2} + \sum_{n=1}^{\infty} a_n \cos(nx) + \sum_{n=1}^{\infty} b_n \sin(nx) \qquad (1.22)$$

Worked Application Example 1.9

Consider a half-rectified cosine wave of period 2π. It is required to build this function up as a series of trigonometric functions or to analyse the frequency structure of the rectified signal.

Solution It is necessary in theory to evaluate an infinite number of integrals of the form

The limits have been changed here due to the fact that the integrand is zero in the intervals $[-\pi, -\pi/2]$ and $[\pi/2, \pi]$.

$$a_n = \frac{1}{\pi} \int_{-\pi/2}^{\pi/2} \cos(x) \cos(nx) \, dx \qquad \text{and} \qquad b_n = \frac{1}{\pi} \int_{-\pi/2}^{\pi/2} \cos(x) \sin(nx) \, dx$$

but this is not as impossible as it seems! Firstly, all of the integrals b_n vanish for all positive values of n: the integrand is of odd symmetry with respect to the range of integration. For the other integrals, a_0 is

$$a_0 = \frac{1}{\pi} \int_{-\pi/2}^{\pi/2} \cos(x) \, dx = \frac{1}{\pi} \left[\sin(x) \right]_{-\pi/2}^{\pi/2} = \frac{2}{\pi} = 0.637$$

while a_1 is given by

$$a_1 = \frac{1}{\pi} \int_{-\pi/2}^{\pi/2} \cos^2(x)\,\mathrm{d}x = \frac{1}{\pi} \int_{-\pi/2}^{\pi/2} 0.5[1 + \cos(2x)]\mathrm{d}x$$

$$= \frac{1}{2\pi}\left[x + \frac{\sin(2x)}{2}\right]_{-\pi/2}^{\pi/2} = 0.5$$

In a similar fashion it is possible to evaluate as many integrals as desired, but, in fact, it is possible to handle all of the remaining integrals with a single integration. Consider the general integral

$$a_n = \frac{1}{\pi} \int_{-\pi/2}^{\pi/2} \cos(x)\cos(nx)\,\mathrm{d}x = \frac{1}{2\pi} \int_{-\pi/2}^{\pi/2} [\cos[(n+1)x] + \cos[(n-1)]x]\,\mathrm{d}x$$

$$= \frac{1}{2\pi}\left[\frac{\sin[(n+1)x]}{n+1} + \frac{\sin[(n-1)x]}{n-1}\right]_{-\pi/2}^{\pi/2} \qquad n \neq 1$$

So that this expression can be evaluated easily for any particular value of $n > 1$:

$$a_2 = \frac{1}{\pi}\left[-\frac{1}{3} + \frac{1}{1}\right] = \frac{2}{3\pi} = 0.212$$

and $\quad a_3 = \frac{1}{\pi}\left[\frac{0}{4} + \frac{0}{2}\right] = 0$

Likewise, $a_4 = -0.0424$, $a_5 = 0$, $a_6 = 0.0182$, and so on, for as many terms as desired. It is possible to conclude that a spectral analysis of the half-rectified cosine wave will exhibit no components for the angular frequencies $n = 3$ and $n = 5$.

One particularly important technique of integration is the approach of partial fractions. Most of the engineering uses of this method arise within the theory of Laplace transforms (see Jeffrey, 1989), where they are extremely useful for examining the detailed properties of the time response of communication systems, circuits and control systems. The uses of the approach are not restricted to such problems however.

Of considerable importance within the field of electronic device fabrication are the techniques of **thin films**. Many devices involve narrow interface regions or surface layers where most of the 'interesting' electronic effects occur. The details of the macroscopic properties of the device will be strongly dependent on the detailed chemical structure/composition of the interface/layer and on the way in which it was produced in practice.

Vapour deposition methods involve exposing a semiconductor wafer to one or more substances in gaseous form inside a heated vacuum chamber from which unwanted contaminants (air and dust!) have been evacuated. The chemical nature of the surface layer and the time required to deposit a certain thickness onto the wafer will depend on the relative concentrations of the vapours introduced into the chamber. If three molecular gases A, B and C are to be combined together to form a number of overlayers of new molecules ABC it turns out that the time dependence of the deposition of the new molecules is governed by the equation

$$\frac{\mathrm{d}x}{\mathrm{d}t} = \alpha(a - x)(b - x)(c - x) \tag{1.23}$$

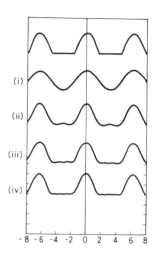

A half-rectified cosine wave of period 2π and its successive Fourier series approximations

(i) $0.318 + 0.5 \cos x$
(ii) $0.318 + 0.5 \cos x + 0.212 \cos(2x)$
(iii) $0.318 + 0.5 \cos x + 0.212 \cos(2x) - 0.0424 \cos(4x)$
(iv) $0.318 + 0.5 \cos x + 0.212 \cos(2x) - 0.0424 \cos(4x) + 0.0182 \cos(6x)$

Clearly, the correct functional form is approached rapidly.

Worked Application Example 1.10

See Sparkes (1987) and Sangwine (1987).

This equation is describing a trimolecular first-order reaction. Each term of the form $(a - x)$ models the fact that the rate of production of the new molecule will be proportional to the current amount of each component substance available: when $x(t)$ reaches a value near that of the smallest of a, b or c the reaction will slow down to a halt as all of that substance is used up. Similarly, if one

13

substance is missing at the start of the process the reaction will not get started at all!

where $x(t)$ is the number of deposited ABC molecules (initially zero); a, b and c are constants specifying the initial concentrations of the constituent gases A, B and C; and α is a constant which governs the natural rate of the chemical reaction of the gases.

Solve Equation (1.23) to obtain $x(t)$ for the cases when $a=1$, $b=2$ and $c=3$.

Solution For this case Equation (1.23) can be rewritten in the form

$$\alpha t = \int \frac{dx}{(1-x)(2-x)(3-x)} + K$$

for some arbitrary constant K. The integrand can be split up as a partial fraction expansion as

$$\frac{1}{(1-x)(2-x)(3-x)} = \frac{1}{2(1-x)} - \frac{1}{(2-x)} + \frac{1}{2(3-x)}$$

leading to

The extra negative sign arises from the fact that terms of the form $(a-x)^{-1}$ are being integrated: a minus arises because of the sign of the x within the bracket.

$$-\alpha t = \frac{\ln|1-x|}{2} - \ln|2-x| + \frac{\ln|3-x|}{2} + K$$

$$\Rightarrow -2\alpha t = \ln\left|\frac{(1-x)(3-x)}{(2-x)^2}\right| + K$$

If $x=0$ when $t=0$ the constant K can be fixed to be $\ln(4/3)$, so that taking the exponential of both sides gives

$$\frac{4(1-x)(3-x)}{3(2-x)^2} = \exp(-2\alpha t) \tag{1.24}$$

This implicit form of solution is sufficient for our current purposes: in this case it is possible to write x as an explicit function of t, as the exercise below indicates.

Exercise 1.6 By rearranging Equation (1.24) as a quadratic equation for x with time-dependent coefficients show that it is possible to obtain x as an explicit function of time:

$$x(t) = 2 - \frac{2\sqrt{[4 - 3\exp(-4\alpha t)]}}{4 - 3\exp(-2\alpha t)}$$

Exercise 1.7 Calculate $x(t)$ from Equation (1.23) for the case $a=1$, $b=1$, $c=2$.

Summary

The techniques of differentiation and integration reviewed in this chapter form the basis of the **differential and integral calculus** of a single variable. Only a limited number of applications have been considered, but it should be clear that the power of the techniques has led to their widespread use in the study of a range of practical systems. In integral applications the form of the integrand is critically dependent on the detailed nature of the problem under consideration and there are a large number of possible standard types that can occur. Chapter T1 reviews some of the commonest together with the basic rules of manipulation of integrals of products. Large tables of definite and indefinite integrals exist (such as Gradshteyn and Ryzhik, 1980), which it is often necessary to consult in practice.

It should be stressed that the idealized view taken here of usually being able to differentiate or integrate a function if a 'clever enough' approach is taken is totally false. It is easy to construct a simple analytic function for which no techniques exist to perform an analytic integration! In a real application the integrals will not always be accommodating, and it is often necessary to resort to numerical methods to perform data smoothing, curve fitting and numerical differentiation and integration. It is also possible to avoid some of the theoretical difficulties with such functions by preprocessing raw experimental data with a differentiating circuit or integrating circuit as appropriate. Such circuits can be constructed readily from resistors, capacitors and operational amplifiers and can be used for the analogue solution of many problems.

For example, a differentiating circuit could transform a position-dependent input into a velocity-dependent output. The practical difficulties with such circuits are that they are not ideal analogue representations of differentiation and integration at all frequencies and can introduce noise amplification and cumulative error drift. See Horrocks (1989) for details of the circuits.

As with many mathematical topics, the real power of the calculus is not clear from the restricted spread of examples considered in this chapter. When the methods are extended to higher orders of differentiation the important engineering field of differential equations arises (see Chapter 4 p. 55); the calculus can be extended to the case of more than one independent variable to produce multivariable calculus (Chapter 5 p. 91); and it can be combined with vector methods (see Chapter 2 p. 16) to produce the vector calculus, which, for example, enables the simple mathematical description of Maxwell's equations (see Carter, 1986).

Further exercises

1.8 Due to thermal drift effects the value of a resistor varies with time according to the law $R = R_0(1 + \alpha t)$ ohms, where t is measured in seconds and both R_0 and α are resistor-specific parameters. If the resistor is subjected to an alternating emf of the form $E \sin(\omega t)$ volts, find the rate of power dissipation within the resistor at any time.

1.9 Find the fifth order Maclaurin expansions of the functions (a) $\sin(t)\exp(-t)$ and (b) $\sin(3t)\exp(-t)$, which arise in the study of the *transient response* of circuits. Calculate the percentage error associated with each expansion at $t = 0.5$ s and $t = 1$ s and explain why the second expansion is a less accurate representation of that response function.

1.10 Application Example 4–10 shows that in a specific series RLC circuit the voltage dropped across the capacitor has the form $V_C(t) = (1 + 2t)\exp(-3t)$ as a function of time. If $C = 1/9$ F and $R = 2 \, \Omega$ find the total energy dissipated in the resistor from time $t = 0$ to $t = \infty$.

2 Vectors and Complex Numbers

- ☐ To illustrate the power of vector methods in practical engineering problems involving the interactions of three-dimensional objects.
- ☐ To introduce the algebra, techniques and basic applications of complex numbers and their geometrical representation in the Argand plane.
- ☐ To ilustrate the more general ideas of vectors and complex numbers as carriers of multivariable information.

Vectors: when, where and why

Vector methods are used in a number of practical applications: where geometrical insight into a system structure is required; where a number of variables of a system vary simultaneously; and where the quantities of interest have a directional nature in three-dimensional space.

In particular, electric and magnetic fields, flow patterns in any fluid medium, forces, velocity and acceleration, rotations and even areas are best represented in vector form. Also, vectors are usually the easiest way to handle problems involving the three-dimensional geometry of the crystalline structure of solids, or the positions and orientations of the segments of a robot arm. Such calculations can be carried out using other methods, but vectors offer a compact and understandable form of representing and processing the information. It is the ability of vectors to allow the manipulation of potentially very large amounts of information in a few lines of algebra that is their greatest strength. The following examples will illustrate the basic tools of vector algebra in a range of engineering applications. The necessary mathematical details are given in Chapter T2.

Fortunately, the advantages apply to man and machine: the shorthand notation provided by vectors is very suitable for human use, while the general idea of an array of variables is one which is incorporated into all high-level computer programming languages.

Worked Application Example 2.1

The atomic structure of crystalline silicon is tetrahedral in nature: each silicon atom possesses four symmetrically positioned, nearest-neighbour atoms. If the origin of an orthogonal Cartesian coordinate is placed on one particular silicon atom the coordinates of the four nearest atoms are:

$$A: \frac{l}{4}(1, 1, 1) \qquad B: \frac{l}{4}(-1, -1, 1)$$

$$C: \frac{l}{4}(-1, 1, -1) \qquad D: \frac{l}{4}(1, -1, -1)$$

where l is the **lattice constant** of silicon: $l = 5.43$ Å. There are six second-neighbour atoms at the coordinates:

$$E: \frac{l}{2}(1, 1, 0) \qquad F: \frac{l}{2}(1, 0, 1) \qquad G: \frac{l}{2}(0, 1, 1)$$

$$H: \frac{l}{2}(-1, -1, 0) \qquad I: \frac{l}{2}(-1, 0, -1) \qquad J: \frac{l}{2}(0, -1, -1)$$

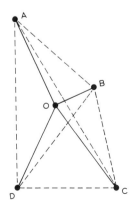

(i) Write down the vectors connecting atoms O to A; O to E; A to E; and C to A. What is the silicon nearest-neighbour bondlength? What is the the second-neighbour bondlength? What relationship is atom E to atom A; and atom C to atom A?

(ii) In calculations on crystal structure it is often more convenient to work with a non-orthogonal basis set of vectors which are chosen to provide a more appropriate, 'natural' description of the internal structure of the solid. Describe the vector positions of atoms D and E in terms of a set of basis vectors defined in terms of the positions of atoms A, B and C.

Solution

(i)

$$\overrightarrow{OA} = \frac{l}{4}\begin{bmatrix} 1 \\ 1 \\ 1 \end{bmatrix} \qquad \overrightarrow{OE} = \frac{l}{2}\begin{bmatrix} 1 \\ 1 \\ 0 \end{bmatrix}$$

$$\overrightarrow{AE} = \overrightarrow{OE} - \overrightarrow{OA} = \frac{l}{4}\begin{bmatrix} 1 \\ 1 \\ -1 \end{bmatrix} \qquad \overrightarrow{CA} = \overrightarrow{OA} - \overrightarrow{OC} = \frac{l}{2}\begin{bmatrix} 1 \\ 0 \\ 1 \end{bmatrix}$$

The nearest-neighbour bondlength is the length (modulus) of the vector from O to A: $l\sqrt{3}/4 \approx 2.35$ Å. Likewise, the modulus of the vector from O to E gives the second-neighbour bondlength as $l/\sqrt{2} \approx 3.84$ Å.

It is clear from the above vectors that atoms A and E are nearest-neighbour atoms, while C and A are a pair of second-neighbour atoms.

(ii) Consider now a new, non-orthogonal set of basis vectors defined in terms of the positions of three of the four nearest-neighbour atoms:

$$\mathbf{a} = \frac{l}{4}\begin{bmatrix} 1 \\ 1 \\ 1 \end{bmatrix} \qquad \mathbf{b} = \frac{l}{4}\begin{bmatrix} -1 \\ -1 \\ 1 \end{bmatrix} \qquad \mathbf{c} = \frac{l}{4}\begin{bmatrix} -1 \\ 1 \\ -1 \end{bmatrix}$$

then the vector from the origin to atom D is given by

$$\mathbf{d} = \overrightarrow{OD} = \frac{l}{4}\begin{bmatrix} 1 \\ -1 \\ -1 \end{bmatrix} = -\mathbf{a} - \mathbf{b} - \mathbf{c}$$

by inspection, and likewise

$$\mathbf{e} = \overrightarrow{OE} = \frac{l}{2}\begin{bmatrix} 1 \\ 1 \\ 0 \end{bmatrix} = \mathbf{a} - \mathbf{b}$$

These vectors are linearly independent (equivalently, they span three-dimensional space). Any vector position can be expressed in terms of a linear combination of the new basis vectors. To evaluate the appropriate coefficients in general will require the solution of a set of simultaneous linear equations (see Chapter 3). Here, the problem is simple enough to solve by inspection.

Using such a vector representation of the structure of a crystalline material it is possible to incorporate a natural model of the periodic nature of the crystal by introducing the idea of a **unit cell**. This can be used to build up a regular structure by translating the unit cell along vectors which are linear combinations of a set of **primitive lattice vectors**. It is possible to have unit cells containing several atoms, calculate the cell volume associated with each atom, and evaluate the effects of the detailed nature of the silicon–silicon covalent bond on the elastic constants of the crystal.

Other applications can arise where vectors may be a natural way to represent the geometry of simple structures, or of the forces imposed on such structures.

The **elastic constants** of a crystal are macroscopic measurements of the compressibility and flexibility of the material. Such effects are of interest in the investigation of strain in the region of an interface of two materials of different lattice constants. Strain effects distorts the atomic positions and change the local electronic properties of the interface, leading to unusual device performance.

Fig. 2.1 illustrates a simplified model of a segmented robot manipulator arm. Three rigid segments are connected by universal joints at points O, A and B, while a manipulator is attached at C. Transducers are incorporated into each joint which

Worked Application Example 2.2

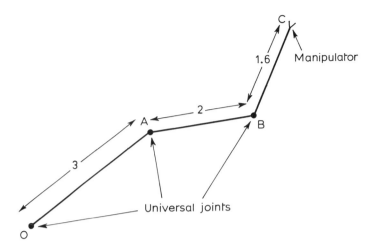

Fig. 2.1 A schematic representation of a robot arm. The directions of the individual sections of the arm are given in Example 2.2. The respective lengths of the jointed segments are 3, 2 and 1.6 units.

A universal joint is one which is capable of being rotated into any angular position, hence allowing full three-dimensional movement.

The direction cosine vectors are unit vectors which specify the direction of each segment: they are free vectors in the sense that a direction need not be associated with any particular point in space. The vectors need only be viewed as bound vectors when they represent quantities whose physical position is of some significance: such as forces exerting turning moments.

record the three-dimensional angular displacements of each segment relative to the previous segment and send this angular information back to a control microprocessor. The microprocessor is programmed to use the data to produce a direction cosine vector for each segment relative to a fixed Cartesian frame (with origin O) on the robot body. If the control module displays calculated direction cosine vectors

$$\begin{bmatrix} 0.41 \\ 0.41 \\ 0.81 \end{bmatrix} \quad \begin{bmatrix} 0.33 \\ -0.67 \\ 0.67 \end{bmatrix} \text{ and } \begin{bmatrix} 0.58 \\ 0.57 \\ -0.58 \end{bmatrix}$$

for the three segments OA, AB and BC respectively, what is the position of the manipulator hand?

Solution The microprocessor has been preprogrammed to take most of the work out of this calculation: since it has already supplied the measured direction of each segment of arm in direction cosine form, it is only necessary to include the information about the length of each segment (3, 2 and 1.6 respectively) to obtain values for the vector position of each joint in terms of its previous neighbour. For example,

$$\overrightarrow{OA} = 3 \begin{bmatrix} 0.41 \\ 0.41 \\ 0.81 \end{bmatrix} = \begin{bmatrix} 1.23 \\ 1.23 \\ 2.43 \end{bmatrix}$$

while

$$\overrightarrow{AB} = \begin{bmatrix} 0.66 \\ -1.34 \\ 1.34 \end{bmatrix} \text{ and } \overrightarrow{BC} = \begin{bmatrix} 0.93 \\ 0.91 \\ -0.93 \end{bmatrix}$$

The position of the manipulator is given by the position vector

$$\overrightarrow{OC} = \overrightarrow{OA} + \overrightarrow{AB} + \overrightarrow{BC} = \begin{bmatrix} 2.82 \\ 0.80 \\ 2.84 \end{bmatrix}$$

Once the geometry of the structure has been calculated it is possible to incorporate the effects of the forces and moments on the struts and joints of the arm. Similar calculations can be performed on quite complicated structures (with rigid or flexible struts), as found in civil engineering or avionics applications, and are often treated using matrix methods (see Chapter 3 p. 43) as well as vectors.

Broadly, vectors are useful for representing the directions and magnitudes of the forces on a structure: a matrix can be used to represent the way in which the forces interact with each other.

Evaluate the position of the hand if the directions of the segments are as above but the length of each segment is 2.5 units.

Exercise 2.1

Products of vectors

Practical problems involving basic geometry and forces are usually fairly easy to deal with, often involving little more than addition or subtraction of vectors. More generally, the description of more complicated geometries or force components will require the use of vector products: the angles between vector quantities are often important in such cases.

Two independent charge distributions a large distance away from a straight conducting wire produce uniform electric fields

Worked Application Example 2.3

$$\mathbf{E}_1 = \begin{bmatrix} 6 \\ -2 \\ 12 \end{bmatrix} \text{ and } \mathbf{E}_2 = \begin{bmatrix} 14 \\ 10 \\ 3 \end{bmatrix} \quad \text{V m}^{-1}$$

in the immediate vicinity of the wire. If the wire passes through the points A: $(1, -1, 3)$ and B: $(4, 5, 9)$, what component of the total electric field acts on the electrons in the wire?

Electric field obeys the **superposition law**: the total field can be constructed as the vector sum of the fields of individual charge distributions. See Compton (1986).

Solution We need to know the total field, $\mathbf{E}$, and the direction of the wire relative to the total field. The former task is straightforward, since

$$\mathbf{E} = \mathbf{E}_1 + \mathbf{E}_2 = \begin{bmatrix} 20 \\ 8 \\ 15 \end{bmatrix}$$

Regarding the wire, define vectors

$$\mathbf{a} = \begin{bmatrix} 1 \\ -1 \\ 3 \end{bmatrix} \text{ and } \mathbf{b} = \begin{bmatrix} 4 \\ 5 \\ 9 \end{bmatrix}$$

Then the vector equation of the line of the wire is

$$\mathbf{r} = \mathbf{a} + \lambda(\mathbf{b} - \mathbf{a})$$

$$= \begin{bmatrix} 1 \\ -1 \\ 3 \end{bmatrix} + \lambda \begin{bmatrix} 3 \\ 6 \\ 6 \end{bmatrix} \quad (2.1)$$

so that the direction of the wire is given by the unit vector $\hat{\mathbf{d}} = (\mathbf{i} + 2\mathbf{j} + 2\mathbf{k})/3$. The component of the field which acts on the charge carriers in the wire will be given by the **projection** of the total field $\mathbf{E}$ onto this direction:

component of field = $\mathbf{E}.\hat{\mathbf{d}} = (20 \times 1 + 8 \times 2 + 15 \times 2)/3 = 22$ V m^{-1}

Note that a projection must be taken onto a unit vector. If the direction vector does not have unit magnitude it is necessary to normalize it by dividing by its magnitude.

19

The **scalar** (or **dot**) **product** of two vectors is easy to apply, and is useful in a number of simple practical applications, including the projection of a vector quantity. The product is defined in such a fashion that when both of the vectors associated with a scalar product are identical, the value of the product gives the square of the length of the vector. It is worth illustrating that the full definition is more powerful than this, and goes beyond the, geometrically obvious, usage in three-dimensional space.

Worked Application Example 2.4

Communication theory employs a number of techniques of vector algebra, but views the vectors in *n*-dimensional space: each vector has *n* elements, where *n* is potentially a large number. In particular, the three-dimensional concept of distance, as embodied in the magnitude of the vector between two points, can be extended to the broader *n*-dimensional mathematical measure **norm**. The norm of a vector **a** is defined by

$$\text{if}\quad \mathbf{a} = \begin{bmatrix} a_1 \\ a_2 \\ \cdot \\ \cdot \\ \cdot \\ a_n \end{bmatrix} \quad \text{then norm } \mathbf{a} = \|\mathbf{a}\| = \left[\sum_{i=1}^{n} a_i^2 \right]^{1/2} = (\mathbf{a}.\mathbf{a})^{1/2} \tag{2.2}$$

so that for $n = 3$ this is just the length of the vector **a**. In *n* dimensions this can still be thought of as defining the 'distance' between two points, an idea which is useful for the rapid determination of the similarity of two digital signals. Suppose that a digital system is designed to react differently on receiving either the coded digital sequence (i) 3, 1, 5, 3, 8, 9, 4, or (ii) 9, 6, 7, 5, 3, 5, 1. If an incoming signal is received which has been corrupted in transmission to be: 7, 4, 6, 3, 6, 6, 2, which expected signal is this closer to?

The signal is assumed to be composed of a sequence of seven positive, single-digit, denary numbers.

Solution The signals can be represented as three seven-element vectors:

$$\mathbf{a} = \begin{bmatrix} 3 \\ 1 \\ 5 \\ 3 \\ 8 \\ 9 \\ 4 \end{bmatrix} \quad \mathbf{b} = \begin{bmatrix} 9 \\ 6 \\ 7 \\ 5 \\ 3 \\ 5 \\ 1 \end{bmatrix} \quad \mathbf{c} = \begin{bmatrix} 7 \\ 4 \\ 6 \\ 3 \\ 6 \\ 6 \\ 2 \end{bmatrix}$$

Situations where an *n*-dimensional vector is employed are more common than might be imagined: as well as communications, they are of considerable importance in the theory of multiprocessor arrays; they arise in modern control theory as carriers of the information about the state of a control system; and they are used in quantum-mechanical calculations of the electron distribution in solid-state device applications.

where **a** and **b** are the two expected signals and **c** represents the actual received signal. Evaluating the distances leads to

$$\|\mathbf{c} - \mathbf{a}\| = [4^2 + 3^2 + 1^2 + 0^2 + 2^2 + 3^2 + 2^2]^{1/2} \approx 6.56$$

and $\|\mathbf{c} - \mathbf{b}\| = [2^2 + 2^2 + 1^2 + 2^2 + 3^2 + 1^2 + 1^2]^{1/2} = 4$

so that the received seven-digit signal is significantly closer to the second of the expected sequences.

Exercise 2.2 Which of the expected control signals does the received signal:

4, 3, 6, 5, 4, 8, 2

correspond to most closely?

Scalar products are useful for problems that require the calculation of projections and distances. However, the result of the scalar product of two vectors is always a number. If the nature of the problem is such that a vector quantity is desired to be the result of the multiplication it is necessary to employ a **vector product**.

Vector products are of practical use in a number of situations: for the rapid calculation of a vector which is orthogonal to a given pair of vectors; for the calculation of areas for a number of problems in electromagnetics; and for the evaluation of the **vector moment** of a number of forces.

The concept of a vector area is useful in the evaluation of the component of an electromagnetic field through a particular surface surrounding a charge distribution. Such surface integrals are introduced in Chapter 5.

The vector moment of a force **F** acting on a point **r** around the origin is given by

$$\mathbf{G} = \mathbf{r} \wedge \mathbf{F}$$

Worked Application Example 2.5

Fig. 2.2 shows the forces acting on the final section of a robot arm. What value of the parameter f in the control force **F** is required to negate the moment due to the 20 N load and the 12 N weight of the arm?

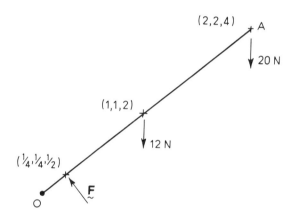

Fig. 2.2   The forces on a manipulator arm. The weight of the arm is represented by a 12 N force acting in the direction $-\mathbf{k}$ at the point (1, 1, 2). The load on the arm is given by a 20 N force acting in the direction $-\mathbf{k}$ at the point (2, 2, 4). The control force is chosen to have the form $\mathbf{F} = f(-\mathbf{i} - \mathbf{j} + \mathbf{k})$ and acts at the point (0.25, 0.25, 0.5).

Solution   The gravitational force acts in the direction $-\mathbf{k}$, so that the total vector moment due to the load and weight is

$$\begin{bmatrix} 2 \\ 2 \\ 4 \end{bmatrix} \wedge \begin{bmatrix} 0 \\ 0 \\ -20 \end{bmatrix} + \begin{bmatrix} 1 \\ 1 \\ 2 \end{bmatrix} \wedge \begin{bmatrix} 0 \\ 0 \\ -12 \end{bmatrix} = \begin{bmatrix} -52 \\ 52 \\ 0 \end{bmatrix}$$

while the moment due to the control force is

$$\begin{bmatrix} 0.25 \\ 0.25 \\ 0.5 \end{bmatrix} \wedge \begin{bmatrix} -f \\ -f \\ f \end{bmatrix} = \begin{bmatrix} 0.75f \\ -0.75f \\ 0 \end{bmatrix}$$

The control force has been designed to act in such a direction as to cancel the applied moment: all that remains is to find out the strength of force that must be applied.

For perfect cancellation these vector moments must be opposite and equal in magnitude, which can be achieved for a value of $f = 208/3$ N.

Simple force problems can be handled readily using both the vector and scalar products. The techniques are more powerful than their simplicity indicates, however, and it is possible to answer questions involving complicated three-dimensional geometries that would be very difficult to analyse in any other fashion.

Worked Application Example 2.6

An electronic air-traffic flight control system must track, calculate and display the current and predicted flight paths of a large number of objects moving independently through three-dimensional space. If any of these aircraft are likely to pass too close to each other the system must trigger an alarm in plenty of time to allow the pilots time for early correction of their flight paths. Relative to a Cartesian coordinate system fixed at an airfield, the current positions (in units of a thousand feet) of two aircraft are found to be

The first two elements of the direction vectors correspond to a particular bearing, while the third component measures the angle of climb/fall.

aircraft 1: $(-3, 4, 10)$ and aircraft 2: $(1, -7, 4)$

and they are moving along directions given by the respective unit vectors

No assumption is being made about the speeds of the aircraft: variable headwinds or pilot adjustment can lead to uncertainty in the arrival times of the aircraft. This question is considering the worst possible case: if circumstances conspire to adjust the speeds of the aircraft so that they arrive in the same local airspace simultaneously, then how close will they pass?

$$\hat{\mathbf{d}}_1 = \frac{1}{\sqrt{137}} \begin{bmatrix} 10 \\ 6 \\ -1 \end{bmatrix} \quad \text{and} \quad \hat{\mathbf{d}}_2 = \frac{1}{\sqrt{90}} \begin{bmatrix} 5 \\ 8 \\ 1 \end{bmatrix} \tag{2.3}$$

If the planes stay on their current (linear) flight paths, what is the closest possible approach distance that can occur?

Solution In three-dimensional space a pair of arbitrary lines will not intersect in general: instead, a pair of **skew lines** will result. It is possible to represent the equations of both lines in vector form:

There is no need to retain the normalization factors in the vector equation of a line: the variable parameter will compensate automatically.

$$\mathbf{r}_\lambda = \begin{bmatrix} -3 \\ 4 \\ 10 \end{bmatrix} + \lambda \begin{bmatrix} 10 \\ 6 \\ -1 \end{bmatrix} \tag{2.4}$$

As λ is varied all points on the first line are scanned out. Likewise, the second line can be generated by varying the parameter μ. If the two parameters are varied simultaneously, the vector $\mathbf{r}_\mu - \mathbf{r}_\lambda$ scans out a surface joining the two lines.

$$\text{and } \mathbf{r}_\mu = \begin{bmatrix} 1 \\ -7 \\ 4 \end{bmatrix} + \mu \begin{bmatrix} 5 \\ 8 \\ 1 \end{bmatrix} \tag{2.5}$$

Thus, it is possible to consider the vector from any point on the first line to any point on the second:

$$\mathbf{r}_\mu - \mathbf{r}_\lambda = \begin{bmatrix} 4 \\ -11 \\ -6 \end{bmatrix} + \begin{bmatrix} 5\mu - 10\lambda \\ 8\mu - 6\lambda \\ \mu + \lambda \end{bmatrix} \tag{2.6}$$

An introduction to some of the ideas of multivariable calculus and minimization is given in Chapter 5, where this particular problem is approached in an alternative fashion.

The length of this vector is a **two-variable function** of the variables λ and μ: we desire the vector with the smallest magnitude. Generally, such a problem requires a **multivariable minimization** of the quantity of interest. In this particular case, however, it is possible to exploit geometrical intuition and take a short-cut by arguing that the vector between the lines which represents the situation of closest approach will be the vector which is perpendicular to both lines. A vector which is orthogonal to both lines is given by the vector product of the direction vectors of the two lines:

$$\mathbf{n} = \begin{bmatrix} 10 \\ 6 \\ -1 \end{bmatrix} \wedge \begin{bmatrix} 5 \\ 8 \\ 1 \end{bmatrix} = \begin{bmatrix} 14 \\ -15 \\ 50 \end{bmatrix} \tag{2.7}$$

so that the particular values of λ and μ which will generate the closest approach vector are those for which the vector of Equation (2.6) is parallel to that of Equation (2.7):

$$\begin{bmatrix} 4 + 5\mu - 10\lambda \\ -11 + 8\mu - 6\lambda \\ -6 + \mu + \lambda \end{bmatrix} = k \begin{bmatrix} 14 \\ -15 \\ 50 \end{bmatrix} \tag{2.8}$$

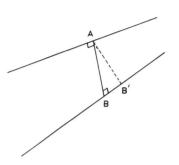

Consider the mutual perpendicular of two skew lines. It is obvious that displacement of the connecting line away from the current positions of A or B will lead to an increase in the length of the segment: $|AB'|^2 = |AB|^2 + |BB'|^2 \Rightarrow |AB'| > |AB|$.

for some constant multiplier k. Since the equality must hold simultaneously for all three components of this vector equation, it follows that Equation (2.8) is actually three individual linear simultaneous equations for the three unknowns λ, μ and k. The solution of such sets of equations is discussed in the next chapter, and it is sufficient for our current purposes to note that the solution of this vector equation is given by

$$\lambda \approx 1.84 \qquad \mu \approx 2.81 \qquad k \approx -0.027$$

so that the vector of closest approach of the flight paths is

$$\mathbf{r}_{ca} = \begin{bmatrix} -0.38 \\ 0.41 \\ -1.35 \end{bmatrix}$$

which has a magnitude of 1.46 thousand feet: in the worst possible case the aircraft will pass no closer than this, provided that they maintain their current courses.

The two aircraft in the above example are found to be simultaneously at a height of 7.5 thousand feet. How far apart are they?

Exercise 2.3

All of the above examples have involved calculations with vectors acting at points or along lines. Quite complicated geometries and interactions can be handled with such basic tools: mainly because of the fact that vectors offer a compact and rapid way of handling large amounts of coordinate data. However, these are still only the simplest form of vector techniques and more general problems in vector algebra will involve vectors interacting with curves, planes or surfaces.

Ion implantation is a useful technique for the introduction of precisely controlled depths of dopant atoms into crystalline silicon. The process involves the impact of a beam of dopant ions upon a pre-masked silicon wafer *in vacuo*. Because the ion beam has a small radius it must be scanned across the wafer a number of times over a range of incident angles in order to ensure an even irradiation of the surface.

Worked Application Example 2.7

A sample holder within an ion implantation vacuum system holds a silicon wafer with its surface in the plane

$$x + 2y + 5z = 8$$

The ion beam source is situated at the coordinates S: (10, 10, 10) within the system. What are the angles of incidence at the points A: (1, 1, 1) and B: (2, -2, 2) on the wafer?

Solution It is conventional to measure the angle of incidence of a beam onto a surface relative to the normal to that surface, so that normal incidence corresponds to an angle of $0°$. The equation of the plane can be expressed in vector form as

$$\mathbf{r} \cdot \begin{bmatrix} 1 \\ 2 \\ 5 \end{bmatrix} = 8 = \mathbf{r} \cdot \mathbf{n} \tag{2.9}$$

The point of this is that the areas of the wafer that are subjected to the ion beam at angles far from normal incidence will receive a reduced number of donor ions relative to those at near-normal incidence: the beam 'spot' will be spread out over a larger area of the wafer. In practice it is necessary to rotate and shift the beam and wafer relative to each other in order to average out these incidence effects.

where $\mathbf{n}$ is a vector normal to the plane of the silicon wafer. Denoting the vector from A to S by $\mathbf{a}$ and that from B to S by $\mathbf{b}$, the angle of incidence at point A is given by

$$\cos \alpha = \frac{\mathbf{a} \cdot \mathbf{n}}{|\mathbf{a}| \, |\mathbf{n}|} = \frac{(9 \times 1 + 9 \times 2 + 9 \times 5)}{\sqrt{243} \times \sqrt{30}} \approx 0.843$$

leading to an incident angle of approximately 32.5°. Similarly, for point B on the wafer, the incidence angle β is given by

$$\cos \beta = \frac{\mathbf{b} \cdot \mathbf{n}}{|\mathbf{b}| \, |\mathbf{n}|} = \frac{(8 \times 1 + 12 \times 2 + 8 \times 5)}{\sqrt{272} \times \sqrt{30}} \approx 0.797$$
$$\Rightarrow \beta \approx 37.2°$$

Space curves

When a vector can be expressed as a function of one or more parameters that appear in a linear fashion in each component the vector will represent a line, a plane or perhaps a surface that can be generated out of lines. In applications involving lines and planes it is easy to calculate quantities such as directions and distances along lines. General problems will require a less restrictive form of vector function, however. For example, the trajectory and velocity of a satellite or aircraft will change in a complicated (but continuous and relatively smooth!) fashion with time; similarly, the usual path of a charged particle in an electric or magnetic field will be a curve, not a line.

A linear function of a parameter t is one of the form $f(t) = a + bt$ where a and b are constants.

For example, Equation (2.6) defines a surface connecting a pair of skew lines.

Worked Application Example 2.8

The most general path of an electron moving in a region of constant uniform magnetic field is a **circular helix**. If the vector equation of the helical path of one particular electron is parameterized in terms of time, t, as

$$\mathbf{r} = \begin{bmatrix} \cos t \\ \sin t \\ \lambda t \end{bmatrix} \tag{2.10}$$

find the direction of motion of the electron at any time t and calculate the distance travelled by the electron from time $t = 0$ to time $t = 2\pi$.

Solution The direction of motion can be obtained by differentiating the position vector with respect to time:

The differentiation of a vector forms the first step beyond vector algebra towards the immensely powerful field of **vector calculus**. Such techniques are invaluable in electromagnetic theory, the study of heat flow, diffusion and fluid dynamics. The general techniques of vector calculus cannot be covered in this text, but the best illustration of the utility of the methods is in the compact and convenient representation of Maxwell's equations. See Carter (1986).

$$\frac{d\mathbf{r}}{dt} = \begin{bmatrix} dx/dt \\ dy/dt \\ dz/dt \end{bmatrix} = \begin{bmatrix} -\sin t \\ \cos t \\ \lambda \end{bmatrix}$$

This vector is tangential to the trajectory of the electron and defines the instantaneous direction of motion at any time: it can be normalized by dividing through by $(1 + \lambda^2)^{1/2}$ if required.

In general, the **arc length**, s, travelled along a curve is given by the expression:

$$s = \int_{t_0}^{t_1} \left[\left[\frac{dx}{dt}\right]^2 + \left[\frac{dy}{dt}\right]^2 + \left[\frac{dz}{dt}\right]^2 \right]^{1/2} dt$$

so that in this particular case the distance travelled from time $t = 0$ to $t = 2\pi$ is

$$s = \int_0^{2\pi} [\sin^2 t + \cos^2 t + \lambda^2]^{1/2} dt$$

$$= \int_0^{2\pi} [1 + \lambda^2]^{1/2} dt = 2\pi[1 + \lambda^2]^{1/2}$$

Note that as $\lambda \to 0$ the electron trajectory tends to a closed circle of unit radius and the distance travelled tends correspondingly to a value of 2π.

Complex numbers and phasors

Any mathematical topic, when viewed in isolation, can appear to be rather remote from apparent applications. Only when a realistic engineering problem is encountered, which usually requires the simultaneous application of a number of mathematical techniques, will an overview of the structure and applicability of the abstract methods be obtained.

The theory of complex numbers is a particularly difficult topic to justify from an engineering point of view: the idea of augmenting the usual algebra of real numbers by the introduction of the so-called imaginary numbers seems remote from practical interpretation. In fact, they have proved to be an extremely valuable tool in a range of applied subjects: ac circuit analysis; communication theory; audio signal processing; and the quantum theory of the electronic structure of solid-state devices. The reason for the considerable utility of complex numbers is that they provide a natural and compact representation of the wave properties of a system: the amplitude and phase of a sinusoidal wave can be related to the two independent parts, real and imaginary, of a complex number.

Consider a general sinusoidal waveform:

$$f(t) = A \cos(\omega t + \phi) = A \cos(2\pi f t + \phi) \tag{2.11}$$

where f is the frequency of the oscillation (in Hz) and ω is the **angular frequency** (in rad s^{-1}). A is the **amplitude** of the wave and ϕ is the **phase**. Waveforms such as this are used in evaluating the **frequency response** of dynamic systems such as RLC circuits, communication lines and control systems. A pure sinusoidal wave of variable frequency is fed into the system of interest and the form of the output as a function of the input frequency is recorded. For a linear system such an output will always be a scaled and phase-shifted sinusoidal wave of the same frequency as the input. A nonlinear system will distort the input in a considerably more complicated fashion: the mathematical treatment of such systems is an advanced topic which will not be pursued in detail in this text.

Equation (2.11) is a perfectly reasonable way to represent the amplitude and phase information of a sinusoidal wave, whether it is an input or the output of a linear system. The main deficiencies of the format are:

1. It is difficult to combine a number of waves of the form of Equation (2.11): awkward trigonometric addition and multiplication formulae are required.
2. Integrals involving a product of functions (one sinusoidal) can be cumbersome to evaluate.
3. Equation (2.11) can be written in a number of equivalent, and confusing, forms by

Many mathematical texts will use the notation i to refer to the pure imaginary number which is the square root of -1. In electronic engineering texts, where there is the possibility of confusion with the notation for current in a circuit, it is more common to use j.

A **sinusoidal** waveform is one that looks like a sine wave, but may be shifted along the Y-axis: a pure sine wave, a pure cosine wave or any weighted sum of a sine and cosine wave are all sinusoidal in form.

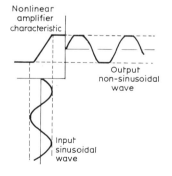

Nonlinear amplifier characteristic

Output non-sinusoidal wave

Input sinusoidal wave

The effect of a nonlinear (saturating) amplifier on an input sinusoid.

redefining ϕ or by expanding the expression into a linear combination of $\cos(\omega t)$ and $\sin(\omega t)$.

The basic techniques of manipulation of complex numbers are covered in detail by Jeffrey (1989) or Stroud (1982). Here their use as a more natural way of representing waves will be emphasized.

Application Example 2.9

The phasor can be plotted on an Argand diagram, and it is common to draw a vector from the origin to the complex number. The vector, the complex number and the original sinusoidal expression are all alternative ways of expressing the same two pieces of information: the amplitude and phase of the input.

When the time variation is taken into account the complex number tracks around a circle of radius 5, at a frequency of 2 Hz. Because of this, it is common to see the time-varying complex voltage referred to as a **rotating vector**. The angular frequency refers to the angle of arc which the vector traverses in each second, in this case 4π.

The ac voltage input to a circuit has the form $5\cos(4\pi t + \pi/6)$ V. In circuit applications it is common to replace this real quantity by a complex input voltage **phasor**: a complex number which carries the same basic information as the real waveform, but in a rather different fashion.

The phasor for this particular case is the complex number

$$5\cos(\pi/6) + 5j\sin(\pi/6) = 5\exp(j\pi/6)$$

so that the amplitude and phase of the wave at $t = 0$ correspond to the modulus and argument respectively of the complex phasor. The time variation of the wave can be added to produce a complex input voltage

$$V(t) = 5\exp[j(4\pi t + \pi/6)] \tag{2.12}$$

so that the original wave can be reconstructed by considering only the real part of Equation (2.12). Likewise, if the input had been of the form $\sin(4\pi t + \pi/6)$, the imaginary part of Equation (2.12) would be a suitable representation.

It may seem odd to think of a physically measurable quantity as being represented by a complex number: the important points are that:

1. Mathematically there is no problem: if the input to a system is complex, then the output and any internal variable may also be complex. The whole problem is released from the restriction of working with purely real numbers.
2. Practically, it is impossible to measure a complex quantity: but no claim is being made that the wave is complex: it is just that the complex number is a convenient way of carrying the information about the amplitude and phase of the wave – which are real and measurable under all circumstances.
3. The basic laws of circuit analysis, KVL and KCL, work perfectly well in complex form for an arbitrary circuit structure: the only difference is that complex current, voltage and power phasors are employed throughout.

Worked Application Example 2.10

This step has been taken to ensure that the sum of the squares of the coefficients of the trigonometric functions is unity: if the expression is of the form $A\cos(\alpha t) + B\sin(\alpha t)$, it is necessary to take out a factor of $(A^2 + B^2)^{1/2}$.

The 0.93 is in radians. The value has been obtained by using both of the facts that $\cos(0.93) \approx 0.6$ and $\sin(0.93) \approx 0.8$: in general it is not enough to work from the relationship $0.93 \approx \tan^{-1}(4/3)$; account must also be taken of the signs of both the sine and cosine terms.

Two independent ac voltage sources: $3\cos(4t)$ V and $4\sin(4t)$ V are connected in series. Describe the total source voltage as a phasor.

Solution In sinusoidal form, the total driving voltage is

$$3\cos(4t) + 4\sin(4t)$$

$$= 5\left[\frac{3}{5}\cos(4t) + \frac{4}{5}\sin(4t)\right]$$

$$= 5(\cos(0.93)\cos(4t) + \sin(0.93)\sin(4t))$$

$$= 5\cos(4t - 0.93)$$

Therefore, the appropriate complex voltage is given by

$$E = 5\exp(-0.93j)\exp(4jt) = 5\exp[j(4t - 0.93)]$$

initial phasor   time variation

Alternatively, consider the two components of the driving voltage in complex form from the beginning:

$$E = 3 \exp(4jt) + 4 \exp(4jt - j\pi/2)$$
$$= [3 + 4 \exp(-j\pi/2)] \exp(4jt)$$

It is easy to combine the two time-independent components into a single, resultant, term using a **phasor diagram**. The new phasor corresponds to the vector resultant of the original pair and is given by $5 \exp(-0.93j)$, a result which can be obtained graphically or by Pythagoras and trigonometry.

It can be seen that the diagrammatic phasor approach provides a simpler, easier to interpret, way of obtaining the overall voltage.

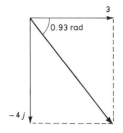

There are a number of points about the phasor representation that help to ease the manipulation of ac quantities:

1. The initial amplitude/phase of the wave and the associated time variation decouple naturally into separate complex functions.
2. To evaluate the superposition of any number of waves of the same frequency it is possible to construct a phasor diagram showing the time-independent phasor of every wave and evaluate the resultant of all of the phasors. The time variation merely has the effect of making the whole diagram rotate at a pre-specified frequency: the relative positions (phases) of the phasors do not change with time.
3. The phasor diagram allows a useful graphical interpretation of the dynamics of a circuit or dynamic system: it also reduces the need for complicated trigonometric addition formulae to be employed to build up the resultant of a number of waves. The technique enables the solution of problems that are beyond an easy analytic solution in trigonometric form.

In a circuit with linear elements, it can be shown that the frequencies of an applied ac voltage, the voltage measured across any circuit component and the current in the circuit are identical. Therefore, it is possible to ignore the time variation temporarily and define voltage and current phasors, V and I, for any element (or group of elements) of the circuit. Ohm's law for a dc circuit can be redefined in terms of these phasors as

$$Z = \frac{E}{I} \; \Omega \tag{2.13}$$

where the complex (phasor) Z defines the **impedance** of the circuit elements. The impedance can be thought of as a complex resistance: its modulus corresponds to the overall opposition to the flow of charge produced by the elements, while its argument specifies the phase shift between the voltage and current phasors.

For an isolated resistor, inductor and capacitor respectively, the appropriate impedances are:

$$\left. \begin{array}{rl} Z_R = & R \\ Z_L = & j\omega L \\ \text{and} \quad Z_C = & -\dfrac{j}{\omega C} \end{array} \right\} \tag{2.14}$$

respectively. What is the amplitude and phase of the impedance of a series RLC circuit?

Solution   The circuit impedance is the total impedance 'experienced' by the source

The concept of a complex number as a rotation is valid beyond this immediate application within phasor methods. The complex number j can be thought of as an operator which applies a rotation of $\pi/2$ to objects in the Argand plane: $j(1 + j) = -1 + j$, for example. Likewise $j^2 = -1$ represents a rotation of π and, in general, any unit modulus complex number, $\exp(j\theta)$, corresponds to a rotation through an angle θ. If the complex number does not have unit magnitude it has the effect of simultaneously scaling and rotating objects in the complex plane.

Worked Application Example 2.11

Chapter 4 covers some examples of the differential properties of RLC circuits. Boctor (1987) gives a good treatment of phasor methods in general.

The phasors are expressed in polar form: the argument of the ratio of the phasors is given by the difference of their respective arguments.

voltage. Each circuit element will have the same current passing though it: an application of KVL shows that the total impedance of the circuit is given by:

$$Z = R + j\omega L - \frac{j}{\omega C}$$ (2.15)

so that the magnitude of the circuit impedance is

$$|Z| = \left[R^2 + \left[\omega L - \frac{1}{\omega C} \right]^2 \right]^{1/2}$$ (2.16)

The phase angle satisfies φ $\epsilon[-\pi/2, \pi/2]$.

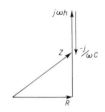

The impedance triangle for a series RLC circuit.

The use of a phasor diagram also occurs in such circuit applications in the form of the power triangle.

and the phase angle, ϕ, satisfies

$$\cos \phi = \frac{R}{|Z|} \qquad \text{and} \qquad \sin \phi = \frac{\omega L - 1/\omega C}{|Z|}$$ (2.17)

Thus, the amplitude and phase of the circuit impedance are multivariable functions of the values of R, L and C and of the frequency of the driving voltage source. The real and imaginary components of this phasor arise from the resistive elements (R) and the reactive elements (L and C) respectively. They can be plotted in the Argand plane to give the **impedance triangle**: a diagram which is extremely useful for ac circuit analysis. See Boctor (1987) for more details.

When the values of these circuit parameters combine to produce a value of ϕ near $-\pi/2$ the circuit is said to be predominantly capacitative: the current waveform leads the voltage waveform by a substantial phase angle.

When ϕ is near zero, the circuit is predominantly resistive: the overall current and voltage waveforms are nearly synchronized.

For values of ϕ near $\pi/2$ the circuit is predominantly inductive: in such a case the current lags the voltage.

Exercise 2.4

The admittance phasor for each element is the inverse of the impedance for that element. The total admittance is the sum of the admittances of the parallel branches: it is the overall admittance that the source 'experiences'.

The use of the **inductive susceptance** $B_L = 1/\omega L$ and the **capacitative susceptance** $B_C = \omega C$ may prove helpful here.

Consider the parallel RLC circuit illustrated in Fig. 2.3. Use KCL to find the magnitude and phase of the total admittance phasor.

Draw an admittance triangle in the Argand plane to illustrate the interactions between the parallel elements.

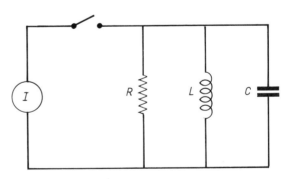

Fig. 2.3 A parallel RLC circuit. The ac current source is sinusoidal in form with frequency ω.

Complex number theory can also be used in some cases where the voltages across circuit elements are varying sinusoidally with a range of frequencies, although usually a pattern or symmetry must be available for the method to be exploited.

A branch of a circuit contains n inductors connected together in series. An e.m.f. is induced in each coil in such a fashion that the kth inductor exhibits an e.m.f. of $\cos(k\omega t)$. Express the total e.m.f. induced across all n inductors in a simple functional form.

Solution   In this arrangement, the e.m.f.s will add together, giving a total e.m.f. of

$$E_{\text{tot}} = \sum_{k=1}^{n} \cos(k\omega t)$$

which can be thought of as merely the real component of a more general summation of complex e.m.f.s:

$$\sum_{k=1}^{n} e^{jk\omega t} = \sum_{k=1}^{n} [e^{j\omega t}]^k$$

This sum can be seen to be a finite geometric progression: the first term is $\exp(j\omega t)$ and each of the n terms is a factor of $\exp(j\omega t)$ different to the previous term. The sum of the series is therefore

$$e^{j\omega t} \left[\frac{1 - e^{jn\omega t}}{1 - e^{j\omega t}} \right] = e^{j\omega t} \left[\frac{1 - e^{-j\omega t} + e^{j(n-1)\omega t} - e^{jn\omega t}}{2 - 2\cos(\omega t)} \right]$$

provided that $\omega t \neq 2\pi m$ for any integer m. The real part of this expression gives the total e.m.f.

$$E_{\text{tot}} = \frac{\cos(\omega t) - 1 + \cos(n\omega t) - \cos[(n+1)\omega t]}{2 - 2\cos(\omega t)}$$

By multiplying above and below by the complex conjugate of the numerator: $1 - \exp(-j\omega t)$.

When $\omega t = 2\pi m$ every term of the series is unity, and so the sum is n.

which is in a (relatively) compact form. Some slight further simplification can be achieved using the formulae for trigonometric addition, but this result is perfectly adequate as an illustration of how the sum of n waves can be compressed into a single functional form.

Phasors and complex waveforms in general provide a useful short-cut in a range of dynamic problems. However, it should be realized that much mathematical detail is being ignored and assumptions are being made about the validity of the phasor approach. A fuller treatment of the dynamics of circuits is given in Chapter 4, where phasors and complex numbers will prove useful once again.

Summary

The basic theories of vectors and complex numbers provide a compact and systematic way of dealing with a wide range of problems involving two or three variables. It is possible to gain geometrical insight into problems that appear obscure on paper, and, conversely, bring powerful analytic tools to bear on problems involving fairly complicated geometries.

At this fairly simplistic level vectors and complex numbers form a bridge between geometry and algebra. At a more advanced level vectors prove to be a natural vehicle for the representation of complicated electrodynamic effects or any problem involving flow, motion or rotations in space, while the theory of complex numbers can be extended to provide a powerful tool in complex variable theory: a technique that can be used to transform an intractable system geometry into one that can be handled readily. Unfortunately, these topics are beyond the scope of this text.

Further exercises

2.5 Two ships are travelling on known bearings with constant speeds such that their positions at time t (hours) are given by

$$\mathbf{s}_1 = \begin{bmatrix} 2 \\ 3 \end{bmatrix} + \begin{bmatrix} 5 \\ 9 \end{bmatrix} t \quad \mathbf{s}_2 = \begin{bmatrix} 4 \\ 9 \end{bmatrix} + \begin{bmatrix} -1 \\ 1 \end{bmatrix} t$$

in a Cartesian coordinate system (measured in miles).

Find the distance of closest approach of the ships, the time at which this occurs and the positions of each ship at this time.

2.6 The piezoelectric effect occurs when certain crystals are subjected to mechanical deformations. Calculate the percentage change in volume when a rectangular crystal defined by the vectors

$$\begin{bmatrix} 1 \\ 0 \\ 0 \end{bmatrix} \quad \begin{bmatrix} 0 \\ 2 \\ 0 \end{bmatrix} \quad \begin{bmatrix} 0 \\ 0 \\ 3 \end{bmatrix}$$

is deformed into a parallelepiped defined by the vectors

$$\begin{bmatrix} 0.98 \\ 0.10 \\ -0.10 \end{bmatrix} \quad \begin{bmatrix} 0.10 \\ 2.10 \\ 0.10 \end{bmatrix} \quad \begin{bmatrix} -0.10 \\ 0.20 \\ 2.95 \end{bmatrix}$$

Obtain the three angular distortions between the undeformed and deformed sides of the crystal.

2.7 In a CRT an electron beam follows a space curve given by

$$\mathbf{r} = \begin{bmatrix} 3 - \lambda + 2\lambda^2 \\ 2 - \lambda + \lambda^2 \\ 2 + \lambda \end{bmatrix}$$

Find the point where this beam is parallel to the deflection plate which lies in the plane $x - y - 4z = 2$.

2.8 An inductor L and capacitor C are connected in parallel, and this pair of parallel components are then connected in series with a resistor R and an ideal ac voltage source. Find the total impedance of the circuit.

2.9 Express the sum of the driving voltages $5 \cos(2t)$ and $12 \sin(2t)$ as a complex voltage (phasor/time variation).

Linear Equations, Determinants and Matrices 3

Objectives

☐ To examine some practical systems requiring a multivariable mathematical description.
☐ To illustrate the relative advantages of using linear equations, determinants and matrices as investigative tools for multivariable systems.
☐ To show that matrix methods provide a natural set of tools for the representation of the structure of a multivariable physical system.

Applications involving linear simultaneous equations

In Chapter T1 the concept of linearity of systems and of their associated mathematical description is introduced, and it is stressed that generally it is much easier mathematically to deal with linear systems than nonlinear systems. This is due to the fact that linear systems obey the principle of superposition, whereby the full solution may be constructed as a linear combination of simpler solutions. Because of this (and despite the fact that most real systems are nonlinear to some degree) it is common to describe engineering systems in terms of linear equations, in essence assuming that the system may be represented as producing an approximately linear response over some (large enough!) operational range. If the linear model is inadequate then further enhancements can often be added, or a full nonlinear model can be analysed by numerical means if necessary. In many cases the linear model is quite good enough for practical purposes and has the added advantage of often giving physical insight into why and how an answer turns out to have the form that it does – it is generally rather harder to interpret the solutions of nonlinear equations.

Another feature of real engineering systems that unfortunately complicates the mathematics somewhat is that real systems are usually multivariable. A system that truly has only one input and one output is rare, and it is frequently necessary to take account of the effect of many input parameters to obtain a reasonable description of how a complicated system responds in practice. Such a multivariable system is influenced by a set of simultaneous inputs in a composite fashion, reacting to the individual inputs to different degrees but in general being affected by them all. The equations which describe such multivariable systems are said to be **coupled equations** – the various outputs of the system depend on how the system reacts to the coupled effect of all the inputs. If any of the elements of the system react in a differential or integral fashion (inductors and capacitors, for example) a set of coupled linear differential equations often arises. If the components of the system react only in a multiplicative manner (resistors, for example) then a system of simultaneous linear algebraic equations arises. Only sets of algebraic equations arising in a variety of applications will be considered in this chapter.

Simple pairs of simultaneous equations are straightforward to deal with by direct substitution: it is merely necessary to scale one equation so that either of the two variables involved can be eliminated by simple addition or subtraction of the two equations. A pair of simultaneous linear equations can arise in a myriad of application

In a linear circuit network the principle of superposition manifests itself in the fact that the total current in any branch is the algebraic sum of the separate currents produced in the branch by the individual sources of e.m.f. considered one by one in isolation.

Such a linearized model is found in the small-signal analysis of a nonlinear device or system, as discussed by Ritchie (1987). The method can be applied to the characteristics of a diode (which is a nonlinear resistor as a function of voltage) to obtain a (linear) **small-signal equivalent circuit** around some nominal operating parameters V_o and I_o.

In any multivariable system it is obviously necessary to make a series of value-judgements about which parameters are most relevant to the behaviour of the system.

Laplace transform methods (see Jeffrey, 1989) can be used to transform such sets of differential equations into related algebraic equations which can be attacked using the methods of this chapter.

models, but it is perhaps worth stressing with an example that they can also appear in a somewhat disguised form.

___

Worked Application Example 3.1

A thermistor is a thermally sensitive resistor – a two-terminal passive device whose resistance is a function of the device temperature. It is not a junction device, but is typically composed of a mixture of metallic oxides. Most thermistors are negative temperature coefficient (NTC) devices: their resistance decreases with increasing temperature.

The resistance of a thermistor is given typically by the equation

$$R = A \exp(b/T) \tag{3.1}$$

to a very good approximation and over a wide temperature range (R is in ohms, T in Kelvin) where A and b are constants which specify the detailed behaviour of this particular type of thermistor.

Assuming that the equation is perfectly valid, if calibration measurements give the resistance at 300 K to be 1000 Ω and at 400 K to be 100 Ω, find the characteristic constants A and b and determine what the resistance should be at a temperature of 350 K.

Solution   The problem amounts to finding the unknown coefficients of the nonlinear Equation (3.1). In general, the characteristic coefficients of such nonlinear equations must be fitted by computer if no analytic approach is feasible. In this particular case, however, it is possible to simplify the problem by taking the natural logarithm of Equation (3.1) to obtain

$$\ln R = \ln A + b/T \tag{3.2}$$

The important point about this equation is that if A is an unknown constant then so is $\ln A$, so that if we define a new constant $C = \ln A$ we have

$$C + b T^{-1} = \ln R$$

and inserting the experimental pairs of values for R and T gives

$$C + 3.3333 \times 10^{-3} b = 6.9078$$

$$\text{and } C + 2.5000 \times 10^{-3} b = 4.6052$$

Generally, a set of linear equations will arise out of problems which exhibit considerable nonlinear behaviour provided that the quantities to be determined appear only in a linear fashion.

which are clearly a pair of simultaneous linear equations in the unknown coefficients C and b. Elimination of C rapidly leads to $b = 2764.2$, and substitution of b into the first equation gives $C = -2.3061$, so that the values of A and b can be summarized as

$$A = \exp C = 0.099649 \ \Omega$$

and $b = 2764.2$ K

It is worth checking the answer if at all possible, and in this particular case it is easy to check that resistances given by the calculated values of A and b at 300 K and 400 K are 1000.1 Ω and 99.923 Ω respectively. The small inaccuracies are merely due to the restricted precision (5 significant figures) of the calculation.

These constants will be characteristic of this particular thermistor and should specify its behaviour over a wide temperature range.

Using these calculated constants the resistance of the thermistor at 350 K can be predicted to be

$$R_{350} = 0.099649 \exp (2764.2/350) = 268.17 \ \Omega$$

___

Simple cases such as this arise frequently and are usually easy to deal with. However, when more than two equations are involved a more systematic and general approach is required. Consider the simple resistance network of Fig. 3.1. Applying Kirchhoff's laws to the three meshes illustrated results in the equations

$$
\begin{aligned}
I_1 R_1 + (I_1 - I_2)R_5 + (I_1 - I_3)R_4 &= E_1 \\
I_2 R_2 + (I_2 - I_3)R_6 + (I_2 - I_1)R_5 &= E_2 \\
I_3 R_3 + (I_3 - I_1)R_4 + (I_3 - I_2)R_6 &= E_3
\end{aligned}
\tag{3.3}
$$

connecting the three (unknown) mesh currents to the known values of the resistances and e.m.f. sources. There is no advantage to be gained by applying Kirchhoff's laws to

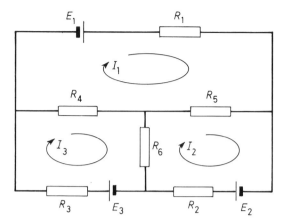

Fig. 3.1   A general three-loop resistance network.

The general three-loop circuit shown in Fig. 3.1 is, perhaps surprisingly at first glance, directly reducible to the standard Wheatstone bridge circuit:

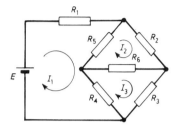

by simply setting $E_2 = E_3 = 0$. It is worth while comparing the circuit with Fig. 3.1 and convincing yourself that they are indeed equivalent. The Wheatstone bridge is an extremely important basic balance circuit with many applications – as a thermometer, a pressure gauge, a strain meter or a fluid velocity gauge (an anemometer) depending on the specific type of test resistor used in the circuit (see Lorrain and Corson, 1978).

any other path through the network – there are only three independent loops within the network, so that the equation for the whole outer loop, for example:

$$I_1 R_1 + I_2 R_2 + I_3 R_3 = E_1 + E_2 + E_3$$

is merely the sum of the three Equations (3.3), which adds no new information.

Straightforward rearrangement of (3.3) leads to

$$
\begin{aligned}
(R_1 + R_4 + R_5)I_1 - R_5 I_2 - R_4 I_3 &= E_1 \\
-R_5 I_1 + (R_2 + R_5 + R_6)I_2 - R_6 I_3 &= E_2 \\
-R_4 I_1 - R_6 I_2 + (R_3 + R_4 + R_6)I_3 &= E_3
\end{aligned}
\tag{3.4}
$$

Equations (3.4) are an example of a set of simultaneous linear algebraic equations in the three unknowns I_i ($i = 1,2,3$). The three equations relate three unknowns; generally it would seem reasonable to expect to be able to use these three relationships to specify uniquely the values of the mesh currents. If the resistors R_i ($i = 4,5,6$) in the common branches were shorted, then this is certainly possible, since the equations would decouple and take the particularly simple form:

$$
\begin{aligned}
I_1 &= E_1/R_1 \\
I_2 &= E_2/R_2 \\
\text{and } I_3 &= E_3/R_3
\end{aligned}
\tag{3.5}
$$

More generally, it is necessary to manipulate the Equations (3.4) to obtain specific values for the currents.

The independent equations for a general three-mesh resistance network such as this can always be summarized in the form

$$
\begin{aligned}
R_{11}I_1 - R_{12}I_2 - R_{13}I_3 &= E_1 \\
-R_{12}I_1 + R_{22}I_2 - R_{23}I_3 &= E_2 \\
-R_{13}I_1 - R_{23}I_2 + R_{33}I_3 &= E_3
\end{aligned}
$$

where R_{ii} is known as the self-resistance of mesh i, while R_{ij} is the **mutual (common) resistance** between meshes i and j. E_i is merely the algebraic sum of the voltage sources in mesh i.

Details of this algorithm are given in Chapter T3.

Solution of linear equations by Gaussian elimination

A number of approaches will be discussed in this chapter for the solution of sets of linear equations arising in a variety of applications. The first to be illustrated is the **Gaussian elimination algorithm**. This is a popular technique that has the advantage of being easy to describe in a systematic format for sets of equations of arbitrary size and which is very straightforward to implement as an automatic computer program.

Consider the particular example:

$$\begin{array}{rcrcrcrcr} 5 & I_1 & - & I_2 & - & I_3 & = & 10 \\ - & I_1 & + & 4\,I_2 & - & I_3 & = & 12 \\ - & I_1 & - & I_2 & + & 11\,I_3 & = & 4 \end{array} \qquad (3.6)$$

obtained from Equation (3.5) by using resistance values of $R_1 = 3\,\Omega$, $R_2 = 2\,\Omega$, $R_3 = 9\,\Omega$, $R_4 = R_5 = R_6 = 1\,\Omega$ and voltage sources $E_1 = 10$ V, $E_2 = 12$ V and $E_3 = 4$ V. Solve these equations by the Gaussian elimination algorithm.

Solution It is possible to add 1/5 of the first equation to each of the second and third, leading to:

$$5I_1 - I_2 - I_3 = 10$$

$$\frac{19}{5}\,I_2 - \frac{6}{5}\,I_3 = 14$$

$$-\frac{6}{5}\,I_2 + \frac{54}{5}\,I_3 = 6$$

so that I_1 no longer appears in the last pair of equations. Similarly, 6/19 times the second equation may now be added to the final equation, leading to

$$5I_1 - I_2 - I_3 = 10$$

$$\frac{19}{5}\,I_2 - \frac{6}{5}\,I_3 = 14 \qquad (3.8)$$

$$\frac{198}{19}\,I_3 = \frac{198}{19}$$

so that the equations are now in an hierarchical form, with each line containing one less unknown current than the one above. This forms the first part of the Gaussian elimination algorithm. The remainder of the method involves a process of back-substitution: the third equation shows that $I_3 = 1$ A; substitution of this result into the second equation gives

$$\frac{19}{5}\,I_2 - \frac{6}{5} = 14 \quad \Rightarrow \quad I_2 = 4 \text{ A}$$

and then, finally, substitution of both of these values into the top equation gives

$$5I_1 - 4 - 1 = 10 \quad \Rightarrow \quad I_1 = 3 \text{ A}$$

so that in a few systematic steps it is possible to obtain values for the three mesh currents in the circuit.

In general, networks such as this can be examined using mesh current analysis or node voltage analysis. If the network contains n nodes and b branches then a mesh analysis will lead to $b - n + 1$ linear independent equations, while nodal analysis will lead to $n - 1$ equations. The circuit here has six branches and four nodes – either method requires the solution of three equations. For further details and comparison of the two approaches see Boctor (1987) or Nilsson (1986).

The Gaussian elimination approach can, in theory, be applied to a set of equations of arbitrarily large dimensions. Unfortunately, the computational effort involved with performing the various multiplication and addition operations increase at a rate proportional to n^3, if the equations involve n unknowns. This makes the approach impractical for systems of more than 10–20 equations, and more advanced techniques are employed by most custom-built computer programs for solving such equations. For small systems of equations, however, the approach is rapid and popular.

Exercise 3.1 A simple three-mesh resistance network is shown in Fig. 3.2. Using mesh analysis and Gaussian elimination evaluate the mesh currents and find the resistor which dissipates the maximum power.

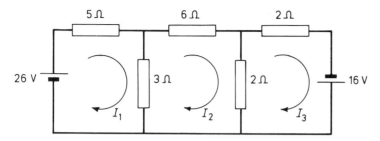

Fig. 3.2   A specific three-loop resistance network.

In some cases a set of equations may exhibit a particular symmetry or structure which can be exploited usefully, or they may simplify by decoupling into sets of smaller independent equations which can be manipulated separately. In such cases it may not be necessary to work through the Gaussian elimination algorithm.

Worked Application Example 3.3.

The manufacturers of a certain photoelectric device have guaranteed that it will produce a photocurrent, I, directly proportional to the incident light flux, f, given by $I = 50f$ (where I is in μA and f is in lumens) with a maximum error of $\pm 1.5\%$ for an operational range of input light intensities of 0.02–0.2 lm. Using accurately calibrated light sources, voltage supplies and meters the following measurements were obtained:

$f = 0.00$ lm: $I = 0.003$ μA
$f = 0.05$ lm: $I = 2.518$ μA
$f = 0.10$ lm: $I = 4.983$ μA

whereas the manufacturer's formula would have predicted values of 0, 2.5 and 5 μA respectively. Within the specified range, the measured discrepancies are all well within the claimed error bracket and do not invalidate the guarantee. Assuming that the photocurrent/light flux relationship is, in fact, more accurately represented by a quadratic formula, is the manufacturer's claim still likely to hold at an incident flux of 0.2 lm?

Solution   The best approach is to fit a general quadratic relationship

$$I = Af^2 + Bf + C$$

with three unknown constant coefficients, to the three accurate measurements and then use this second-order model to predict the photocurrent at 0.2 lm.

The measurements lead to the relationships

$$0.003 = 0.00\,A + 0.0000\,B + C$$
$$2.518 = 0.05\,A + 0.0025\,B + C$$
$$\text{and } 4.983 = 0.10\,A + 0.0100\,B + C$$

that is, a set of linear equations in the three unknown coefficients A, B and C. This is, in fact, another example of a nonlinear (in this case quadratic) problem leading to equations which are linear in the unknown coefficients. These equations can be solved readily without using Gaussian elimination, since it follows immediately that $C = 0.003$ to within experimental accuracy and then, subtracting twice the second equation from the third, that $B = 50.8$ and $A = -10$. The new experimental quadratic law is therefore

$$I = 0.003 + 50.8\,f - 10\,f^2$$

In theory this approach can be applied to fit a polynomial of any degree (say n) to a number of data points ($n + 1$) and the fit will require the solution of a set of ($n + 1$) linear equations for the ($n + 1$) unknown constant coefficients of the polynomial. In practice this is not sensible beyond a few (certainly less than 10) data points, however, and more suitable techniques exist for curve fitting to large numbers of data values.

The small nonzero value of C is an example of a constant offset in an instrument. It can be removed by a simple recalibration.

This formula predicts that an input light flux of 0.2 lm would produce a photocurrent of 9.763 μA, which is 2.4% below the manufacturer's predicted value. This indicates that further measurements are necessary to check that the device meets the specifications at higher light intensities and that it may possibly require replacing.

Insufficient and contradictory equations

Things can go wrong with the simple Gaussian algorithm outlined above, however, and it is useful to illustrate how some problems can arise in practice.

Worked Application Example 3.4

At the heart of any digital computer is the central processing unit (c.p.u.), which is where the binary numbers (the data) held in the computer's memory are transferred in order to undergo some desired mathematical operation (an instruction, as defined by the program). The c.p.u. carries out each instruction at very high speeds, but can carry out only a small number of very basic operations such as addition or subtraction and scaling a number by a power of two. More complicated operations are available only as pre-defined subprograms which break the single operation of multiplication, for example, into a series of simpler processes of addition and scaling. This means that certain mathematical manipulations take far longer for a computer to perform than others. For example, addition and subtraction are fairly basic (and, in fact, equivalent) operations, while each multiplication is a composite operation and takes rather longer to carry out. Likewise, division is a little more complicated than multiplication, and hence slightly slower, while raising numbers to any power is a significantly more difficult task for the c.p.u. and will take up much more time than any of its more basic actions.

A test program has given the results that a million evaluations of each of the four expressions:

$$\frac{(1 + 3)^2}{2} \qquad \frac{7 \times (1 + 2 + 3^2 + 4^3)^2}{11}$$

$$\frac{(7 + 4 \times 3)^2}{(3 + 11)} \times \frac{(1 + 3)^2}{(1 + 99)} \quad \text{and} \quad \frac{(2^2 + 3^3 + 4^4)}{(1 + 2 \times 3 + 3 \times 4 + 4 \times 5)}$$

take the c.p.u. times of 20 seconds, 53 seconds, 47 seconds and 61 seconds, respectively. How long does each of the arithmetic operations take?

Solution If the time required for the operations of addition, multiplication, division and raising to a power are denoted by a, m, d and p, respectively, then the first expression involves one a operation, none of m, one d and one p for each of the million evaluations, leading to a total time of

$$(a \qquad + \ d + \ p) \times 10^6 = 20 \text{ seconds}$$

Likewise, the other three expressions require that

$$(3a + \ m + \ d + 3p) \times 10^6 = 53 \text{ seconds}$$
$$(4a + 2m + 2d + 2p) \times 10^6 = 47 \text{ seconds}$$
$$(5a + 3m + \ d + 3p) \times 10^6 = 61 \text{ seconds}$$

Hence, the aim is to find the solution of the four linear equations:

$$\begin{aligned}
a \qquad + \ d + \ p &= 20 \times 10^{-6} \\
3a + \ m + \ d + 3p &= 53 \times 10^{-6} \\
4a + 2m + 2d + 2p &= 47 \times 10^{-6} \\
5a + 3m + \ d + 3p &= 61 \times 10^{-6}
\end{aligned} \qquad (3.9)$$

Applying the first step of the Gaussian elimination algorithm leads to

$$
\begin{array}{rcl}
a \quad\; + \; d + \; p = & 20 \times 10^{-6} \\
m - 2d \quad\;\;\; = & -7 \times 10^{-6} \\
2m - 2d - 2p = & -33 \times 10^{-6} \\
3m - 4d - 2p = & -39 \times 10^{-6}
\end{array}
$$

It is then possible to continue with the reduction to triangular form to obtain

$$
\begin{array}{rcl}
a + \quad\; + \; d + \; p = & 20 \times 10^{-6} \\
m - 2d \quad\;\;\; = & -7 \times 10^{-6} \\
2d - 2p = & -19 \times 10^{-6} \\
2d - 2p = & -18 \times 10^{-6}
\end{array}
$$

which cannot lead to a sensible solution: the last two equations are clearly inconsistent. These are known as a set of **contradictory** equations. They have arisen due to a combination of two factors: firstly, the expressions which have led to the l.h.s. of the equations were badly chosen in that they are not independent; and secondly, the numbers which have been listed on the r.h.s. are inappropriate, almost certainly because some important factor has been neglected in the system model or because the measured numbers are subject to experimental uncertainties.

This result is the reason that it was sensible to avoid finding the time per addition operation by the simple expedient of timing 10^6 additions alone: any such measured time would be the time required for the additions plus contributions from other unknown effects. By taking five independent measurements it would be possible to solve five equations for the (desired) variables $a, m, d, p,$ and another, c (say), where c is the contribution from all other effects which take c.p.u. time consistently from each program.

Worked Application Example 3.5

In the above example, further examination of the problem has shown that in each test exactly one second of c.p.u. time is used up as the variable which counts out the number of evaluations is incremented from 1 to 10^6. Solve the modified problem for the required times of the operations a, m, d and p.

Solution   The equations are similar to (3.9); the only difference is that the numbers on the r.h.s. are reduced by one to remove the contribution of the loop counter:

$$
\begin{array}{rcl}
a \quad\;\;\; + \; d + \;\; p = & 19 \times 10^{-6} \\
3a + \;\; m + \;\; d + 3p = & 52 \times 10^{-6} \\
4a + 2m + 2d + 2p = & 46 \times 10^{-6} \\
5a + 3m + \;\; d + 3p = & 60 \times 10^{-6}
\end{array} \tag{3.10}
$$

The Gaussian elimination algorithm will produce exactly the same results for the l.h.s., but, after reduction to triangular form, the new equations take the form:

$$
\begin{array}{rcl}
a \quad\;\; + \; d + \;\; p = & 19 \times 10^{-6} \\
m - 2d \quad\;\;\; = & -5 \times 10^{-6} \\
2d - 2p = & -20 \times 10^{-6} \\
0 = & 0
\end{array}
$$

These are a set of **insufficient** equations: the measured data are not inconsistent in any way with the equations, but the four equations form a dependent set. Since there are really only three independent constraints on the four unknown variables it is quite impossible to pinpoint a single solution: the best that can be done is to obtain a family of parameterized solutions. Suppose that the value of p is $k \times 10^{-6}$, for some parameter k, then clearly, from the third, second and first equation in sequence:

$$
d = (k - 10) \times 10^{-6} \quad m = (2k - 25) \times 10^{-6} \quad \text{and} \quad a = (29 - 2k) \times 10^{-6}
$$

so that the solution can be expressed in vector form as

$$
\begin{bmatrix} a \\ m \\ d \\ p \end{bmatrix} = \begin{bmatrix} 29 \\ -25 \\ -10 \\ 0 \end{bmatrix} + k \begin{bmatrix} -2 \\ 2 \\ 1 \\ 1 \end{bmatrix} \quad \text{microseconds}
$$

In cases where the set of equations turns out be insufficient, it may be possible to insert additional information by the use of 'sensible' physical constraints. For example, it is reasonable to restrict the range of allowable temperatures of a controlled system (such as a thermal regenerator) by disallowing values less than absolute zero or greater than the melting point of the weakest exposed system component. In this particular example the requirement that the time predicted for any of the four arithmetic operations be positive restricts the value of the parameter k to lie in the range (12.5, 14.5) – any value of k outside of this narrow range will predict a negative time for one or more of the operations!

This is the parametric equation of a line in four-dimensional space and is the most general form of solution that can be given from the information available.

In summary, it can be seen that there are three basic forms of behaviour which can occur in sets of n linear equations in n unknowns:
1. It may be that the set may be solved to obtain a unique solution with no difficulty.
2. An insufficient set may be obtained, giving rise to an infinite family of solutions.
3. The equations may be contradictory and lead to no possible solution whatsoever.

These cases will manifest themselves in the Gaussian elimination method respectively by:
1. No particular problems being encountered.
2. Two equations turning out to be exact multiples of each other, or the trivial result $0 = 0$ being obtained.
3. An obvious contradiction being obtained at any stage in the algorithm.

Ill-conditioning of linear equations

The mathematical tools discussed so far in this chapter assume implicitly that the equations are, in fact, exactly true. In practice, such an assumption is usually invalid and the methods must be extended to cope with such practical realities. In particular, one point that must be raised is the **robustness** of any solution of a set of equations to errors in the values of the measured coefficients of the original equations. Clearly, it is undesirable that small numerical uncertainties introduced into the equations should be able to have any unduly large effect on the nature of the solution. The problem is best illustrated by some examples.

Application Example 3.6

For further details see O'Reilly (1989) or Smol *et al.* (1981).

The design of colour television broadcast systems in the 1960s was constrained severely by two operational requirements: that the older monochrome televisions should be capable of receiving a good black-and-white picture from a colour transmission and that the new colour receivers should accept an old monochrome form of signal and produce a good black-and-white picture. It was found to be possible to meet these requirements of compatibility and reverse compatibility by adding a narrowband high-frequency chrominance (colour) signal on top of the existing luminance (relative brightness) signal, which tends to be concentrated towards the low-frequency side of the video band. The signals were transmitted as a luminance signal, E_y, given by

$$E_y = l E_r + m E_g + n E_b$$

composed of a weighted sum of red–green–blue (RGB) signals, which was compatible with the old system, and two new signals carrying the extra colour information in a strange form – as colour difference signals. These are defined by

$$d_r = E_r - E_y$$
$$\text{and } d_b = E_b - E_y$$

for the red and blue difference signals respectively.

The decoding circuitry is based on a network of resistors and operational amplifiers which produce three CRT grid cathode voltages proportional to E_r, E_g and E_b. Such a circuit is sometimes known as a matrix circuit.

These three signals are decoded at the receiver to obtain individual cathode voltages for the three colours, so that the circuitry effectively has to solve the set of simultaneous equations:

$$\begin{aligned} l E_r + m E_g + n E_b &= E_y \\ E_r &= E_y + d_r \\ E_b &= E_y + d_b \end{aligned}$$

for the unknowns E_r, E_g and E_b in terms of the received signals E_y, d_r and d_b and a preset triad of luminosity coefficients l, m and n (chosen such that $l + m + n = 1$). This may seem a fairly trivial set of equations, but it is enlightening to consider a realistic set of values. The standard values of the luminosity coefficients are 0.30, 0.59 and 0.11, so that if signals $E_y = 2.81$ V, $d_r = -0.81$ V and $d_b = 1.19$ V are input into the decoding network then the above equations readily lead to

$E_r = 2$ V, $E_g = 3$ V and $E_b = 4$ V

(substituting into the first equation). If the video signals are now corrupted by a constant positive offset of 0.02 V, so that new input voltages of $E_y = 2.83$ V, $d_r = -0.79$ V and $d_b = 1.21$ V are received, then the decoded RGB signals now turn out to be

$E_r = 2.040$ V, $E_g = 3.006$ V and $E_b = 4.040$ V

so that the disturbance to the RGB output is only about 2% at worst.

It may seem somewhat arbitrary to choose to transmit the red and blue difference values along with the luminosity signal. Three signals are definitely needed because three unknown and independent cathode voltages must be obtained at the receiver. The luminosity signal is necessary for compatibility, and the choice of the red and blue difference signals arises from a desire to minimize the effects of noise. To see this, suppose that an alternative broadcast system employs a green difference signal, d_g, instead of the blue. This leads to very similar equations:

$$\begin{aligned} l E_r + m E_g + n E_b &= E_y \\ E_r &= E_y + d_r \\ E_g &= E_y + d_g \end{aligned}$$

so that with the standard luminosity coefficients and received signal values of $E_y = 2.81$ V, $d_r = -0.81$ V and $d_g = 0.19$ V the full decoded values are

$E_r = 2$ V, $E_g = 3$ V and $E_b = 4$ V

as above. If all of the transmitted signals are again corrupted by a positive offset of 0.02 V, the decoded cathode voltages are

$E_r = 2.040$ V, $E_g = 3.040$ V and $E_b = 3.858$ V

showing that the final effect is significantly more severe in this case. These decoded signals are less robust to outside interference.

Generally, it is a bad idea to use a green difference signal because of the large luminosity coefficient assigned to E_g: a value of m near unity produces

$d_g = E_g - E_y = l E_r + (1 - m) E_g + n E_b$

where l, $(1 - m)$ and n are all small numbers. This means that the green difference signal will be weaker than the others and is rather more prone to corruption by noise.

These apparently arbitrary values of the luminosity coefficients arise because of the different electron/optical properties of the phosphors used to coat the screen of a colour receiver.

Nature has assigned these luminosity coefficients: there is nothing that can be done except to transmit those signals which make best use of the magnitudes and bandwidths available, given the natural physical restrictions.

The green difference signal has the smallest **signal-to-noise** ratio.

In cases where a set of simultaneous equations arises from a set of experimental measurements, as in the TV transmission example above, the values of the coefficients may be uncertain and subject to experimental error. The different degrees to which the solution of the equations is disturbed by noise is referred to as the **conditioning** of the equations: if the solutions are disturbed only by the same broad percentage errors as are introduced into the coefficients then the equations are described as being **well conditioned**, while those that change rather more than might be hoped arise from **ill-conditioned** equations.

Clearly, it is necessary to define some reliable measure which determines the extent to which such inaccuracies actually disturb the solution of the equation. A suitable indicator of the likely robustness of a solution to data uncertainties is the determinant of the n^2 coefficients which appear on the l.h.s. of the equations. Chapter T3 defines determinants and shows that the magnitude of the determinant relative to the magnitudes of the largest elements in the equations can be used as a measure of the conditioning of the equations:

Worked Application Example 3.7

Consider again the set of Equations (3.6) arising from the resistance network of Example 3.2. Examine the conditioning of the equations.

Solution The determinant of the l.h.s. of the equations is given by

$$\Delta = \begin{vmatrix} 5 & -1 & -1 \\ -1 & 4 & -1 \\ -1 & -1 & 11 \end{vmatrix}$$

which can be evaluated from the definitions given in Chapter T3 (p. 142) or, preferably, by using some of the rules given therein for the manipulation of the determinant before expansion:

$$\Delta = \begin{vmatrix} 5 & -1 & -1 \\ -1 & 4 & -1 \\ -1 & -1 & 11 \end{vmatrix} = \begin{vmatrix} 0 & 0 & -1 \\ -6 & 5 & -1 \\ 54 & -12 & 11 \end{vmatrix}$$

$$= -1[(-6)(-12)-(5)(54)] = 198$$

where five times the third column has been added to the first column, the third column has also been subtracted from the second column, and then the determinant has been expanded by the first row.

The conditioning of the equations is determined by the size of this determinant relative to that of the product of the largest elements. It is possible to scale each equation so that the size of the largest element in each equation is unity: in this particular case it is necessary to divide by 5, 4 and 11 respectively. Hence, the determinant of the scaled equations is $198/(5 \times 4 \times 11) = 0.9$. This is close to unity and it seems safe to conclude that the equations will be fairly well conditioned.

As a test of this conclusion, it is interesting to inspect the effect on the solution of altering the coefficient of I_3 in the third equation from 11 to 12 and 10. This 9% change in the coefficient corresponds to a value of 9 ± 1 ohm for the R_3 resistor of Equations (3.3). A series of standard manipulations with the Gaussian algorithm lead to;

$$R_3 = 8 \; \Omega: I_1 = 3.03 \;\text{A}, I_2 = 4.03 \;\text{A, and } I_3 = 1.11 \;\text{A}$$
$$R_3 = 9 \; \Omega: I_1 = 3.00 \;\text{A}, I_2 = 4.00 \;\text{A, and } I_3 = 1.00 \;\text{A}$$
$$R_3 = 10 \; \Omega: I_1 = 2.98 \;\text{A}, I_2 = 3.97 \;\text{A, and } I_3 = 0.91 \;\text{A}$$

so that, as indicated by the determinant, the worst percentage variation in any of the solution values is only of the same order as the percentage change in the uncertain coefficient.

Effectively, each row of the determinant is being scaled by a constant, and hence the determinant is adjusted by the product of all such multiplicative constants: see Chapter T3 for details.

Worked Application Example 3.8

The set of equations

$$\begin{aligned} a \quad\quad + d + p &= 19 \times 10^{-6} \\ 3a + m + d + 3p &= 52 \times 10^{-6} \\ 4a + 2m + 2d + 2p &= 46 \times 10^{-6} \\ 5a + 3m + d + 2p &= 46 \times 10^{-6} \end{aligned}$$

(3.11)

is similar to that obtained in Example 3.5 for the c.p.u. times required for different mathematical operations with a digital computer. The fourth equation is slightly different from that of Equation (3.9), a different mathematical test expression having been chosen to ensure that these equations form an independent set. Examine the conditioning of these equations.

Solution The determinant of the l.h.s. is

$$\Delta = \begin{vmatrix} 1 & 0 & 1 & 1 \\ 3 & 1 & 1 & 3 \\ 4 & 2 & 2 & 2 \\ 5 & 3 & 1 & 2 \end{vmatrix}$$

which can be evaluated to give $\Delta = -2$ (check! – ideally by manipulation of the rows and columns). The product of the largest element in each row is $(1)(3)(4)(5) = 60$, so that the measure of the conditioning of the equations is $|-2/60| = 1/30$. This indicates that the solution is going to tend to react badly to changes in any of the coefficients.

Use Gaussian elimination to show that the solution of the Equations (3.11) is $a = 1$ μs, $m = 3$ μs, $d = 4$ μs, and $p = 14$ μs.

Also solve the modified set where the r.h.s. of the fourth equation is increased by approximately 2% to a value of 47×10^{-6}, and show that the solution is changed significantly to: $a = 3$ μs, $m = 1$ μs, $d = 3$ μs, and $p = 13$ μs.

Exercise 3.2

If the r.h.s. of the third equation is instead modified in this fashion the solution becomes $a = -1.5\,\mu$s, $m = 6\,\mu$s, $d = 5.5$ μs, and $p = 15\,\mu$s which is physically ridiculous.

Solution of linear equations using determinants

The Gaussian elimination approach has considerable utility for small sets of linear equations, but other approaches are possible and may be more suitable in certain circumstances. One common approach is Cramer's rule, which expresses the solution of a set of $n \times n$ equations in a compact determinantal form.

Chapter T3 gives a complete discussion of Cramer's rule.

An in-flight satellite navigational system interchanges precisely timed signals with three ground-based tracking stations. By accurate measurement of the time-lag and bearing of the incoming signal, each station can define a plane in which the satellite lies at that instant, and at one particular time the measurements give the three planes

$$\begin{aligned} x - 2y - z &= 1 \\ 2x + y - z &= -1 \\ \text{and } 3x - 2y - 2z &= 2 \end{aligned}$$

in Cartesian coordinates.

Find the measured position of the satellite (a) by Gaussian elimination, (b) by Cramer's rule, evaluating the determinants from first principles, (c) by Cramer's rule, manipulating and simplifying the determinants before evaluation.

Worked Application Example 3.9

Solution (a) Proceeding through the steps of the Gaussian elimination algorithm transforms the original equations into

$$\begin{aligned} x - 2y - z &= 1 \\ 5y + z &= -3 \quad (r_2 \leftarrow r_2 - 2r_1) \\ \text{and} \qquad 4y + z &= -1 \quad (r_3 \leftarrow r_3 - 3r_1) \end{aligned}$$

It is sensible to include some such brief notes at the sides of the equations as an indication of the specific moves carried out at each stage.

and then into

$$x - 2y - z = 1$$
$$5y + z = -3$$

and $\qquad z/5 = 7/5 \qquad (r_3 \leftarrow r_3 - 4/5\, r_2)$

where the notation $r_i \leftarrow r_i + \lambda r_j$ indicates that a new row has been created by adding a multiple λ of row j to the old row i.

The process of back-substitution can then proceed, leading to

(i) $\quad z = 7$
(ii) $\quad 5y + 7 = -3 \Rightarrow y = -2$
and (iii) $\quad x + 4 - 7 = 1 \Rightarrow x = 4$

(b) The Cramer's rule formulation gives

$$\frac{x}{\begin{vmatrix} 1 & -2 & -1 \\ -1 & 1 & -1 \\ 2 & -2 & -2 \end{vmatrix}} = \frac{y}{\begin{vmatrix} 1 & 1 & -1 \\ 2 & -1 & -1 \\ 3 & 2 & -2 \end{vmatrix}} = \frac{z}{\begin{vmatrix} 1 & -2 & 1 \\ 2 & 1 & -1 \\ 3 & -2 & 2 \end{vmatrix}} = \frac{1}{\begin{vmatrix} 1 & -2 & -1 \\ 2 & 1 & -1 \\ 3 & -2 & -2 \end{vmatrix}}$$

or, in shorthand notation,

$$\frac{x}{|\Delta_x|} = \frac{y}{|\Delta_y|} = \frac{z}{|\Delta_z|} = \frac{1}{|\Delta|}$$

where the determinants are given by (expanding by the first row)

$$|\Delta_x| = -4 + 8 + 0 = 4$$
$$|\Delta_y| = 4 + 1 - 7 = -2$$
$$|\Delta_z| = 0 + 14 - 7 = 7$$
$$|\Delta| = -4 - 2 + 7 = 1$$

so that the solution is

$$\frac{x}{4} = \frac{y}{-2} = \frac{z}{7} = \frac{1}{1}$$

Check these expansions in full from first principles – and note how long it takes!

(c) As for part (b) there are four determinants to simplify. Here,

$$|\Delta_x| = \begin{vmatrix} 1 & -2 & -1 \\ -1 & 1 & -1 \\ 2 & -2 & -2 \end{vmatrix} = \begin{vmatrix} 1 & -2 & -1 \\ 0 & -1 & -2 \\ 0 & 2 & 0 \end{vmatrix} = \begin{vmatrix} -1 & -2 \\ 2 & 0 \end{vmatrix} = 4$$

$$\begin{aligned} r_2 &\leftarrow r_2 + r_1 \\ r_3 &\leftarrow r_3 - 2r_1 \end{aligned}$$

where the notation is similar to that used in part (a) and the final 3×3 determinant has been expanded by the first column, thus exploiting the zeros that have been (deliberately) created by the manipulations. Similarly,

$$|\Delta_y| = \begin{vmatrix} 1 & 1 & -1 \\ 2 & -1 & -1 \\ 3 & 2 & -2 \end{vmatrix} = \begin{vmatrix} 1 & 1 & -1 \\ 0 & -3 & 1 \\ 0 & -1 & 1 \end{vmatrix} = \begin{vmatrix} -3 & 1 \\ -1 & 1 \end{vmatrix} = -2$$

$$\begin{aligned} r_2 &\leftarrow r_2 - 2r_1 \\ r_3 &\leftarrow r_3 - 3r_1 \end{aligned}$$

$$|\Delta_z| = \begin{vmatrix} 1 & -2 & 1 \\ 2 & 1 & -1 \\ 3 & -2 & 2 \end{vmatrix} = \begin{vmatrix} 1 & -2 & 1 \\ 0 & 5 & -3 \\ 0 & 4 & -1 \end{vmatrix} = \begin{vmatrix} 5 & -3 \\ 4 & -1 \end{vmatrix} = 7$$

$$\begin{aligned} r_2 &\leftarrow r_2 - 2r_1 \\ r_3 &\leftarrow r_3 - 3r_1 \end{aligned}$$

$$|\Delta| = \begin{vmatrix} 1 & -2 & -1 \\ 2 & 1 & -1 \\ 3 & -2 & -2 \end{vmatrix} = \begin{vmatrix} 1 & -2 & -1 \\ 0 & 5 & 1 \\ 0 & 4 & 1 \end{vmatrix} = \begin{vmatrix} 5 & 1 \\ 4 & 1 \end{vmatrix} = 1$$

$$r_2 \leftarrow r_2 - 2r_1$$
$$r_3 \leftarrow r_3 - 3r_1$$

$$\Rightarrow \quad \frac{x}{4} = \frac{y}{-2} = \frac{z}{7} = \frac{1}{1}$$

as before.

It would be quite acceptable to manipulate the determinant by adding columns or making zeros appear elsewhere. The main trick is to simplify at least one row or column – exploiting structure or symmetry if there happens to be any – and then expand the determinant by that row or column.

In terms of sheer effort, the above example indicates that for a third-order problem Gaussian elimination is probably easiest while Cramer's rule from first principles is likely to be hardest. For small systems of equations it is very much a matter of personal choice which method you employ and it is sensible to practise both for the time being. For medium systems of equations (say 4–8) Gaussian elimination should be the most suitable by far for hand calculation and for larger systems even the most dedicated masochist will tend to reach for a computer (which for up to a few tens of equations will probably also use a form of Gaussian elimination).

For an equation with functional coefficients (such as: $t^2 x + 2ty + (t^2 - 4)z = 3e^{-t}$, where the numerical coefficients are functions of time) it is probably easier and neater, however, to use Cramer's rule rather than Gaussian elimination.

Solve the resistance network Equations (3.6) by using Cramer's rule and simplifying the determinants using the manipulation rules 1–6 given in Chapter T3.

Exercise 3.3

The remainder of this chapter will illustrate the application of matrix methods to the investigation of problems involving sets of linear equations. The theory of matrices provides a more powerful tool than those discussed so far and has a more wide-reaching applicability in practical problems.

Why should matrices interest an engineer?

Matrix algebra forms the basis for theoretical studies of multivariable engineering systems as reflected by the frequent appearances of chapters on 'matrix methods' in books on modern control theory or circuit theory. Some particular reasons why matrices are so useful are:

1. They form a compact representation, and enable the rapid solution of systems of linear algebraic equations (arising in a multitude of applications).
2. Matrices give a neat mathematical form for expressing the effect of rotations in, for example, aerospace applications and computer graphics for CAD, or the transformations/distortions associated with general mechanical stress as occurs in the piezoelectric effect in ferroelectric crystals.
3. They allow the modelling of networked systems – resistance networks and linear element networks specifically, but also flow and transportation systems in general. In particular their use for circuit analysis in mesh or nodal form is very common – it is possible to manipulate matrices in a fashion that would be near impossible with the corresponding set of linear equations.
4. Systems of multivariable coupled linear differential equations may be examined by

Such as Boctor (1987), Franklin *et al.* (1986) and Nilsson (1986).

Computer aided design (CAD) is now an established and important approach to system design in many fields, including circuit design and analysis, device manufacture and control system applications.

Such a search for internal structure is closely connected to the mathematical topic called group theory.

See, for example, Lindsay (1967).

This probabilistic approach to transitions using matrices is based on the mathematical topic of Markov processes or Markov chains.

An application of the least squares technique is given in Example 3.13.

combining the theory of the Laplace transforms (Jeffrey, 1989) with matrix methods. The detailed treatment of such systems is beyond the scope of this text.

5. Matrices enable the investigation of the structure of a physical system – whether it partitions naturally into smaller sub-units, whether these sub-units are perhaps independent, what their important time-dependent properties are, and so on.

6. The quantum theory of the electronic structure of devices relies heavily on matrices. In fact, quantum mechanics was formulated originally in two forms; matrix mechanics and wave mechanics, which later proved to be effectively equivalent. Modern quantum theory uses both notations and approaches in a hybrid fashion, applying the more appropriate tool as required.

7. Matrices arise in probability theory and the transition probability matrix may be used, for example, to contain the information about the likelihood of electronic or optical transitions occurring in a quantum electrical system such as a laser.

8. Optimization techniques are used for finding the optimum operating conditions of a multivariable controlled system (a plant), sometimes subject to constraints on the system variables – matrices can provide a useful tool in these circumstances using least squares techniques.

9. Finally (in this far from complete list!), matrices are useful as straightforward carriers of information – for holding lookup tables of data, sets of experimental values, digitized images or encrypted signals, etc.

Before going on to illustration the techniques of matrix algebra in a range of applications, it is worth giving an example which stresses that cases may arise where the standard concept of matrix multiplication as defined in Chapter T3 (p. 148) is meaningless or of little use.

Application Example 3.10

These methods are widely used in areas such as signal analysis, image processing and digital holography.

Fourier series and transforms (see Jeffrey, 1989) are the tools commonly used with regard to the frequency analysis of periodic and non-periodic functions respectively. The methods enable the functions to be broken up into component sine and cosine contributions of varying frequencies and allow a detailed spectral analysis of a signal or image.

Image processing involves the use of matrices as information arrays. A monochrome still picture may be scanned by, for example, a video camera and submitted to an analog-to-digital converter which digitizes the image by sampling the value of the light intensity over some rectangular mesh of coordinate points. This set of values (say $m \times n$ of them) may be readily stored in an $m \times n$ matrix on a computer – where it can be rapidly manipulated and modified. This matrix carries all of the information about the digitized picture, but it is not necessarily sensible to manipulate the matrix by the ordinary rules of matrix algebra. It is not really meaningful, for example, to try to assign physical significance to the determinant of the matrix – and multiplication by another matrix would produce very odd effects if the resultant matrix was still interpreted as a picture! Such information arrays still need to be manipulated, however. An information array such as this, where shades of grey are stored as numerical matrix elements, can be subjected to a two-dimensional finite Fourier transform. This mathematical procedure simulates the operation of a perfect lens – transforming the basic array of luminance information into an array containing the same information in spatial frequency form.

When dealing with acoustic signals it is possible to consider the signal as being constructed out of many sinusoidal components of varying frequencies (a spectral analysis of the signal). The frequencies, f, and wavelengths, λ, of the component signals being related by the usual expression: $f = v/\lambda$, where v is the speed of sound in that medium. In image processing it is possible in a similar fashion to consider an optical signal to be composed of sinusoidal signals which correspond to different degrees of detail within the image. For images it is thus possible to define a spatial frequency which is related to the component spatial wavelength in a similar reciprocal fashion. A pattern of close, narrow black-and-white strips would contain a great deal of short-wavelength optical information and thus is composed of high spatial frequencies. A broader, less detailed, pattern of wide strips would contain rather

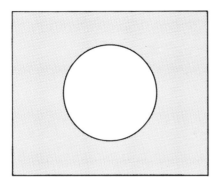

Fig. 3.3   The form of a low-pass filter for use with two-dimensional information arrays. The corresponding matrix elements are assigned the value 1 if they lie within the central circle and 0 if they lie in the shaded outer section. The radius of the circle defines a cut-off for the pass band of the matrix, because this matrix will pass unchanged those elements in the centre of the matrix when element-by-element multiplication is used.

larger wavelength information and thus corresponds to the lower spatial frequencies.

The Fourier-transformed array has no obvious visual significance, but may be interpreted as containing the information about the fine detail of the picture (the high spatial frequency information) near its edges and the less detailed broad light/dark trends (the low spatial frequency information) near its centre. Subjecting the frequency array to a similar Fourier transform operation (another lens) reconstructs the original image.

The frequency array may, however, be modified, attenuated or filtered before reconstruction – thus dramatically affecting the reconstructed image. For example, multiplying the frequency information matrix element by element with the filter shown in Fig. 3.3 simulates the effect of a low pass filter – the zero elements outside of the central circle destroy the high-frequency information so that upon reconstruction a rather fuzzier image is obtained. The operation of element-by-element multiplication used here is very different to the ordinary algebra of matrix multiplication – the method is chosen to suit this particular task.

It turns out that ordinary matrix multiplication is most usually the appropriate tool, arising commonly in a wide variety of engineering applications – particularly circuit analysis and control systems.

To redress the balance a little, however, it is useful to consider some of the many physical situations where ordinary matrix multiplication is the appropriate tool to use.

A **two-port** network, sometimes known as a **quadripole** or **four-terminal** network, usually consists of a number of impedances connected together in such a fashion as to present a black-box system with two input terminals and two output terminals. Such units may be designed with a variety of detailed properties and connected together in series, the output of one unit forming the input of another, to construct attenuators or filters which modify the input electrical signal in a frequency-dependent fashion. The frequency-dependent problem will not be discussed here, but the matrix techniques commonly used in such transistor (*amplifying*) circuits may be illustrated with simple two-port d.c. resistance networks.

For example, consider the (very) simple network displayed in Fig. 3.4a, which consists of a single shunt resistor. Clearly, the output electrical parameters can be expressed in terms of the electrical inputs by

Application Example 3.11

Perhaps passing low-frequency signals to the output terminals unattenuated but effectively suppressing the higher frequencies beyond some cut off frequency – acting as a low pass filter.

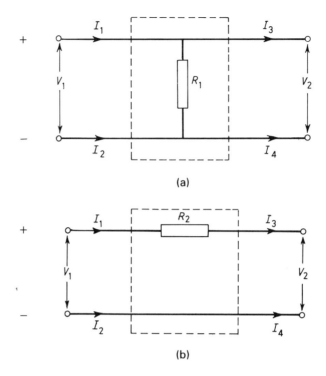

Fig. 3.4 (a) A single parallel resistor two-port section.
(b) A single series resistor two-port section.

Laplace transform techniques (see Jeffrey, 1989) are commonly used to reduce the description of two-port networks involving inductors and capacitors to a straightforward algebraic form. A detailed discussion, including definitions of hybrid matrices, inductance matrices, admittance matrices and transmission matrices can be found in Desoer and Kuh (1969).

$$V_2 = V_1$$
$$I_3 = I_1 - V_1/R_1$$
and $I_4 = I_2 + V_1/R_1$

and this can be expressed in matrix form as

$$\begin{bmatrix} V_2 \\ I_3 \\ I_4 \end{bmatrix} = \begin{bmatrix} 1 & 0 & 0 \\ -1/R_1 & 1 & 0 \\ 1/R_1 & 0 & 1 \end{bmatrix} \begin{bmatrix} V_1 \\ I_1 \\ I_2 \end{bmatrix}$$

summarized in the notation

$$s_{out} = P \, s_{in}$$

where s contains the electrical information at the input and output ports and P is the matrix which expresses the detailed resistive properties of this particular system.

An even simpler two-port element arises for a single series resistor, as shown in Fig. 3.4b. For this configuration the outputs are

$$V_2 = V_1 - I_1 R_2$$
$$I_3 = I_1$$
and $I_4 = I_2$

or

$$\begin{bmatrix} V_2 \\ I_3 \\ I_4 \end{bmatrix} = \begin{bmatrix} 1 & -R_2 & 0 \\ 0 & 1 & 0 \\ 0 & 0 & 1 \end{bmatrix} \begin{bmatrix} V_1 \\ I_1 \\ I_2 \end{bmatrix}$$

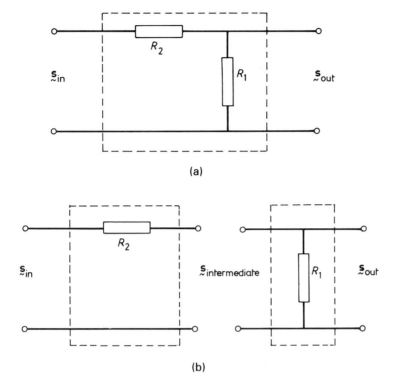

Fig. 3.5   (a) A more complicated two-port section.
(b) The individual components of this particular example.

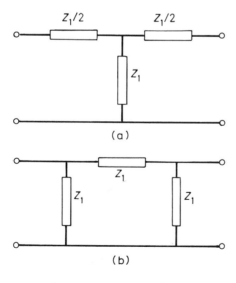

Fig. 3.6   (a) A T-section.
(b) A π-section.

which can be shortened to

$$s_{out} = S \, s_{in}$$

These two, very simple, two-port elements may now be used to build up more general structures so that, for example, the quadripole shown in Fig. 3.5a may be partitioned up into the two basic elements shown in Fig. 3.5b. It is easy to check that the correct way to combine the matrix representations of these subsystems is, in fact, ordinary matrix multiplication, which means that we can combine

$$s_{out} = P \, s_{intermediate}$$
with
$$s_{intermediate} = S \, s_{in}$$
leading to
$$s_{out} = P \, S \, s_{in}$$

In this way it is possible to express the properties of a general black-box two-port system of this type in terms of a 3×3 system matrix which can be constructed out of a product of only two or three basic types of component matrices. In realistic filter applications many impedances may be connected together in a ladder network which can be broken down into named, well understood subsections such as those shown in Fig. 3.6.

Certain types of matrix appear in diverse applications frequently enough to merit specific names. For instance, in Example 3.11 the system matrices **P** and **S** represent the transfer characteristics of the circuit sections shown in Fig. 3.4a and 3.4b. **P** and **S** are examples of **lower** and **upper triangular** matrices respectively.

Now consider the five-mesh circuit shown in Fig. 3.7. The matrix equation relating the vector of mesh currents to the vector of sources of e.m.f. can rapidly be seen to be

$$\begin{bmatrix} 3R & -2R & 0 & 0 & 0 \\ -2R & 5R & -2R & 0 & 0 \\ 0 & -2R & 5R & -2R & 0 \\ 0 & 0 & -2R & 5R & -2R \\ 0 & 0 & 0 & -2R & 3R \end{bmatrix} \begin{bmatrix} I_1 \\ I_2 \\ I_3 \\ I_4 \\ I_5 \end{bmatrix} = \begin{bmatrix} E \\ 0 \\ 0 \\ 0 \\ 0 \end{bmatrix}$$

This is effectively a multivariable statement of Ohm's law: the resistive properties of the circuit network as a whole are collected together in the resistance matrix and a more general form of Ohm's law, $v = Ri$, applies to the whole network. In this particular case the structure of the network leads to a resistance matrix which is said to be **banded** in form.

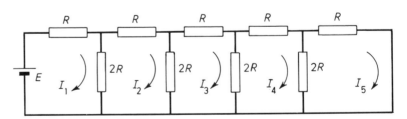

Fig. 3.7 A simple 5-loop resistance network.

Solution of linear equations using matrices

Matrices provide a more powerful and general approach to the solution of sets of linear equations than either Gaussian elimination or Cramer's rule. When a set of

---

(margin notes)

Note that the left–right order of the matrices is reversed relative to the left–right order of the quadripole subelements. This is because operations $A_1 \ldots A_n$ applied to a vector **x** in the order $1, \ldots, n$ will produce a final vector given by $A_n A_{n-1} \ldots A_1 x$ – the rightmost vector operates first upon the operand **x**.

This particular type of banded matrix is often referred to as a **tridiagonal matrix**.

48

linear equations are expressed in matrix form, the matrix of coefficients operates on all of the unknown variables gathered together into a single vector. If it is possible to multiply both sides of the matrix equation by the inverse of the matrix of coefficients then the values of all unknown variables can be obtained directly. Chapter T3 (p. 151) discusses the definition of an inverse matrix and the circumstances under which it can be obtained.

The linear Equations (3.6), describing a particular three-loop resistance network, can be expressed in matrix form as

$$\begin{bmatrix} 5 & -1 & -1 \\ -1 & 4 & -1 \\ -1 & -1 & 11 \end{bmatrix} \begin{bmatrix} I_1 \\ I_2 \\ I_3 \end{bmatrix} = \begin{bmatrix} 10 \\ 12 \\ 4 \end{bmatrix}$$

Obtain the unknown currents by inverting the matrix.

Solution If the matrix of coefficients is denoted by **A**, then

$$\mathrm{adj}(\mathbf{A}) = \begin{bmatrix} 43 & 12 & 5 \\ 12 & 54 & 6 \\ 5 & 6 & 19 \end{bmatrix}$$

and $|\mathbf{A}| = 198$, leading to

$$\mathbf{A}^{-1} = \frac{1}{198} \begin{bmatrix} 43 & 12 & 5 \\ 12 & 54 & 6 \\ 5 & 6 & 19 \end{bmatrix}$$

$$\Rightarrow \begin{bmatrix} I_1 \\ I_2 \\ I_3 \end{bmatrix} = \frac{1}{198} \begin{bmatrix} 43 & 12 & 5 \\ 12 & 54 & 6 \\ 5 & 6 & 19 \end{bmatrix} \begin{bmatrix} 10 \\ 12 \\ 4 \end{bmatrix} = \begin{bmatrix} 3 \\ 4 \\ 1 \end{bmatrix}$$

as before.

Worked Application Example 3.12

One major advantage of this approach over Gaussian elimination or Cramer's rule is that it is not necessary to re-solve the problem if the values of the e.m.f.s are altered, thus changing the numbers appearing in the vector of known voltages. All that needs to be done is to premultiply the new e.m.f. vector by the previously calculated inverse matrix – leading immediately to new values of the currents.

The matrix formulation of linear equations is generally rather more compact and natural than some of the cumbersome formulae given earlier in this chapter. It also eases the physical interpretation of many applied problems. For example, the general three-loop circuit discussed at the beginning of the chapter and defined by Equation (3.3) and Fig. 3.1 may be expressed in matrix form as

$$\begin{bmatrix} R_1 + R_4 + R_5 & -R_5 & -R_4 \\ -R_5 & R_2 + R_5 + R_6 & -R_6 \\ -R_4 & -R_6 & R_3 + R_4 + R_6 \end{bmatrix} \begin{bmatrix} I_1 \\ I_2 \\ I_3 \end{bmatrix} = \begin{bmatrix} E_1 \\ E_2 \\ E_3 \end{bmatrix}$$

or **R i** = **v** for short.

All of the resistance information about the network is contained in the matrix **R** – any symmetry within the circuit should be reflected in the mathematical description and any special features should have an interpretable effect upon the equations. In this particular case **R** can be split up as

$$\mathbf{R} = \begin{bmatrix} R_1 & 0 & 0 \\ 0 & R_2 & 0 \\ 0 & 0 & R_3 \end{bmatrix} + \begin{bmatrix} R_4 + R_5 & -R_5 & -R_4 \\ -R_5 & R_5 + R_6 & -R_6 \\ -R_4 & -R_6 & R_4 + R_6 \end{bmatrix}$$

Generally, nonzero elements in the off-diagonal elements of a matrix signify coupling or direct interaction between subsystems or subunits. Contributions which appear only down the diagonal arise from properties which are specific to the individual subelements and do not involve direct interaction.

49

which reflects two important features of the circuit:

1. The circuit has three-fold symmetry (try redrawing it as a triangle!) as can be seen by the fact that reordering the equations simply corresponds to renumbering the resistors – the structure does not change.
2. The R_1, R_2 and R_3 resistors play very different roles to the R_4, R_5 and R_6 resistors. The latter set couple the individual loops of the network together – they appear on shared wires within the circuit. The resistors which appear on the exterior of each loop are individual to each loop – they do not directly interact with any other loop and they thus appear only down the diagonal of the matrix description.

Many problems leading to linear equations can be attacked using a matrix formalism. If n independent equations are available to fix the n unknown variables there will be no difficulty in inverting the matrix of coefficients. However, if the equations form a dependent set the determinant of the coefficients will be zero and the inverse matrix will not exist: as before, such equations cannot be solved for a unique solution.

Least squares solution of overdetermined linear equations

One particular advantage of matrices is that they allow the straightforward solution of sets of m equations in n unknowns, where $m > n$: such equations arise frequently in real applications. Measurements are usually made on practical systems either in a continuous fashion or as a series of discrete samples: in either case there are usually far more numerical values available than there are unknowns to be determined. Unfortunately, all measurements are subject to noise and inaccuracies so that the large sets of equations turn out to be inconsistent – there is no single solution that satisfies all m equations. Such overdetermined, inconsistent equations can be treated by the least squares approach: this attempts to find the solution point which comes 'closest' to satisfying all of the m constraint equations. This is most commonly used to fit 'best' straight lines through a series of uncertain data points, although the technique can be extended to deal with more general curves.

Worked Application Example 3.13

This is a measure of the average pressure of the impinging sound wave.

An electroacoustical transducer (a microphone) has been designed to produce an electrical output which, after amplification, is linearly dependent on the r.m.s. acoustic pressure of the sound waves being detected. Six measurements with an accurate sound generator produced the results:

r.m.s. acoustic pressure (Pa):	0	50	100	150	200	250
Output current (A):	0.00	0.49	1.05	1.53	2.01	2.44

Assuming that the pressures given are exact, fit a least squares line to the experimental data. Which measurement lies furthest from the line?

Solution Before proceeding, it is a very worthwhile exercise to plot the six data points on a sheet of graph paper and produce your own estimate of a best line 'by eye'.

To evaluate the best line analytically, let the line be given by

$$y = mx + n$$

Then the six data points lead to the equations:

$$n = 0.00$$
$$50\,m + n = 0.49$$
$$100\,m + n = 1.05$$
$$150\,m + n = 1.53$$
$$200\,m + n = 2.01$$
$$250\,m + n = 2.44$$

or in matrix form:

$$\begin{bmatrix} 0 & 1 \\ 50 & 1 \\ 100 & 1 \\ 150 & 1 \\ 200 & 1 \\ 250 & 1 \end{bmatrix} \begin{bmatrix} m \\ n \end{bmatrix} = \begin{bmatrix} 0.00 \\ 0.49 \\ 1.05 \\ 1.53 \\ 2.01 \\ 2.44 \end{bmatrix}$$

These overdetermined, contradictory equations cannot be solved exactly, but the 'best' solution is given by the least squares equation:

$$\mathbf{x}_{ls} = (\mathbf{A}^T\mathbf{A})^{-1}\,\mathbf{A}^T\mathbf{b}$$

where

$$\mathbf{A}^T\mathbf{A} = \begin{bmatrix} 0 & 50 & 100 & 150 & 200 & 250 \\ 1 & 1 & 1 & 1 & 1 & 1 \end{bmatrix} \begin{bmatrix} 0 & 1 \\ 50 & 1 \\ 100 & 1 \\ 150 & 1 \\ 200 & 1 \\ 250 & 1 \end{bmatrix} = \begin{bmatrix} 137500 & 750 \\ 750 & 6 \end{bmatrix}$$

so that

$$(\mathbf{A}^T\mathbf{A})^{-1} = \frac{1}{262500} \begin{bmatrix} 6 & -750 \\ -750 & 137500 \end{bmatrix}$$

Also, $\quad \mathbf{A}^T\mathbf{b} = \begin{bmatrix} 0 & 50 & 100 & 150 & 200 & 250 \\ 1 & 1 & 1 & 1 & 1 & 1 \end{bmatrix} \begin{bmatrix} 0.00 \\ 0.49 \\ 1.05 \\ 1.53 \\ 2.01 \\ 2.44 \end{bmatrix} = \begin{bmatrix} 1371 \\ 7.52 \end{bmatrix}$

leading to $\quad \mathbf{x}_{ls} = \dfrac{1}{262500} \begin{bmatrix} 6 & -750 \\ -750 & 137500 \end{bmatrix} \begin{bmatrix} 1371 \\ 7.52 \end{bmatrix} = \begin{bmatrix} 0.0098514 \\ 0.0219048 \end{bmatrix}$

so that the best line is given by

$$y = 0.0098514\,x + 0.0219048$$

The values given by this equation are compared with experiment in the table.

Pressure (Pa)	Experiment (A)	Least squares (A)	Exp. − l.s.
0	0.00	0.0219	− 0.0219
50	0.49	0.5145	− 0.0245
100	1.05	1.0070	+ 0.0430
150	1.53	1.4996	+ 0.0304
200	2.01	1.9922	+ 0.0178
250	2.44	2.4848	− 0.0448

The table shows that the final data point lies furthest from the 'best' line.

Solution of linear equations using elementary transformations

The final example of this chapter illustrates an alternative numerical technique which is rather more reliable for hand calculation and which leads directly to the solution of a given set of linear equations and the inverse of the matrix of coefficients. The method depends on applying a series of elementary transformations to an augmented matrix. The details of the approach are reviewed briefly in Chapter T3 (p. 151).

Worked Application Example 3.14

The satellite navigation system described in Example 3.9 produces the equations

$$
\begin{aligned}
2x - y + z &= 4 \\
-x + 2y + 3z &= -3 \\
-x + 3y + 7z &= -2
\end{aligned}
$$

which define the position of the satellite at their intersection point. Use a series of elementary transformations to solve the equations and obtain the inverse of the matrix of coefficients.

Solution Perform a series of elementary operations on the augmented matrix

$$
\left[\begin{array}{ccc|ccc}
2 & -1 & 1 & 4 & 1 & 0 & 0 \\
-1 & 2 & 3 & -3 & 0 & 1 & 0 \\
-1 & 3 & 7 & -2 & 0 & 0 & 1
\end{array}\right]
$$

$r_1 \leftarrow r_1/2$

$$
\Rightarrow \left[\begin{array}{ccc|ccc}
1 & -1/2 & 1/2 & 2 & 1/2 & 0 & 0 \\
-1 & 2 & 3 & -3 & 0 & 1 & 0 \\
-1 & 3 & 7 & -2 & 0 & 0 & 1
\end{array}\right]
$$

$r_2 \leftarrow r_2 + r_1$
$r_3 \leftarrow r_3 + r_1$

$$
\Rightarrow \left[\begin{array}{ccc|ccc}
1 & -1/2 & 1/2 & 2 & 1/2 & 0 & 0 \\
0 & 3/2 & 7/2 & -1 & 1/2 & 1 & 0 \\
0 & 5/2 & 15/2 & 0 & 1/2 & 0 & 1
\end{array}\right]
$$

$r_2 \leftarrow 2r_2/3$

$$
\Rightarrow \left[\begin{array}{ccc|ccc}
1 & -1/2 & 1/2 & 2 & 1/2 & 0 & 0 \\
0 & 1 & 7/3 & -2/3 & 1/3 & 2/3 & 0 \\
0 & 5/2 & 15/2 & 0 & 1/2 & 0 & 1
\end{array}\right]
$$

$r_1 \leftarrow r_1 + r_2/2$
$r_3 \leftarrow r_3 - 5r_2/2$

$$
\Rightarrow \left[\begin{array}{ccc|ccc}
1 & 0 & 5/3 & 5/3 & 2/3 & 1/3 & 0 \\
0 & 1 & 7/3 & -2/3 & 1/3 & 2/3 & 0 \\
0 & 0 & 5/3 & 5/3 & -1/3 & -5/3 & 1
\end{array}\right]
$$

$r_3 \leftarrow 3r_3/5$

$$
\Rightarrow \left[\begin{array}{ccc|ccc}
1 & 0 & 5/3 & 5/3 & 2/3 & 1/3 & 0 \\
0 & 1 & 7/3 & -2/3 & 1/3 & 2/3 & 0 \\
0 & 0 & 1 & 1 & -1/5 & -1 & 3/5
\end{array}\right]
$$

$r_1 \leftarrow r_1 - 5r_3/3$

$r_2 \leftarrow r_2 - 7r_3/3$

$$\Rightarrow \quad \left[\begin{array}{ccc|c|ccc} 1 & 0 & 0 & 0 & 1 & 2 & -1 \\ 0 & 1 & 0 & -3 & 4/5 & 3 & -7/5 \\ 0 & 0 & 1 & 1 & -1/5 & -1 & 3/5 \end{array} \right]$$

so that the solution is $x=0$, $y=-3$ and $z=1$, while the inverse of the matrix of coefficients of the equations is

$$\left[\begin{array}{ccc} 1 & 2 & -1 \\ 4/5 & 3 & -7/5 \\ -1/5 & -1 & 3/5 \end{array} \right]$$

Summary

This chapter has illustrated that linear equations arise in a wide range of practical applications and can be solved by a number of different mathematical approaches. Linear equations, determinants, matrices and, to an extent, vectors can be seen to be different aspects of the same mathematical structure and the advantages of each subject can be exploited when possible. Matrix methods in particular provide a compact and logical notation and allow the investigation of the internal structure of a complicated multivariable engineering system. Also, the strength of the coupling between subsystems and the effect of the transfer function of a general system are natural concepts when investigated with matrix methods.

These topics are often grouped together in texts on **linear algebra**.

Chapter 4 discusses the applications of differential equations, while Chapter 5 gives an introduction to some of the methods of the multivariable calculus. At a more advanced level, the algebraic techniques illustrated in this chapter can be combined with the differential calculus to obtain an extremely powerful and general set of tools for the modelling and investigation of the properties of time-dependent multivariable systems.

Further exercises

3.4 Use Gaussian elimination to solve the circuit equations (3.4) for the particular case:

$R_1 = 2\ \Omega, R_2 = 2\ \Omega, R_3 = 5\ \Omega, R_4 = 3\ \Omega, R_5 = 4\ \Omega, R_6 = 6\ \Omega,$
$E_1 = 5\ V, E_2 = 10\ V, E_3 = 5\ V.$

3.5 Use Cramer's rule to solve the circuit equations (3.4) for the particular case:

$R_1 = 4\ \Omega, R_2 = 7\ \Omega, R_3 = 8\ \Omega, R_4 = 3\ \Omega, R_5 = 4\ \Omega, R_6 = 6\ \Omega,$
$E_1 = 5\ V, E_2 = 10\ V, E_3 = 5\ V.$

3.6 Establish which of the sets of linear equations arising in Exercises 3.4 and 3.5 exhibit the better conditioning.

3.7 Solve Exercises 3.4 and 3.5 by calculating inverse matrices. Hence find the loop currents if the 10 V source is replaced by a 12 V source in both cases.

3.8 Find the total power dissipated in the circuit of Figure 3.7 if $R = 4\ \Omega$ and $E = 10$ V.

3.9 The source-free discharge of an ideal capacitor in a series RC circuit is governed by the equation

$$V_C(t) = V_0 \exp(-t/RC)$$

where V_0 is the initial voltage across the capacitor and the product RC determines the *time constant* of the circuit.

By linearizing the equation use the four experimental measurements of voltage:

$t = 0.5$	$V_C = 3.92$ V
$t = 1.0$	$V_C = 3.00$ V
$t = 2.0$	$V_C = 1.79$ V
$t = 4.0$	$V_C = 0.71$ V

to show that the least-squares estimates of the values of V_0 and RC are 4.89 V and 2.06 s respectively.

Differential Equations and their Applications   4

Objectives

☐ To discuss the varied uses of differential equations in electronic engineering as mathematical vehicles for the representation of the dynamics of a system.
☐ To introduce the ideas of the natural response and the forced response of any dynamic system.
☐ To explain the different types of differential equations that are used commonly in a variety of engineering applications.
☐ To illustrate the techniques of representing systems by differential equations and solving them to model the output of the system.
☐ To indicate some of the reasons why linearity and superposition are of such importance in the modelling and interpretation of many problems in practical electronic engineering.

Differential equations and system dynamics

Differential equations have formed the keystone of science and engineering for a considerable number of years. Practical systems will react to a wide range of inputs in a variety of ways: the reaction may be broadly internal to the system structure and not immediately obvious; or it may be clearly observable in the effect of the input on a measured output. In either case the system is exhibiting a **dynamic response** – it is reacting in a variable and detectable fashion to the different inputs. For example, any component of the system that has any degree of flexibility (mechanical or electrical) will be set into vibration by most forms of input. Also, a system will often resist a changing input by responding with a 'back' force which depends on the rate of change of the input. In circuit applications it will be seen that the reactive components of a series circuit (inductor and capacitor) correspond to the masses and elasticity of the springs of a mechanical system, while the resistance acts in a similar fashion to a frictional effect.

Perfect inductors and capacitors, like a perfectly flexible spring, are energy storage elements: they are all associated with the gradual and reversible conversion of energy from one form to another. Resistances and frictional effects are dissipative in nature: they introduce the possibility of energy losses from the system, via conversion to heat, for example. The dissipative components of a system tend to act against the motion of that system.

Differential equations represent the mathematical model of this dynamic structure of a physical system. To obtain the response of a system it is usually necessary to solve at least one differential equation.

As a result of numerous applications in a wide variety of systems, much investigative and development work has been performed on differential equations – many different types are known and documented. It is possible to write down a set of differential equations which describe extremely complex situations, but unfortunately it is usually impossible to solve the resulting complicated equations without resorting to advanced mathematical techniques or obtaining an approximate solution by computer. For example, the solution of many realistic, nonlinear systems is beyond the capabilities of these analytic techniques. However, it still remains possible to describe a surprising range of important systems and processes to a high degree of accuracy by equations that can be handled with a few common rules and techniques.

Most circuit elements are really nonlinear to some extent, but there are a number of important components that are highly nonlinear, including diodes, frequency dividers, harmonic generators and transistors.

Because the methods of differential equations are common to a number of application areas, a system-independent set of mathematical jargon has been developed to

If the Mathematical Toolkit fails to answer any of your queries try looking at Jeffrey (1989) or any text on basic mathematical techniques for engineers.

classify the equations into recognizable types. If differential equations are completely new to you, some of the descriptions in a specialized text can seem daunting at first glance! A list of nearly all of the basic terminology and techniques for differential equations is given in Chapter T4 (p. 156) of the Mathematical Toolkit; the only way that you will come to understand the specific techniques fully is to use the information in the Toolkit to help you to follow the individual steps given in the specific applications covered in this chapter.

First-order equations and their applications

The general form of a first-order differential equation is

$$\frac{dy}{dx} = f(y, x) \qquad \text{or perhaps} \qquad \frac{dx}{dt} = f(x, t) \tag{4.1}$$

where the first equation describes how a **dependent variable** y reacts to an **independent variable** x in such a way that the current rate of change of y with respect to x is specified by some function of the current values of x and y. Similarly, the second equation relates how the rate of change of some system output x depends on the state of x at a particular time t.

First-order equations such as these arise in system models where the primary reaction of a system is to resist change or motion, via frictional or resistive energy dissipation effects, or to store energy in some internal system component in a time-dependent fashion, such as the build-up of charge on a capacitor. They have widespread applications within circuit theory, electromechanical systems, control theory and filter theory, to name but a few.

A range of first-order equations can arise in practice, the main differences being in the particular form of the function, f. The commonest types are discussed in Chapter T4 and some examples of applications are given below.

The equation 'types' mentioned here merely refer to the list given in Chapter T4.

Worked Application Example 4.1

Consider the purely inductive circuit shown in Fig. 4.1 and find the time variation of the loop current.

Solution   At time $t = 0$ the switch is closed and the ac voltage source is connected to the inductor. After the switch is closed the relationship between the circuit current and voltage is

$$L \frac{dI}{dt} = E(t) \tag{4.2}$$

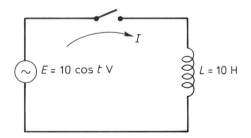

Fig. 4.1   A purely inductive circuit with $L = 10$ H and $E = 10 \cos t$ V. The switch is closed at time $t = 0$.

where the inductance L is assumed to be constant. In this case $L = 10$ H and the time dependence of the input voltage is given by $E = 10 \cos t$ volts. Therefore, the differential equation is

$$10 \frac{\mathrm{d}I}{\mathrm{d}t} = 10 \cos t \quad \Rightarrow \quad I = \sin t + C \qquad (4.3)$$

In Chapter T4 this is described as a Type I first-order differential equation.

by direct integration. However, since the system was in open circuit before $t = 0$, the initial value of the current must be zero. This fixes the value of the arbitrary constant as zero to give $I = \sin t$ amperes as the time response of the loop current to the cosine voltage input.

The above example illustrates the idea of a system reacting to a single input in such a way as to produce a measurable response. In this example the system is simply a single, linear, time-invariant inductor, but a more realistic model could include some of the effects associated with a nonlinear inductor.

The use of a linear, time-invariant inductor assumes that the circuit element may be modelled by assuming that the relationship between the time-varying flux $\phi(t)$ and current $I(t)$ takes the form of a constant proportionality law, $\phi(t) = L\,I(t)$, for all values of I, ϕ and t. However, for large currents, an inductor will **saturate** – the flux through the inductor will not increase as rapidly as the current is increased. More generally, then, it is necessary to define inductance by the expression $L(I) = \mathrm{d}\phi/\mathrm{d}I$, where a more realistic flux/current relationship is illustrated in Fig. 4.2. The inductance itself will therefore be a nonlinear function of the current through the inductor.

Even this is not necessarily a general enough model for this single circuit element – it is entirely possible that the shape of the inductor characteristic will also change with time, perhaps due to resistive heating effects or some effect external to the circuit such as ambient temperature.

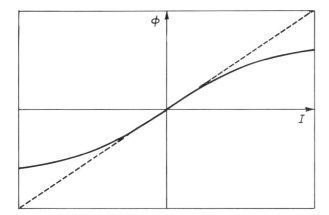

Fig. 4.2   Typical *characteristics* for a linear (-------) and a nonlinear (————) inductor. For the linear inductor L is just the slope of the line and for the nonlinear inductor the inductance is given by $L = \mathrm{d}\phi/\mathrm{d}I$ at any point on the curve.

Consider the same circuit as in Example 4.1, but as a refined approximation, assume that an improved model of the inductor characteristic can be obtained by using $L = \mathrm{d}\phi/\mathrm{d}I = 10/(1 + \lambda^2 I^2)$. For this type of characteristic the inductance will tend to zero for large current magnitudes, so that some account is being taken of the effect of saturation. Find the time variation of the loop current.

Worked Application Example 4.2

Solution Within the above expression λ is a parameter which controls the degree of the nonlinear contribution; λ = 0 corresponds to the purely linear case covered in Example 4.1. The differential equation for the system with this modification is

$$\frac{10}{1 + \lambda^2 I^2} \frac{dI}{dt} = 10 \cos t \tag{4.4}$$

which is **variables separable** (Type III in Chapter T4) in form. Conveniently, the variables are already separated in this case, and it is merely necessary to carry out two integrations, giving

$$\frac{10 \operatorname{arctanh}(\lambda I)}{\lambda} = 10 \sin t + C \qquad \lambda \neq 0$$

Again, $I = 0$ when $t = 0$, so that the arbitrary constant satisfies $C = 0$. The variation of I as a function of t is thus given by

$$I = \frac{\tanh[\lambda \sin t]}{\lambda} \tag{4.5}$$

First-order differential equations arise in a variety of applications involving mechanical components, electromagnetics, diffusion and fluid flow/heat transfer, but simple circuits with one or two elements are perhaps the commonest application in electronic engineering and illustrate many of the effects arising in other systems.

Worked Application Example 4.3

Fig. 4.3 illustrates a general RL circuit. An application of KVL shows that the circuit is characterized by a differential equation

$$L \frac{dI}{dt} + RI = E \tag{4.6}$$

Find the time response of the current if E, L and R are all constant.

Solution At first sight it might seem that Equation (4.6) is a Type IV equation which will require an integrating factor, but since the coefficients are all constants it is possible to rearrange the equation as

$$L \frac{dI}{dt} = E - RI \tag{4.7}$$

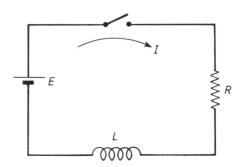

Fig. 4.3   A general series RL circuit.

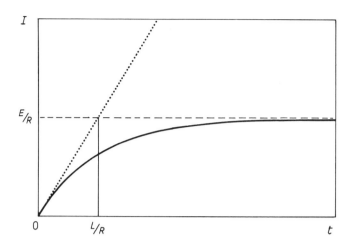

Fig. 4.4 The time response of the current in a series RL circuit after closing the switch at time $t=0$. The tangent to the response curve at $t=0$ crosses the line of limiting current value at $t=L/R$ – the time constant of the circuit.

which is merely Type II in structure – it can be integrated directly simply by dividing through by $(E - RI)$. This leads to

$$-\frac{L}{R} \int \frac{-R}{[E - R\,I]}\ \mathrm{d}I = \int \mathrm{d}t + K$$

$$\Rightarrow\ -\frac{L}{R}\ \ln|E - RI| = t + K$$

$$\Rightarrow\ E - R\,I = A \exp\left[-\frac{Rt}{L}\right] \qquad\qquad (4.8)$$

Where $A = \exp\left[-\frac{RK}{L}\right]$

If the initial current is again zero, the arbitrary constant must be given by $A = E$. The full solution can then be written as

$$I = \frac{E}{R}\left[1 - \exp\left[-\frac{Rt}{L}\right]\right] \qquad\qquad (4.9)$$

This solution is plotted in Fig. 4.4.

In Equation (4.9) it can be seen that the ratio L/R plays an important role in determining the properties of the current response. For $L \ll R$ the $\exp(-Rt/L)$ component will tend to zero quickly – leading to a rapid rise of the circuit current towards the limiting value of E/R. As L/R is increased, the rate of current response will correspondingly decrease. Given any 'target' value of current $(<E/R)$ the ratio L/R determines how long the circuit current will take to reach that value – L/R is thus often called the **time constant** of this circuit. The idea of such a **reaction time** of a first-order system is not restricted to this particular circuit type.

It is easy to show that the time constant is inversely proportional to the slope of the **current response** curve at $t = 0$ (see Fig. 4.4) – thus a small time constant corresponds to a steep initial slope. If a rapid current response is required of the circuit it must be designed with a small time constant, $L \ll R$.

Consider the switched RC circuit shown in Fig. 4.5. For time $t < 0$ the switch is held at position 1 (open circuit), the capacitor has previously been charged and has a voltage $V_0\,(V_0 < E)$ across it, and (of course) no current is flowing.

Worked Application Example 4.4

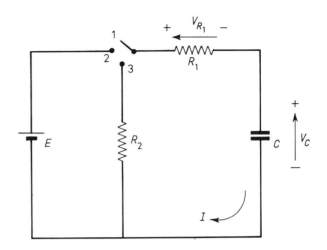

Fig. 4.5   A switched RC circuit.

The steady state component of a circuit response (or the output of any dynamic system) is that part of the solution which remains after all transient contributions to the solution have died away – it is the form of the solution for large values of time.

If at time $t = 0$ the switch is turned to position 2, write down a differential equation for the capacitor voltage V_C in terms of the circuit parameters (E, C, R_1 and R_2) and find the steady-state value of the voltage across the capacitor.

At some later time $t = t_1$, when the capacitor voltage has reached some value V_1, the switch is turned to position 3 forming a **source-free** RC circuit. Examine the future behaviour of the capacitor voltage.

Solution   For the circuit shown, after the switch is moved to position 2, application of KVL leads to

$$E = I R_1 + V_C \qquad \text{and} \qquad I = C \frac{\mathrm{d} V_C}{\mathrm{d} t}$$

so that eliminating the current from the first equation leads to a differential equation for the capacitor voltage:

$$E = C R_1 \frac{\mathrm{d} V_C}{\mathrm{d} t} + V_C \tag{4.10}$$

$$\Rightarrow \quad \frac{1}{E - V_C} \frac{\mathrm{d} V_C}{\mathrm{d} t} = \frac{1}{CR_1}$$

in a separated variables form. This leads to

$$\int \frac{\mathrm{d} V_C}{E - V_C} = \int \frac{\mathrm{d} t}{CR_1} + K$$

$$\Rightarrow -\ln |E - V_C| = \frac{t}{CR_1} + K \tag{4.11}$$

The initial condition $V_C = V_0$ when $t = 0$ gives $K = -\ln[E - V_0]$, so that

$$\ln \left| \frac{E - V_C}{E - V_0} \right| = -\frac{t}{CR_1}$$

$$\Rightarrow \quad E - V_C = [E - V_0] \exp \left[-\frac{t}{CR_1} \right]$$

For this **charging cycle** of the circuit, the time constant is CR_1.

or $\qquad V_C - V_0 = [E - V_0] \left[1 - \exp \left[-\frac{t}{CR_1} \right] \right] \tag{4.12}$

so that for large values of t the capacitor voltage tends to E.

If at time $t = t_1$ the switch is turned to position 3 the effect is to modify the dynamics of the circuit – the voltage source is switched out and is replaced by a second resistor. Application of KVL shows that a new differential equation comes into force for times beyond t_1:

$$[C R_1 + C R_2] \frac{dV_C}{dt} + V_C = 0 \qquad (4.13)$$

$$\Rightarrow \quad -\frac{1}{V_C} \frac{dV_C}{dt} = \frac{1}{C(R_1 + R_2)}$$

$$\Rightarrow \quad -\ln|V_C| = \frac{t}{C(R_1 + R_2)} + K \qquad (4.14)$$

Whenever the internal dynamic structure of a system undergoes a change, a new differential equation must be constructed and solved to obtain the behaviour of the system under the new circumstances.

so that, clearly, a very similar form of solution will be obtained. The key point lies in how to determine the value of the arbitrary constant for this differential equation. The correct approach is to recognize that there cannot be an instantaneous change in the value of the voltage across the capacitor, and so the value of the capacitor voltage at the end of the previous period of operation of the circuit will automatically provide the approprite initial value for the current period of operation.

If the switching takes place after the capacitor has been charged by the voltage source from $t = 0$ to $t = t_1$ then the capacitor voltage will have reached a value

$$V_1 = V_0 + [E - V_0] \left[1 - \exp\left[-\frac{t_1}{CR_1} \right] \right] \qquad (4.15)$$

Most physical variables cannot undergo instantaneous changes in their values – changes in the dynamics of a system will lead to changes in the behaviour of a variable, and hence gradient discontinuities will be seen at the switching points when the output is plotted against time – but the value of the output will be continuous from one period to the next. In this case an instantaneous change of voltage would correspond to an infinite current.

so that the appropriate initial condition for the general solution (4.14) is $V_C = V_1$ when $t = t_1$. This fixes the value of the arbitrary constant and allows Equation (4.14) to be rearranged as:

$$V_C = V_1 \exp\left[-\frac{t - t_1}{C(R_1 + R_2)} \right] \quad \text{for } t \geqslant t_1 \qquad (4.16)$$

where V_1 is given by Equation (4.15). The complete time variation of capacitor voltage is specified by Equation (4.12) for $t \leqslant t_1$ and by Equation (4.16) for $t \geqslant t_1$.

For this source-free circuit the capacitor is in a discharge cycle, with time constant $C(R_1 + R_2)$.

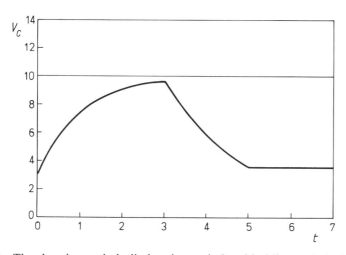

Fig. 4.6 The charging period, discharging period and holding period of the RC circuit specified in Example 4.4.

Equations (4.12) and (4.16) comprise a concise mathematical solution of the voltage response of the capacitor in a simple, switched, inductance-free network. However, in most engineering applications it is useful to examine a graph of the solution for a 'realistic' set of circuit values – it can be difficult to gain an immediate impression of the important characteristics of a system from the equations alone. With this in mind, Fig. 4.6 shows a graph of the time dependence of the capacitor voltage for Example 4.4 with the specific values of

$$E = 10 \text{ V} \qquad\qquad C = 20 \text{ } \mu\text{F}$$
$$R_1 = 50 \text{ k}\Omega \qquad\qquad R_2 = 50 \text{ k}\Omega$$
$$V_0 = 3 \text{ V}$$

The switch is moved from position 1 to position 2 at $t=0$. After three seconds the switch is moved to position 3, and after a further two seconds it is turned back to position 1. The analytic solutions take the form:

$$V_C = 10 - 7\exp(-t) \qquad\qquad 0 \text{ s} \leqslant t \leqslant 3 \text{ s}$$
$$V_C = 9.6515 \exp\left[-\left[\frac{t-3}{2}\right]\right] \qquad 3 \text{ s} \leqslant t \leqslant 5 \text{ s}$$
$$V_C = 3.5506 \qquad\qquad 5 \text{ s} \leqslant t$$

so that the graphical representation makes it possible to gain an immediate insight into the effects of the different time constants on the charge and discharge rates of the circuit.

Many of the important properties of simple circuits can be well represented by simple first-order differential equations similar in form to those above. What is less obvious is that, at least for first-order systems, it is quite straightforward to examine some of the more unusual circuit properties. Consider, for example, a single-loop RC circuit where the resistor value is allowed to vary with time.

Worked Application Example 4.5

Fig. 4.7 illustrates such a simple RC circuit. Suppose that the resistor is variable and is continuously adjusted so that its time dependence is given by $R = R_0(1 + \alpha t)$ for some positive parameter α. Find the time response of the capacitor voltage if $V_C = V_0$ at time $t=0$, for a constant input voltage E.

Solution Using exactly the same circuit relationships that established Equation (4.10) gives

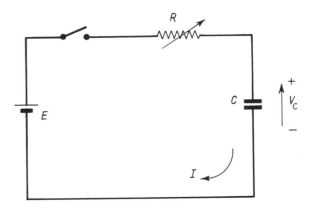

Fig. 4.7 A single-loop RC circuit with a time-varying resistor.

$$E = CR_0(1 + \alpha t)\frac{dV_C}{dt} + V_C \tag{4.17}$$

as the differential equation that describes the dynamic response of the capacitor voltage. Taking V_C over to the l.h.s. separates the variables and leads to

$$\int \frac{dV_C}{E - V_C} = \frac{1}{CR_0} \int \frac{dt}{1 + \alpha t} + K$$

$$\Rightarrow \quad -\ln|E - V_C| = \frac{1}{\alpha CR_0}\ln|1 + \alpha t| + K \qquad \alpha \neq 0$$

The initial condition fixes K as $-\ln|E - V_0|$, so that

$$-\ln\left|\frac{E - V_C}{E - V_0}\right| = \frac{1}{\alpha CR_0}\ln|1 + \alpha t|$$

$$\Rightarrow \quad \left[\frac{E - V_C}{E - V_0}\right] = [1 + \alpha t]^{-1/\alpha CR_0}$$

$$\Rightarrow \quad V_C - V_0 = [E - V_0][1 - [1 + \alpha t]^{-1/\alpha CR_0}] \tag{4.18}$$

which is the desired expression for V_C as a function of time and the (unspecified) circuit parameters.

> Certainly, it is not at all obvious that as $\propto$ tends to zero this power law result tends to the previous exponential law. It does, but it is beyond the needs of the text to justify the result.

A particularly interesting point about this result is that the capacitor is no longer charging with an exponential approach to its fully charged value. For large values of t the same limiting value, E, is obtained as the steady-state value of the capacitor voltage, but the shape of the response curve can be significantly different from that obtained in Example 4.4, depending on the magnitude of α.

In the above example, the practical effect of increasing the value of R as time passes is to make it increasingly difficult for current to pass through the circuit, and hence charge the capacitor. Correspondingly, it takes longer for the capacitor to reach any pre-specified voltage than for the constant-resistance case. This has the broad effect of increasing the time constant of the system, but also the more detailed effect of altering the way in which the charging process occurs. By deliberately controlling the time dependence of the resistor it is possible to make the capacitor charge up in a pre-determined fashion.

Alternatively, the introduction of a variable resistance can be used to provide a model of the thermal drift of the circuit resistance as the resistor heats up, for example, explaining why a series of experimental results might fail to correlate systematically with the expected exponential approach to a limit.

Note that any given time the equation is still linear – it is the slope of the resistor characteristic that is changing with time, not its shape.

For the particular case

Exercise 4.1

$$\begin{aligned} E &= 10\text{ V} & C &= 20\ \mu\text{F} \\ R_1 &= 50(1 + \alpha t)\ \text{k}\Omega \\ V_0 &= 3\text{ V} \end{aligned}$$

draw graphs of V_C against time for the cases $\alpha = 0$ (constant resistance), $\alpha = 0.1$, and $\alpha = 1$.

These examples have introduced several important concepts. In addition to the ideas of dynamic response and time constant, the steady-state solution has been defined. Next, it must be stressed that a clear comprehension of the utility of differential equations as an engineering tool hinges on understanding that the solution (output) of a linear differential equation (system) can always be split into two components: the steady-state component and the transient component.

The steady-state output is due only to the form of the input function and the structure of the differential equation.

The transient component arises only because of the structure of the differential equation and because of the initial conditions of the system. It reflects the transitory reaction of the system to being required to switch its state from one level to another – the magnitude of the transient response will depend on the size of the step that the system is being asked to make.

In Equation (4.12), for example, the steady-state component of the solution is E and the transient component is $-(E - V_0) \exp(-t/CR_1)]$.

Worked Application Example 4.6

Find the steady-state and transient responses of the capacitor voltage if the battery of the RC circuit shown in Fig. 4.5 is replaced by an ac source, $E = E_0 \cos(\omega t)$.

Solution The differential equation for the voltage, Equation (4.10), becomes

$$C R_1 \frac{dV_C}{dt} + V_C = E_0 \cos(\omega t) \tag{4.19}$$

which is Type IV in structure and can be solved using an integrating factor. Putting the equation in standard form

$$\frac{dV_C}{dt} + \frac{V_C}{CR_1} = \frac{E_0 \cos(\omega t)}{CR_1} \tag{4.20}$$

shows that the integrating factor is given by $\exp(t/CR_1)$, so that

$$\frac{d}{dt}\left[V_C \exp\left[\frac{t}{CR_1}\right]\right] = \frac{E_0 \cos(\omega t)}{CR_1} \exp\left[\frac{t}{CR_1}\right] \tag{4.21}$$

shows the equation partitioned by the integrating factor into a form suitable for direct integration. The integral of a product of a cosine and an exponential is not particularly easy to remember:

$$\int \exp(ax) \cos(nx)\, dx = \frac{\exp(ax)\,[a \cos(nx) + n \sin(nx)]}{a^2 + n^2} \tag{4.22}$$

but can be obtained from first principles using integration by parts (see Chapter T1, p. 119), or complex number theory (see Chapter T2 p. 135). Using Equation (4.22) to facilitate integration of Equation (4.21) gives

$$V_C \exp\left[\frac{t}{CR_1}\right] = E_0 \frac{[\omega CR_1 \sin(\omega t) + \cos(\omega t)]}{[1 + (\omega CR_1)^2]} \exp\left[\frac{t}{CR_1}\right] + K$$

$$\Rightarrow \quad V_C = E_0 \frac{[\omega CR_1 \sin(\omega t) + \cos(\omega t)]}{[1 + (\omega CR_1)^2]} + K \exp\left[\frac{-t}{CR_1}\right] \tag{4.23}$$

The arbitrary constant of this general solution may be fixed using an initial value for the capacitor voltage of V_0 when $t = 0$, giving

$$K = V_0 - \frac{E_0}{[1 + (\omega CR_1)^2]} \tag{4.24}$$

so that the full time dependence of the capacitor voltage for a cosine input and an initial charge of V_0 is given by Equations (4.23) and (4.24). The solution can be split up as a steady-state component:

$$V_C(\text{steady-state}) = E_0 \frac{[\omega CR_1 \sin(\omega t) + \cos(\omega t)]}{[1 + (\omega CR_1)^2]} \tag{4.25}$$

and a transient component

$$V_C(\text{transient}) = \left[V_0 - \frac{E_0}{[1 + (\omega CR_1)^2]} \right] \exp\left[\frac{-t}{CR_1} \right] \tag{4.26}$$

As ω tends to zero these solutions approach the form already derived in Equation (4.12), which corresponds to a constant voltage input.

This example emphasizes that the steady-state response of a system will generally be a function of t and not merely a number. It also shows that the nature of the transient and steady-state responses will depend on the detailed form of the input – in this case different values of angular frequency of the cosine input will provoke different forms of circuit response. This change in behaviour of the above circuit is an example of a concept of interest in a number of electronic engineering disciplines, but particularly in circuit analysis, communication theory and control theory, known as the **frequency response** of a system.

The frequency-response approach is an experimental method which examines the effect of a system on an input sinusoidal signal of a known frequency and phase as a function of the input frequency. It can often be used as a tool of system identification – to find out what order of differential equation is necessary to describe realistically the dynamics of a system. It can also provide information about the important parameters (values of key internal components) of a system. The deficiencies of the frequency-response approach are that to build up a reasonable picture of a system it may be necessary to consider a large number of input frequencies, and for each frequency it is necessary to wait for the transient components of the output to die down – enabling comparison of the steady-state output with its corresponding input.

For first-order systems, it is easy to show that the results of the previous example mean that the steady-state frequency response of a general linear first-order system with time constant T to an input of amplitude A and phase ϕ:

$$\frac{dx}{dt} + \frac{x}{T} = A \cos(\omega t + \phi) \tag{4.27}$$

is given by

$$x(\text{steady-state}) = AT \frac{[\omega T \sin(\omega t + \phi) + \cos(\omega t + \phi)]}{[1 + (\omega T)^2]}$$

$$= \frac{AT \cos(\omega t + \phi - \alpha)}{[1 + (\omega T)^2]^{1/2}} \tag{4.28}$$

where α satisfies

$$\sin \alpha = \frac{\omega T}{[1 + (\omega T)^2]^{1/2}} \quad \text{and} \quad \cos \alpha = \frac{1}{[1 + (\omega T)^2]^{1/2}} \tag{4.29}$$

In other words, the system dynamics are examined by attaching a signal generator to the input of the system, producing a range of sinusoidal input signals and monitoring the output on an oscilloscope for each input sinusoid of a given frequency.

The connection between the experimental frequency-response results and the theoretical models may be made by calculating the expected output from a range of system models with a sinusoidal input of variable frequency (as in Example 4.6) and comparing the model answers with the experimental data.

The corresponding transient response is

$$x(\text{transient}) = \left[x_0 - \frac{AT[\omega T \sin \phi + \cos \phi]}{[1 + (\omega T)^2]} \right]$$

$$\exp \left[\frac{-t}{T} \right]$$

This shows that the effect of a first-order linear system on a sinusoidal input is to modulate and phase shift the input signal in a frequency-dependent fashion – but the output still has the form of a sinusoid of the same frequency as the input.

The differential equation represents the dynamic response of a first-order system to an input: if the input is sinusoidal, it has been shown that the resultant output also will be so, but phase and amplitude modified as a function of input frequency. The phase

In circuit and control applications it is common to find the amplitude/frequency information represented on a log-log plot and the corresponding phase/frequency curve drawn on a linear/log plot. The representation is useful for the graphical combination of the properties of several subsystems and such plots are usually referred to as **Bode plots**. Examples of Bode plots are given in Example 4.14.

When the differential equation arises from a circuit example, the quantity $[1 + (\omega T)^2]^{1/2}$ corresponds to the **impedance** of the circuit, while $\propto$ determines whether the circuit will act as a **first-order phase lag filter** ($\propto > 0$) or a **first-order phase lead filter** ($\propto < 0$).

More generally, an input may be non-sinusoidal or a complicated mixture of many frequencies. It is possible to express such functions in terms of simple sinusoidal functions of the form discussed here using Fourier analysis (Jeffrey, 1989).

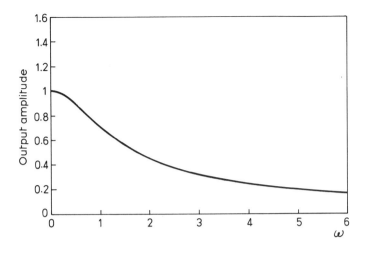

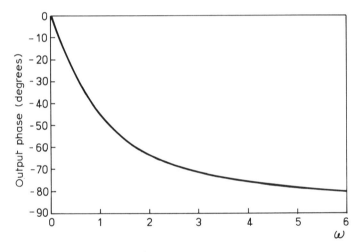

Fig. 4.8   The frequency response functions for the general first-order system given by Equation (4.27).
(a) The amplitude response.
(b) The phase response.
The graphs correspond to a unit time constant.

shift is given by Equation (4.29), while the amplitude modulation as a function of frequency is given by Equation (4.28), which shows that the amplitude of the output signal relative to that of the input is given by $T/[1 + (\omega T)^2]^{1/2}$.

The phase and amplitude variations of the output as a function of the frequency of an input sinusoidal signal correspond to information about the filter characteristics of a system, and are illustrated for the first-order case in Fig. 4.8.

Before moving on to higher-order equations, it is worth while considering an example of a first-order differential equation arising in another application.

Application Example 4.7   A component on a printed circuit board is subject to overheating due to a power dissipation which increases as a function of time during its period of operation. To combat this a fan blows air across cooling fins to draw heat away from the board. The equations governing the respective heating and cooling processes are:

$$\text{Rate of heat gain} = \frac{dQ_{in}}{dt} = \text{power dissipated in resistor} = P(t) \quad \text{J s}^{-1}$$

$$\text{and rate of heat loss} = \frac{dQ_{out}}{dt} = K(T - T_a) \quad \text{J s}^{-1}$$

where T_a is the ambient air temperature, K specifies the thermal conductivity of the contacts of the device with the board, and it is being assumed that the fan keeps the cooling fins effectively at the ambient temperature. The rise in temperature of the device is governed by the equation

$$\frac{dQ}{dT} = C \quad \text{or} \quad \frac{dT}{dQ} = \frac{1}{C}$$

Fourier's law states that the rate of heat transfer between two bodies is proportional to the temperature difference between them. K is the **thermal conductivity** of the channel of heat transfer.

where C is the **heat capacity** of the device and Q is the total heat energy supplied to the device. Using $Q = Q_{in} - Q_{out}$, these equations can be combined to give

$$\frac{dT}{dt} = \frac{1}{C}[P(t) - K(T - T_a)]$$

or

$$\frac{dT}{dt} + \frac{K}{C}T = \frac{P(t)}{C} + \frac{KT_a}{C} \tag{4.30}$$

which is a first-order differential equation. It can be solved readily by using an integrating factor $\exp(Kt/C)$ if the precise form of the power dissipation is specified.

The limited range of differential equations covered in the last few pages illustrates several basic points that are worth remembering about the representation of the differential dynamics of a system:
1. Similar equations arise in a wide range of applications.
2. The introduction of more complicated models produces correspondingly more complicated equations.
3. The solution of a linear differential equation can be split into a transient component and a steady-state component.

As will now be discussed, these observations are also applicable to higher-order systems.

Second-order differential equations

The main restriction of first-order differential equations is that it is only possible to build into a system model an allowance of the nature of the rate of response of that system under a change in the value of some system variable. Second-order equations also allow the inclusion of effects which hinge upon the derivative of the rate of response. These second-order terms terms arise in systems which react with a force which is proportional to the displacement of some system variable from an average value – such as obtained via a spring or internal flexibility in a system.

Circuit examples again offer useful illustrations of the detailed properties of the equations, but the concepts are transferable to other systems with similar dynamics.

First-order differential terms are usually associated with dissipative or resistive effects. Second-order terms often reflect the 'elasticity' of a system and govern its vibrational characteristics.

Figs. 4.9 and 4.10 illustrate two general resistor–inductor–capacitor circuit layouts in series and parallel networks respectively. The series circuit is viewed as being driven

Application Example 4.8

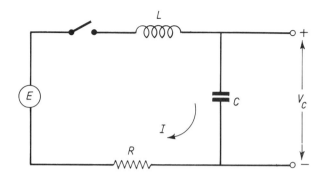

Fig. 4.9   A series RLC circuit.

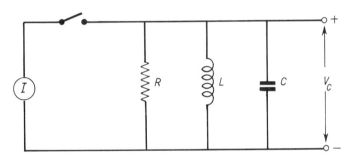

Fig. 4.10   A parallel RLC circuit.

by a time-dependent voltage source and the parallel circuit by a time-dependent current source. In both cases, the physical value of interest (the system output) to be taken as the dependent variable is assumed to be the time variation of the capacitor voltage. After the switch in each circuit is closed (at time $t = 0$) for linear, time-invariant circuit elements the voltage dropped across each element satisfies

$$V_R = I_R R \qquad \text{for the resistor}$$

$$V_L = L \frac{dI_L}{dt} \qquad \text{for the inductor} \qquad (4.31)$$

and $V_C = \dfrac{1}{C} \displaystyle\int_0^t I_C(\tau) \, d\tau \qquad$ for the capacitor

Note the use of a dummy variable of integration, τ, to avoid conflict with the fact that V_C is a function of time t.

Consider the series circuit configuration first, so that $I_R = I_L = I_C = I$, then KVL gives

$$V_L + V_R + V_C = E \qquad (4.32)$$

$$\Rightarrow \quad L \frac{dI}{dt} + IR + V_C = E$$

$$\Rightarrow \quad \frac{d^2 V_C}{dt^2} + \frac{R}{L} \frac{dV_C}{dt} + \frac{1}{LC} V_C = \frac{1}{LC} E \qquad (4.33)$$

where the loop current has been related to the capacitor voltage by the expression $I = C \, dV_C/dt$. This equation shows that the dynamic response of a series RLC circuit with constant elements may generally be represented by a second-order linear differential equation with constant coefficients.

Consider now the parallel network in Fig. 4.10. For this configuration $V_C = V_R = V_L$, and KCL gives

$$I_L + I_R + I_C = I \tag{4.34}$$

$$\Rightarrow \quad \frac{dI_L}{dt} + \frac{dI_R}{dt} + \frac{dI_C}{dt} = \frac{dI}{dt}$$

$$\Rightarrow \quad \frac{1}{L} V_L + \frac{1}{R} \frac{dV_R}{dt} + C \frac{d^2 V_C}{dt^2} = \frac{dI}{dt}$$

$$\text{or} \quad \frac{d^2 V_C}{dt^2} + \frac{1}{RC} \frac{dV_C}{dt} + \frac{1}{LC} V_C = \frac{1}{C} \frac{dI}{dt} \tag{4.35}$$

using the fact that the same potential difference applies over all three circuit elements. This is also a second-order linear differential equation with constant coefficients for the dependent variable V_C. The structure of the two Equations (4.33) and (4.35) differ only in that the coefficients of V_C and dV_C/dt will have different numerical values and the time-dependent functions on the r.h.s. have different physical interpretations.

Mathematically, it is clear that the most powerful approach is to consider any second-order equation of this form and apply the general results to specific applications as required. As before, the more complicated the equation, the more work is needed to obtain a full solution.

Chapter T4 provides a summary of the theory of second-order linear differential equations.

Homogeneous second-order equations

The solution of second-order equations is greatly simplified when the functions on the r.h.s. of Equations (4.33) or (4.35), for example, are identically zero. In such cases the equations are described as **homogeneous**. In a practical sense, the system represented by the equations can be said to be undriven: the r.h.s. usually represents a **driving function** – an input to the system which produces a further **forced response** of the system variables. When this driving input is absent the system is said to exhibit a **natural response** as a function of time.

As with first-order equations, it is common to view the function which appears on the r.h.s. of the inhomogeneous equation as representing a driving, or forcing, input to the system.

Consider the series RLC circuit of Fig. 4.9 whose dynamics are expressed in Equation (4.33). In the special case of $R = 0$ and $E = 0$ the circuit becomes a source-free LC circuit. Calculate the time response of such a circuit with the circuit parameters $L = 1$ H and $C = 4$ F, if the measurements $I = 4$ A and $V_C = 3$ V are made at $t = 0$.

Application Example 4.9

Solution The specific differential equation is

$$\frac{d^2 V_C}{dt^2} + \frac{1}{4} V_C = 0$$

which is an example of a homogeneous, second-order linear differential equation with constant coefficients (see the appropriate part of Chapter T4, p. 162). It has a **characteristic equation** $m^2 + 1/4 = 0$ and corresponding **characteristic roots** $m = \pm j/2$. The **general solution** of this equation can therefore be written as

$$V_C = A \cos \left[\frac{t}{2} \right] + B \sin \left[\frac{t}{2} \right] \tag{4.36}$$

Any two independent measurements are sufficient to fix the two arbitrary constants – they need not be initial conditions such as these.

where A and B are arbitrary constants. These should be able to be given fixed values which provide a specific solution appropriate to the given initial value $V_C(t=0) = 3$ and $I(t=0) = 4$. Since $I = C\,\mathrm{d}V_C/\mathrm{d}t$ relates the current flowing through the capacitor to the voltage variation across it, the second condition is equivalent to $\mathrm{d}V_C/\mathrm{d}t(t=0) = 1$. Equation (4.36) can be differentiated to give

$$\frac{\mathrm{d}V_c}{\mathrm{d}t} = -\frac{A}{2}\,\sin\left[\frac{t}{2}\right] + \frac{B}{2}\cos\left[\frac{t}{2}\right] \tag{4.37}$$

so that setting $t=0$ in Equations (4.36) and (4.37) respectively requires $V_C(t=0) = A$ and $\mathrm{d}V_C/\mathrm{d}t(t=0) = B/2$. The specific measurements therefore give a **particular solution** for the time response of the form

$$V_C = 3\cos\left[\frac{t}{2}\right] + 2\sin\left[\frac{t}{2}\right] \tag{4.38}$$

More generally, the LC circuit discussed in the above example will have a differential equation

$$\frac{\mathrm{d}^2 V_C}{\mathrm{d}t^2} + \frac{1}{LC}\,V_C = 0 \tag{4.39}$$

This perfect sinusoidal response is often described as **simple harmonic motion** and the system that leads to it is called a **simple harmonic oscillator**.

and a corresponding general solution

$$\left. \begin{aligned} V_C &= A\cos(\omega_n t) + B\sin(\omega_n t) \\ \text{or} \quad V_C &= D\cos(\omega_n t - \alpha) \end{aligned} \right\} \tag{4.40}$$

where these two forms of solution are equivalent and ω_n satisfies $\omega_n = [1/LC]^{1/2}$. Therefore, we can see that the natural response of an LC circuit is sinusoidal with a **natural angular frequency** ω_n.

Next, it is necessary to examine a more realistic model which allows the effect of circuit resistance to be taken into account.

Application Example 4.10

Consider the source-free series RLC circuit which is described by Equation (4.33) with E set to zero. The characteristic equation is

$$m^2 + \frac{R}{L}m + \frac{1}{LC} = 0 \tag{4.41}$$

so that the characteristic roots are given by

$$m = -\frac{R}{2L} \pm \sqrt{\left[\left[\frac{R}{2L}\right]^2 - \frac{1}{LC}\right]} \tag{4.42}$$

The form of these roots means that different behaviours of the natural response of the circuit will be observed as the relative values of R, L and C are altered. For example, values of:

(i) $R = 10\ \Omega$, $C = 1/9$ F, $L = 1$ H lead to characteristic roots -1 and -9 and thus a general solution of the form

$$V_C = A\exp(-t) + B\exp(-9t) \tag{4.43}$$

(ii) If $R = 6\ \Omega$, $C = 1/9$ F, and $L = 1$ H, repeated characteristic roots $m = -3$ (twice) are obtained and the general solution is

$$V_C = (A + Bt)\exp(-3t) \tag{4.44}$$

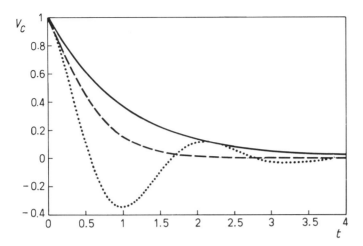

Fig. 4.11   Three specific types of natural response curve for the capacitor voltage
in a source-free series RLC circuit.

Overdamped	——	$V_C = \exp(-t)$
Critically damped	------	$V_C = (1 + 2t)\exp(-3t)$
Underdamped	······	$V_C = \exp(-t)\cos(\sqrt{8}\,t)$

with initial conditions $V_C(t=0) = 1$ and $dV_C/dt(t=0) = -1$.

(iii) $R = 2\ \Omega$, $C = 1/9$ F, and $L = 1$ H lead to $m = -1 \pm \sqrt{8}\,j$ and a general solution

$$V_C = \exp(-t)[A\cos(\sqrt{8}\,t) + B\sin(\sqrt{8}\,t)] \tag{4.45}$$

The introduction of initial conditions $V_C(t=0) = 1$ and $dV_C/dt(t=0) = -1$ gives a set
of particular solutions for these parameter values:

(i) $V_C = \exp(-t)$
(ii) $V_C = (1 + 2t)\exp(-3t)$
(iii) $V_C = \exp(-t)\cos(\sqrt{8}\,t)$

and these are plotted in Fig. 4.11. Clearly, very similar sets of curves will be obtained
for the response of the parallel RLC circuit.

The response curves of Fig. 4.11 are important enough to merit a further, more
detailed, discussion. To keep the theory completely general it is useful to introduce the
second-order equation

$$\frac{d^2x}{dt^2} + 2\zeta\frac{dx}{dt} + \omega_n^2 x = 0 \tag{4.46}$$

which is the equation describing a **free, damped harmonic oscillator**. ζ/ω_n is called the
damping factor or **damping ratio** of the system and ω_n is the natural angular frequency
of the system in the absence of the term involving dx/dt. For positive values of ζ the
central term corresponds to a damping, or retardation, effect: in practice arising from
energy dissipation in a resistor, from friction or from any movement of an object
through a viscous medium. The amount of damping within a system is controlled by
the magnitude of ζ. The corresponding characteristic equation is

$$m^2 + 2\zeta m + \omega_n^2 = 0$$
$$\Rightarrow \quad m = -\zeta \pm [\zeta^2 - \omega_n^2]^{1/2}$$

$$\text{or} \quad m = -\zeta \pm \omega_n\left[\left[\frac{\zeta}{\omega_n}\right]^2 - 1\right]^{1/2} \tag{4.47}$$

This general equation can
represent any second-order
homogeneous differential
system and, in particular,
setting $\omega_n = 1/\sqrt{(LC)}$ and $\zeta = 1/(2RC)$ corresponds to the
parallel Equation (4.35). Both
Equations (4.33) and (4.35)
can be compared usefully with
the equation

$$\frac{d^2x}{dt^2} + \frac{f}{m}\frac{dx}{dt} + \frac{k}{m}x = 0$$

which is the equation describing
the motion of a mass (m)
attached to a spring (the
strength of which is determined

71

by k) and subject to a force which resists any motion of the mass (the strength of this resistance is governed by f). Hence, it is possible to draw meaningful parallels between the various roles played by the mechanical quantities and the corresponding circuit elements.

If the damping ratio, ζ/ω_n, is less than unity, then the characteristic roots will be complex in nature, and the general solution will take the form of an exponentially decaying sinusoid: as in the specific case (iii) in Example 4.10. The solution is said to be **underdamped** in this case.

If it happens that $\zeta/\omega_n = 1$, then the square root in Equation (4.47) vanishes identically, leading to repeated characteristic roots. The solution type for this situation is exemplified in case (ii) and is known as **critical damping**.

For values of ζ/ω_n greater than unity, the characteristic roots are guaranteed to be real and distinct. This occurs in case (i) and the solution is described as being **overdamped**.

The table summarizes these results.

It is conventional (and sensible) always to define the amplitude and frequency of a sinusoidal signal to be positive quantities. A positive value of ζ corresponds to a system involving frictional damping of the output. Negative values of ζ can arise in systems that involve a physical effect that tends to increase the speed of an oscillation – such a system will produce solutions that tend to increase in magnitude with time. Instability of this form can occur in feedback circuits, using operational amplifiers, for example (see Horrocks, 1989).

Damping ratio	Description	General solution
$\dfrac{\zeta}{\omega_n} = 0$	Undamped (free)	$A \cos(\omega_n t - \alpha)$
$\dfrac{\zeta}{\omega_n} \in (0,1)$	Underdamped	$A \exp(-\zeta t) \cos[(\omega_n^2 - \zeta^2)^{1/2} t - \alpha]$
$\dfrac{\zeta}{\omega_n} = 1$	Critically damped	$(A + Bt) \exp(-\zeta t)$
$\dfrac{\zeta}{\omega_n} \in (1,\infty)$	Overdamped	$A \exp(m_1 t) + B \exp(m_2 t)$

In the table, m_1 and m_2 refer to the distinct roots defined by Equation (4.47) for $\zeta/\omega_n > 1$. Fig. 4.11 shows the form of these responses for the particular values of ω_n and ζ appropriate for the RLC circuits of Example 4.10.

Thus, there are a series of possible forms for the natural response of a system. If the damping ratio of a system can be controlled in some fashion independently of its natural frequency, it is possible to view the output or solution changing its nature from pure sinusoidal to an exponentially decaying sinusoidal as ζ is increased from zero, losing any trace of an oscillatory component as the point of critical damping is reached, and finally becoming a superposition of exponentials as the damping ratio exceeds unity. If the damping ratio is increased further, the arguments of the exponentials will approach -2ζ and zero (but not actually reach these values). They correspond to a fast mode and a slow mode of the solution respectively, since the exponential with the more negative argument will tend to zero more rapidly. Practical examples of these effects will be given shortly.

Before moving on to a discussion of the properties of inhomogeneous second-order equations, it is worth showing how powerful and general results can be obtained from a simple model of the dynamic properties of a complicated physical system.

Application Example 4.11   In device applications, interest often centres upon the properties of the potential that electrons and holes experience in the region of an interface. At a semiconductor p–n junction, for example, an interface is formed between doped semiconductor slabs of p-type (acceptor impurities) and n-type (donor impurities). At the interface the difference in concentration densities of holes and electrons leads to a short-range equilibrium diffusion of electrons into the p-type material and a corresponding diffusive spread of holes into the n-type material. Thus, a **barrier space-charge** is built up in the region of the interface, leading to a local **barrier electric field** and an associated **contact potential**. This, relatively rapid, microscopic step in electrostatic

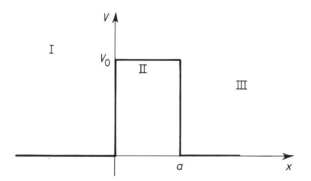

Fig. 4.12   A simplified view of the internal electrostatic potential barrier appropriate to the quantum-well laser.

The concept of a particle of energy E being able (sometimes) to pass through a barrier of higher energy is a completely quantum idea – in classical dynamics the particles would forever be trapped on one side of the barrier. However, in the quantum picture some transmission is always possible for a finite barrier. The phenomenon is known as the **tunnel effect**.

Other applications of the concepts of potential barriers and tunnelling include the spontaneous ionization of atoms in an applied electric field, and the thermionic emission of electrons from a metal. Tunnelling is also the reason that some very high-energy radiation is detected emerging from black holes.

The representation of waves as complex quantities is discussed in Chapter 2.

internal potential is critical in determining the macroscopic properties of the device under an external applied potential. Many complicated device structures can be envisaged as extensions of this basic idea (see Sparkes, 1987, for more details).

The **quantum-well laser**, for example, has the structure of a symmetrical 'sandwich' where a thin, intermediate layer sets up an internal potential barrier. This is illustrated in a simplified form in Fig. 4.12. The point of interest here is the relative probability of electrons approaching this barrier from the left-hand side being able to reach the right-hand side or being 'reflected' at the barrier.

The mathematical tools necessary to attack this problem are the concept of representing a wave as a complex number in exponential form: $\exp(jkx)$ and $\exp(-jkx)$ representing waves travelling in the positive and negative x-directions respectively; and the wave-mechanical description of the properties of quantum-mechanical particles/ waves.

Wave mechanics is built around the representation of the quantum object of interest by a **wave function**, ψ, which is the solution of the **Schrödinger wave equation**. The one-dimensional Schrödinger equation for a particle of mass m and energy $E(>0)$ moving within a potential $V(x)$ is

$$-\frac{1}{2m}\left[\frac{h}{2\pi}\right]^2\frac{d^2\psi}{dx^2} + [V(x) - E]\psi = 0 \qquad (4.48)$$

h is **Planck's constant**, and is equal to approximately 6.6262 $\times 10^{-34}$ J s.

and the solution of this second-order linear differential equation is a (generally complex) wave function $\psi(x)$, which can be interpreted as a statistical representation of the properties of the particle that it describes. Information about measurable, or observable, properties can be obtained by examining the function $\psi(x)\psi^*(x)$, which is guaranteed to be real and which can be viewed as a probability distribution for the position of the particle – larger values of $\psi(x)\psi^*(x)$ corresponding to likelier positions for that particle to be detected.

Where ψ^* is the complex conjugate of the wave function ψ.

The main difference from previous examples is that complex solutions of the differential Equation (4.48) are allowed, whereas previously only real functions have been considered to be valid.

Consider the application of the Schrödinger equation to the simple potential barrier illustrated in Fig. 4.12. In regions I and III the potential is constant and nominally set to zero. Within these regions the Schrödinger equation is:

It is always possible to assign the zero of potential to any level within a problem – it is potential differences that matter.

$$-\frac{1}{2m}\left[\frac{h}{2\pi}\right]^2\frac{d^2\psi}{dx^2} - E\psi = 0$$

which has a general solution (in complex form)

$$\psi(x) = A \exp(jkx) + B \exp(-jkx)$$

$$\text{where} \quad k^2 = 2mE \left[\frac{2\pi}{h}\right]^2$$

(4.49)

so that the general complex solution of the Schrödinger equation in a region of constant potential, where the energy of the particle is greater than the level of the potential (here $E > 0 = V$), is a superposition of two complex waves moving in the positive and negative x-directions as specified by Equation (4.49).

Now consider region II and assume that the particle energy is less than the barrier height, $E < V_0$. Then within region II the appropriate differential equation is

$$-\frac{1}{2m}\left[\frac{h}{2\pi}\right]^2 \frac{d^2\psi}{dx^2} + [V_0 - E]\psi = 0$$

so that, clearly, the general solution can be seen to be

$$\psi(x) = F \exp(\alpha x) + G \exp(-\alpha x)$$

(4.50)

$$\text{where} \quad \alpha^2 = 2m\,[V_0 - E]\left[\frac{2\pi}{h}\right]^2$$

Thus, for $E < V_0$, the complex form of solution is inappropriate for region II. Because the barrier height is greater than the particle energy, wave-like transmission of the particle through the barrier is impossible. Instead, the wave function takes the form of a superposition of real exponentials.

In short, the Schrödinger differential equation leads to the conclusion that the appropriate general wave function solutions are:

$$\psi(x) = A \exp(jkx) + B \exp(-jkx) \quad \text{in region I}$$
$$\psi(x) = F \exp(\alpha x) + G \exp(-\alpha x) \quad \text{in region II}$$
$$\text{and} \quad \psi(x) = C \exp(jkx) + D \exp(-jkx) \quad \text{in region III}$$

In the context of this particular problem $A \exp(jkx)$ represents a quantum wave approaching the barrier in region I, and B corresponds to the amount of that wave which is turned back by the change in potential at $x = 0$, forming a reflected wave moving in the negative x-direction.

Within the barrier wave propagation is inappropriate and instead an exponentially decaying component of the incoming wave function occurs, represented by (most of) the term $G \exp(-\alpha x)$. This component suffers a partial reflection itself at the other side of the barrier and sends a component proportional to $\exp(\alpha x)$ back in the negative x-direction. The overall wave function $F \exp(\alpha x) + G \exp(-\alpha x)$ represents the sum of all of the internally reflected transients, in both directions.

Some component of the decaying wave function is transmitted through to region III, however, where wave propagation is again possible, represented by a quantum wave function $C \exp(jkx)$. Since this particular problem involves no particles approaching from the right in region III it is possible to assume $D \equiv 0$.

Thus, it is possible to form a realistic physical interpretation of all of the coefficients of the wave functions listed above. The original question regarding the relative probabilities of transmission or reflection at the barrier corresponds to examining the quantities

$$\left|\frac{B}{A}\right|^2 - \text{the probability of reflection at the barrier}$$

$$\text{and} \quad \left|\frac{C}{A}\right|^2 - \text{the probability of transmission at the barrier}$$

which arise because the relative probabilities are observable and thus correspond to the squares of the wave functions involved. For many incoming particles, A^2 can be interpreted as the incoming particle flux, B^2 as the reflected particle flux, and C^2 as the transmitted particle flux.

The mathematical problem is how to obtain the ratios B/A and C/A. The respective wave functions contain five parameters, A, B, C, F and G. So far, no connection between these parameters has been stated. The necessary information can be gained from the quantum-mechanical boundary conditions, which demand that at a finite discontinuity of potential the value of a wave function and its first derivative must be continuous.

Applying these boundary conditions leads to the four equations:

$$\psi(x=0): A + B \qquad\qquad = F + G$$

$$\left.\frac{d\psi}{dx}\right|_{x=0} : jkA - jkB \qquad = \alpha F - \alpha G$$

$$\cdot\psi(x=a): F \exp(\alpha a) + G \exp(-\alpha a) \quad = C \exp(jka)$$

$$\left.\frac{d\psi}{dx}\right|_{x=a} : \alpha F \exp(\alpha a) - \alpha G \exp(-\alpha a) = jkC \exp(jka)$$

(4.51)

so that four independent **constraint equations** are available to relate the five parameters. Thus, it should be possible to evaluate uniquely any ratio of the parameters. These four equations can be reorganized as:

$$[(\alpha + jk)A + (\alpha - jk)B] \exp(\alpha a) = 2\alpha F \exp(\alpha a) = (\alpha + jk)C \exp(jka)$$

and $[(\alpha + jk)A + (\alpha + jk)B] \exp(-\alpha a) = 2\alpha G \exp(-\alpha a) = (\alpha - jk)C \exp(jka)$

so that it is possible to ignore the central terms involving F and G, divide through both equations by C, and effectively reduce the equations to a pair of simultaneous equations in A/C and B/C. Solving this pair of equations for A/C leads to

$$[(\alpha + jk)^2 - (\alpha - jk)^2] \frac{A}{C} = [(\alpha + jk)^2 \exp(-\alpha a) - (\alpha - jk)^2 \exp(\alpha a)] \exp(jka)$$

$$\Rightarrow \quad 4j\alpha k \frac{A}{C} = [2(k^2 - \alpha^2) \sinh(\alpha a) + 4j\alpha k \cosh(\alpha a)] \exp(jka)$$

This expression gives the ratio A/C in terms of the (given) potential and particle parameters a, α and k. To obtain probability information we need to obtain A^2/C^2, so multiplying both sides of the above equation by the appropriate complex conjugates leads directly to

$$4\alpha^2 k^2 \frac{A^2}{C^2} = [(k^2 - \alpha^2)^2 \sinh^2(\alpha a) + 4\alpha^2 k^2 \cosh^2(\alpha a)]$$

$$= [(k^2 + \alpha^2)^2 \sinh^2(\alpha a) + 4\alpha^2 k^2]$$

Therefore, the transmission probability is given by

$$\frac{C^2}{A^2} = \frac{4\alpha^2 k^2}{[(k^2 + \alpha^2)^2 \sinh^2(\alpha a) + 4\alpha^2 k^2]}$$

or $\dfrac{C^2}{A^2} = \dfrac{4E(V_0 - E)}{V_0^2 \sinh^2\left[[2m(V_0 - E)]^{1/2} \dfrac{2\pi a}{h} \right] + 4E(V_0 - E)}$

(4.52)

in terms of the original parameters of the interface. A similar procedure leads to a related expression for B^2/A^2.

See Chapter T4 for a discussion of particular integrals.

Exercise 4.2

1. Using the same procedure as immediately above eliminate A/C instead of B/C and obtain an expression for the reflection probability.
2. Confirm that the sum of the probability of reflection and the probability of transmission is unity.
3. Show that as the width of the barrier is reduced to zero the transmission probability tends to unity.
4. What happens to the transmission probability as the barrier height is increased?

The above example indicates the powerful results which can be obtained when a set of diverse mathematical tools are applied simultaneously. In this case the tools of differential equations were used to describe the dynamics of the interface, while exponential complex numbers formed a natural description of the nature of the wavefunction and the solution of a set of linear algebraic equations enabled the expression of output particle flux densities in terms of an input flux density. The original model, with a rectangular barrier, is highly idealized, but gives considerable insight into the details of the real quantum tunnelling effect. More complicated barrier profiles can be attacked numerically once the basic theory has been established.

Inhomogeneous second-order equations

The general form of the second-order inhomogeneous differential equation is

$$\frac{d^2x}{dt^2} + a\,\frac{dx}{dt} + b\,x = f(t) \tag{4.53}$$

The function $f(t)$ could, for example, represent a time-varying input to the system, in which case the solution, $x(t)$, would represent a corresponding output. Clearly, changing the form of $f(t)$ will generally have a considerable effect on $x(t)$.

It is often notationally convenient to rewrite this equation as

$$\frac{d^2x}{dt^2} + 2\zeta\,\frac{dx}{dt} + \omega_n^2 x = f(t) \tag{4.54}$$

using a notation similar in form to that for the homogeneous Equation (4.46).

The main mathematical difficulty with inhomogeneous equations is obtaining a suitable particular integral for the solution to augment the complementary solution. The general solution is built up as the superposition of these two components. Fortunately, some systems of practical interest need only very simple particular integrals.

Application Example 4.12

Consider again the series RLC circuit shown in Fig. 4.9 with dynamics described by the equation

$$\frac{d^2V_C}{dt^2} + \frac{R}{L}\,\frac{dV_C}{dt} + \frac{1}{LC}\,V_C = \frac{1}{LC}\,E \tag{4.33}$$

Previously, the source-free case with $E = 0$ has been considered, leading to the natural response of the circuit for a number of different sets of circuit parameters, as shown in Fig. 4.11. Instead, suppose that a perfect constant voltage source is supplied, so that when the switch is closed at time $t = 0$ the circuit experiences a constant driving voltage V_0. For the same three cases as discussed before,

    (i) $R = 10\ \Omega$, $C = 1/9$ F, and $L = 1$ H

    (ii) $R = 6\ \Omega$, $C = 1/9$ F, and $L = 1$ H

and (iii) $R = 2\ \Omega$, $C = 1/9$ F, and $L = 1$ H
the respective general solutions of the homogeneous equation were

$$V_C = A \exp(-t) + B \exp(-9t) \tag{4.43}$$

$$V_C = (A + Bt) \exp(-3t) \tag{4.44}$$

$$V_C = \exp(-t)\,[A \cos(\sqrt{8}\ t) + B \sin(\sqrt{8}\ t)] \tag{4.45}$$

and these form the complementary solution component of the solution to the inhomogeneous equation. The particular integral for a constant input voltage V_0 is clearly PI $= V_0$, giving general solutions

$$V_C = V_0 + A \exp(-t) + B \exp(-9t) \tag{4.55}$$

$$V_C = V_0 + (A + Bt) \exp(-3t) \tag{4.56}$$

$$V_C = V_0 + \exp(-t)[A \cos(\sqrt{8}\ t) + B \sin(\sqrt{8}\ t)] \tag{4.57}$$

for the three sets of circuit parameters. Taking a specific battery voltage of $V_0 = 2$ V and the same initial conditions as for the source-free circuit: $V_C(t=0) = 1$ and $\mathrm{d}V_C/\mathrm{d}t\,(t=0) = -1$, leads to specific solutions

$$V_C = 2 - \frac{5}{4} \exp(-t) + \frac{1}{4} \exp(-9t)$$

$$V_C = 2 + (-1 - 4t) \exp(-3t)$$

and $V_C = 2 + \exp(-t)\left[-\cos(\sqrt{8}\ t) - \frac{2}{\sqrt{8}} \sin(\sqrt{8}\ t) \right]$

for the three sets of values of the circuit elements. These solutions are illustrated in Fig. 4.13 and describe the **step response** of the capacitor voltage – the reaction to a step change in the source voltage from 0 V (open circuit) to 2 V (switch closed at $t=0$).

Very similar results hold for the parallel RLC circuit.

In fact, to provide a consistent definition of the natural response and step response of a system it is more usual to set the initial conditions to be a unit function value and zero gradient for the natural response (sometimes known as the **unit impulse response**) and zero for both function value and gradient for the step response. This enables comparison of the responses of different systems irrespective of any transient effects due to a particular set of initial conditions.

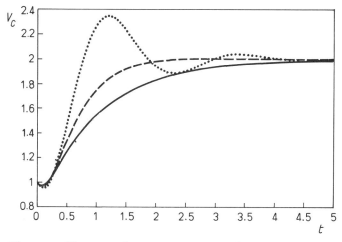

Fig. 4.13   Three specific types of step response curve for the capacitor voltage in a series RLC circuit with a dc source of 2 V.

Overdamped   —— $V_C = 2 - \dfrac{5}{4} \exp(-t) + \dfrac{1}{4} \exp(-9t)$

Critically damped   ----- $V_C = 2 + (-1 - 4t) \exp(-3t)$

Underdamped   ..... $V_C = 2 + \exp(-t)\left[-\cos(\sqrt{8}\ t) - \dfrac{2}{\sqrt{8}} \sin(\sqrt{8}\ t) \right]$

with initial conditions $V_C(t=0) = 1$ and $\mathrm{d}V_C/\mathrm{d}t\,(t=0) = -1$.

The most important point about the above solutions is that they are each composed of the sum of a particular integral (in this case, a constant, 2) and a complementary solution. In circuit, control and communication applications these contributions may be described alternatively:

Mathematical description	*Engineering interpretation*
Complementary function	Natural/transient response
Particular integral	Forced/driven/steady-state response
General solution = CF + PI	Total response/output

As mentioned above, cases can occur where the roots of the characteristic equation have positive real parts. If this is so the magnitude of the natural response will increase with time and the system will be unstable. Control theory is largely concerned with the design of feedback structures that modify the nature of an unstable system to produce desirable transient properties – 'desirable' usually meaning decaying rapidly and smoothly to zero.

As for first-order linear differential equations, the natural response is due to the system dynamics (structure of the differential equation) and the initial conditions (arbitrary constants) alone. For stable systems the magnitude of the natural response will decrease with time (hence the description 'transient response').

The driven response arises from the system dynamics and the form of the system input (driving function/forcing function) alone. It is independent of the initial conditions and will not necessarily decrease in magnitude with time. It will persist when any transient contributions have died away and is hence described as the **steady-state** component of the solution.

The **complete response** is the sum of the transient response and the steady-state response and represents the total output of a system, as would be measured experimentally.

This partitioning is only valid for a linear system: it is the linearity which allows the principle of superposition of the solutions of the equation.

Thus, the mathematical treatment of breaking up the solution of a linear differential equation (of any order) into two components is equivalent to examining the properties of the system response separately for small and large values of t and, effectively, decoupling these two contributions to the total output. This is true for any input function, not just for the constant values used for the step responses above. In particular, a sinusoidal form of input function is often of great practical importance.

Application Example 4.13

Consider the series RLC circuit of Equation (4.33) with the specific circuit parameters: $R = 4\ \Omega$, $L = 1$ H, $C = 1/3$ F, and $E = \cos(3t)$. Assume that $V_C(t=0) = 9/10$ V and $dV_C/dt(t=0) = 8/5$ V s^{-1}.

The specific differential equation is

$$\Rightarrow \quad \frac{d^2 V_C}{dt^2} + 4\frac{dV_C}{dt} + 3V_C = 3\cos(3t) \tag{4.58}$$

which has a characteristic equation

$$m^2 + 4m + 3 = 0 \quad \Rightarrow \quad (m+1)(m+3) = 0 \quad \Rightarrow \quad m = -1 \text{ or } -3$$

and a corresponding complementary solution

$$\text{CS} = A\exp(-t) + B\exp(-3t) \tag{4.59}$$

One way to establish a suitable particular integral is to use a trial solution with undetermined coefficients (see Chapter T4, p. 165 for details), the appropriate form of particular integral for any sinusoidal input being

$$\text{PI} = C\cos(3t) + D\sin(3t)$$

where the undetermined coefficients C and D are fixed by substituting this expression into the original differential equation, and requiring that the overall coefficients of the independent functions $\cos(3t)$ and $\sin(3t)$ should balance on each side of the equation.

Differentiating this trial expression twice and inserting the expressions into Equation (4.58) gives

$[- 9C\cos(3t) - 9D\sin(3t)] + 4[-3C\sin(3t) + 3D\cos(3t)] + 3[C\cos(3t) + D\sin(3t)] \equiv 3\cos(3t)$

so that equating the coefficients of $\sin(3t)$ and $\cos(3t)$ leads to

$$-\ 6C + 12D = 3$$
$$-12C -\ 6D = 0$$

which are a pair of independent, simultaneous equations, which fix the values of the coefficients to be $C = -1/10$ and $D = 1/5$. This leads to a general solution of the original differential equation:

$$V_C = A\exp(-t) + B\exp(-3t) - \frac{1}{10}\cos(3t) + \frac{1}{5}\sin(3t) \qquad (4.60)$$

or $\quad V_C = A\exp(-t) + B\exp(-3t) + \dfrac{1}{2\sqrt{5}}\cos(3t - 116.6°) \qquad (4.61)$

and the initial conditions require that

$$\frac{9}{10} = A + B - \frac{1}{10} \quad \Rightarrow \quad A + B = 1$$
$$\frac{8}{5} = -A - 3B + \frac{3}{5} \quad \Rightarrow \quad A + 3B = -1$$

so that these initial conditions fix the values of the arbitrary constants to be $A = 2$ and $B = -1$. The specific solution is thus

$$V_C = \underbrace{2\exp(-t) - \exp(-3t)}_{\text{transient response}} + \underbrace{\frac{1}{2\sqrt{5}}\cos(3t - 116.6°)}_{\text{driven response}} \qquad (4.62)$$

where, as before, this represents the complete response of the circuit and is composed of a transient response and a driven response. These response curves are shown in Fig. 4.14.

The important point is that we are demanding that the functions on either side of this expression should be identically equal for all time. This is a much stronger condition than equality. The two linear equations could then be derived by considering $t = 0$ and $t = \pi/2$ respectively, for example.

This equivalent form of the solution has been designed to have a positive magnitude associated with the sinusoidal response – any combination of signs of the $\cos(3t)$ and $\sin(3t)$ can be encompassed in the phase part of the composite function. In this case there is a phase lag of 116.6° or 2.034 radians associated with the output sinusoid. Note that it is conventionally assumed that the $3t$ part of the argument of the cosine is measured in radians – while it is common to see the associated phase lag/lead expressed in degrees, as in this equation.

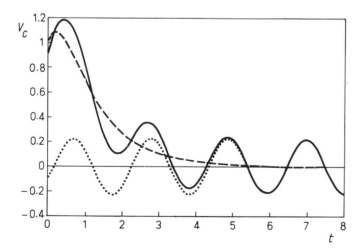

Fig. 4.14   The complete response (———) of the series RLC circuit of Example 4.13. The transient (-------) and steady-state (·····) components are also illustrated.

As for first-order systems, this is true for a sinusoidal input of any frequency – a linear system will produce a steady-state output of the same frequency, but scaled in magnitude and shifted in phase. The **gain** of the circuit – the amplitude of the output relative to the amplitude of the input.

This is one reason why some poorly protected ac driven systems (e.g. older computers) can exhibit occasional strange behaviour on start-up.

It is seen that the steady-state portion of the solution consists of a sinusoid of the same frequency as the input, but with a different magnitude and phase. As for the first-order circuit examples, the input function has undergone amplitude and phase modulation by the internal structure of the circuit.

The magnitude of the transient response (the sizes of A and B) will vary according to the specified values of the initial conditions. In particular, it is possible to find a pair of initial conditions that will produce a zero transient response. The transient response arises physically as the reaction of the system to being asked to switch from one mode of operation (specified by the initial conditions) to another (specified by the steady-state solution). If the switch between modes takes place smoothly, it is possible to eliminate the transient component of the solution entirely. In this case, this can be done mathematically by demanding that A and B must be zero and finding the corresponding initial conditions that will achieve this. It will be found that the zero transient initial conditions are those that match smoothly onto the value and gradient of the steady-state solution at $t = 0$.

Exercise 4.3   Calculate the initial conditions for the above example which will produce a zero transient response.

It is worth commenting that there are other, more advanced, ways of obtaining particular integrals in cases that might seem difficult with the trial function approach. In particular, for sinusoidal inputs it is possible to use a phasor approach (discussed in Chapter 2) to solve the above example rapidly.

For a more general discussion on the use of complex exponentials to represent real sinusoidal signals see Meade and Dillon (1986).

The phasor method represents a real sinusoidal signal as merely a component of a more general complex phasor signal. In general, a real input $u \cos(\omega t + \phi)$, is replaced by a complex input $u \exp(j\omega t + j\phi)$, where the phasor $u \exp(j\phi)$ represents the initial angular position of the phasor (see Chapter 2) and the time variation is built into the multiplying factor $\exp(j\omega t)$. If we are going to use a complex function on the r.h.s. of the differential equation, however, it is necessary to extend the allowable forms of the solution to be complex as well. Ignoring transient effects, which can be obtained readily from the complementary function, the appropriate form for the steady-state solution is an output phasor $v \exp(j\psi)$ with an associated time variation $\exp(j\omega t)$ – the same form of time variation as the input. The corresponding (complex) differential equation for the above problem is given by

$$\frac{d^2 V_C}{dt^2} + 4 \frac{d V_C}{dt} + 3 V_C = 3 \exp(3jt) \tag{4.63}$$

since the input phase is zero. Inserting a (complex) solution $V_C = v \exp(3jt + j\psi)$ gives

$$-9v \exp(3jt + j\psi) + 12jv \exp(3jt + j\psi) + 3v \exp(3jt + j\psi) = 3 \exp(3jt)$$

$$\Rightarrow \quad -6v \exp(j\phi) + 12jv \exp(j\phi) = 3$$

$$\Rightarrow \quad v \exp(j\phi) = \frac{3}{-6 + 12j} = \frac{-1 - 2j}{10} = \frac{1}{2\sqrt 5} \exp(-j116.6°)$$

This gives information about the magnitude and phase of the driven component of the solution directly – requiring only the manipulation of a few complex numbers. The difficult matching of the independent sine and cosine components of the steady-state solution is avoided, but the same results are obtained as those shown in Equation (4.61).

The important point about the phasor approach is that the time-dependent portion, exp($j\omega t$), can simply be cancelled out of the equation at some stage since it appears in both the output and input. In fact, the only way that it contributes to the solution at all is via the factors of $j\omega$ and $-\omega^2$ that appear when the output function term is differentiated. The presence of these factors is critical, however – they mean that the nature of the amplitude and phase of the solution phasor will depend directly on the specific value of ω. Thus, the gain and phase shift will be functions of the value of the frequency of the sinusoidal input.

The forced, damped harmonic oscillator, frequency response and resonance

The fact that an input signal of a given frequency will undergo phase and amplitude modulation when passing through a differential system is the basis of the theory of filters in communication applications and frequency response in control system evaluation and circuit analysis.

As discussed above for first-order systems.

Consider the equation

$$\frac{d^2x}{dt^2} + 2\zeta\frac{dx}{dt} + \omega_n^2x = u\cos(\omega t + \phi) \tag{4.64}$$

This equation represents any second-order dynamic system (circuit, filter, electro-mechanical apparatus) subject to a general sinusoidal input of amplitude u, angular frequency ω and initial phase ϕ. It is often referred to as the equation of the **forced, damped harmonic oscillator** (cf. Equation (4.54)). As for the **free, damped harmonic oscillator** (Equation (4.46)), ω_n describes the natural angular frequency of the oscillatory system and ζ determines the degree of damping incorporated into the system. The concepts of overdamping, critical damping and underdamping are all still applicable in this specific inhomogeneous case where the system is driven by a sinusoidal input.

Using a phasor approach, it is possible to replace the input by $u\exp(j\omega t + j\phi)$ and the steady-state output (forced response) by $v\exp(j\omega t + j\psi)$, leading to

$$[-\omega^2 + 2j\zeta\omega + \omega_n^2]\,v\exp(j\psi) = u\exp(j\phi) \tag{4.65}$$

where the time variation $\exp(j\omega t)$, common to both sides, has been cancelled. This gives the relationship between the complex input and output phasors as:

If the input phasor has the same frequency as one of the components of the natural response of the system it will be necessary to consider instead an output of the form $t\exp(j\omega t + j\psi)$, just as for the case of real trial functions.

$$v\exp(j\psi) = u\exp(j\phi)\,\frac{1}{[(\omega_n^2 - \omega^2) + 2j\omega\zeta]}$$

$$\Rightarrow \quad G = \left|\frac{v}{u}\right| = [(\omega_n^2 - \omega^2)^2 + 4\omega^2\zeta^2]^{-1/2} \tag{4.66}$$

and $\psi = \phi - \alpha$ $\tag{4.67}$

where G is the gain of the system and α satisfies

These results are obtained by using the standard result that the modulus of the ratio of two complex numbers is the ratio of their respective moduli and the corresponding argument (phase) of the ratio is the difference of the individual moduli.

$$\left.\begin{array}{l} \cos\alpha = \dfrac{\omega_n^2 - \omega^2}{[(\omega_n^2 - \omega^2)^2 + 4\omega^2\zeta^2]^{1/2}} \\[4mm] \text{and } \sin\alpha = \dfrac{2\omega\zeta}{[(\omega_n^2 - \omega^2)^2 + 4\omega^2\zeta^2]^{1/2}} \end{array}\right\} \tag{4.68}$$

For positive values of ω and ζ, the angle α must lie in the range $(0,\pi)$ so that the output of a sinusoidally driven, damped system of this type will always exhibit a phase lag. For example, in the series RLC circuit described by Equation (4.58) the capacitor voltage must lag the input sinusoidal voltage. Other circuit 'outputs' are related to the capacitor voltage by differentiation – the current by a single differentiation and the inductor voltage by two differentiations. This means that the inductor voltage will be $180°$ out of phase with the capacitor voltage and will thus always lead the input by a

Recall that, although it is mathematically convenient to represent the input and solution in the form of a complex exponential quantity, the quantities of physical interest are the amplitude and phase of the output, which are real. No measurable variable is being represented by a complex number: it is merely that the complex phasor is a compact and symmetric way of containing the same information as the real sinusoid.

81

A series RLC circuit which is predominantly capacitative will result in the loop current leading the source voltage. A predominantly inductive circuit will exhibit a current lag.

phase angle in the range $(0,\pi)$. The resistor voltage, and hence the loop current, leads the capacitor voltage by only 90° and may lag or lead the source voltage depending on the relative magnitudes of the circuit elements.

For a given second-order dynamic system (specified values of ω_n and ζ) Equation (4.66) expresses the gain of the system as a function of driving angular frequency ω. To examine the properties of this frequency response of the amplitude of the output, note that for small values of ω (near constant input) the gain tends to a value of ω_n^{-2} and that for large values of ω (very high-frequency input) the gain will tend to zero at a limiting rate of ω^{-2}. Differentiating Equation (4.66) with respect to angular frequency leads to

$$\frac{dG}{d\omega} = \frac{\omega[2\omega_n^2 - 4\zeta^2 - 2\omega^2]}{[(\omega_n^2 - \omega^2)^2 + 4\omega^2\zeta^2]^{3/2}} \tag{4.69}$$

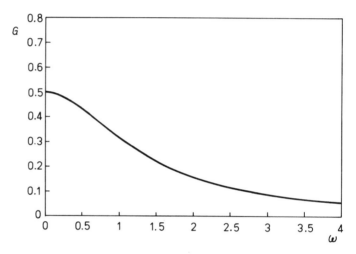

Fig. 4.15a The gain/angular frequency relationship for an overdamped system with $\omega_n = \sqrt{2}$ rad s^{-1} and $\zeta/\omega_n = 3/\sqrt{8}$.

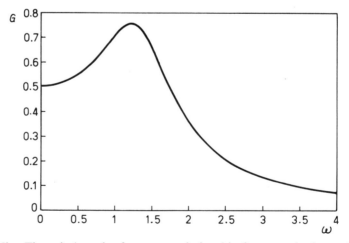

Fig. 4.15b The gain/angular frequency relationship for an underdamped system with $\omega_n = \sqrt{2}$ rad s^{-1} and $\zeta/\omega_n = 1/\sqrt{8}$.

so that there will be a stationary point of the gain curve where the equality

$$\omega[2\omega_n{}^2 - 4\zeta^2 - 2\omega^2] = 0$$

is satisfied. Therefore, there are stationary points of this function when $\omega = 0$ and when $\omega^2 = \omega_n{}^2 - 2\zeta^2$. It follows that the function has only one stationary point if $\omega_n{}^2 < 2\zeta^2$ and two stationary points if $\omega_n{}^2 > \zeta^2$. Differentiating again to examine the properties of these stationary points leads to two distinct cases:

1. If $\omega_n{}^2 < 2\zeta^2$ the gain curve has only a local maximum at zero frequency.
2. If $\omega_n{}^2 > 2\zeta^2$ the gain curve has a local minimum at zero frequency and a local maximum at $\omega = [\omega_n{}^2 - 2\zeta^2]^{1/2}$.

Check these results by evaluating $d^2G/d\omega^2$.

Examples of these two types of gain curve are plotted in Fig. 4.15. The corresponding phase variations as a function of ω are shown in Fig. 4.16.

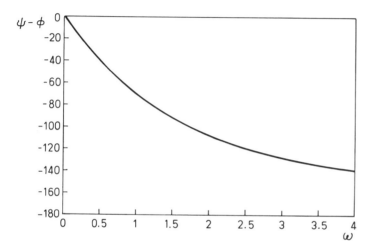

Fig. 4.16a The phase/angular frequency relationship for an overdamped system with $\omega_n = \sqrt{2}$ rad s^{-1} and $\zeta/\omega_n = 3/\sqrt{8}$.

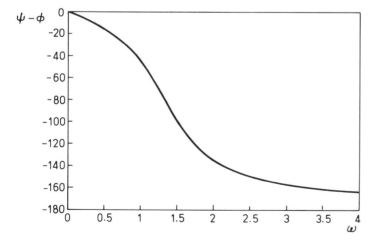

Fig. 4.16b The phase/angular frequency relationship for an underdamped system with $\omega_n = \sqrt{2}$ rad s^{-1} and $\zeta/\omega_n = 1/\sqrt{8}$.

The appearance of a maximum in the gain curve was not possible in a first-order system – it is the mathematical reflection of the phenomenon of **resonance** in dynamic systems.

Substitution of the value of ω which corresponds to the maximum in case (1) leads to a peak value of gain of

Note that as ζ tends to zero, the magnitude of the resonance can become arbitrarily large. This means that driving a lightly damped system near its resonance frequency (which is near its natural frequency for small ζ) can lead to an extremely large output magnitude. On a large scale this can lead to catastrophic results, such as the collapse of a bridge in a variable wind which is gusting near the appropriate frequency.

$$G_{max} = \frac{1}{2\zeta[\omega_n{}^2 - \zeta^2]^{1/2}} \tag{4.70}$$

Remembering that an underdamped system corresponds to $\zeta < \omega_n$ we can say that:

An underdamped second-order system with a damping ratio $\zeta/\omega_n < 1/\sqrt{2}$ will exhibit resonance at the **resonance angular frequency** $\omega_{res} = [\omega_n{}^2 - 2\zeta^2]^{1/2} \, \text{rad s}^{-1}$ (the

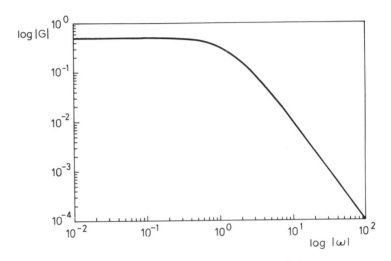

Fig. 4.17a   The amplitude Bode plot for an overdamped system with $\omega_n = \sqrt{2} \, \text{rad s}^{-1}$ and $\zeta/\omega_n = 3/\sqrt{8}$.

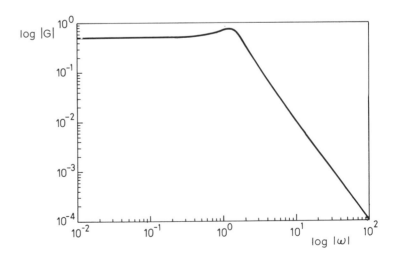

Fig. 4.17b   The amplitude Bode plot for an underdamped system with $\omega_n = \sqrt{2} \, \text{rad s}^{-1}$ and $\zeta/\omega_n = 1/\sqrt{8}$.

resonance frequency in Hz is this value divided by 2π). The magnitude of the resonance will be given by Equation (4.70).

Examine the resonance properties of the series RLC circuits:
(i) With $R = 1.5$ Ω, $L = 0.5$ H and $C = 1$ F.
(ii) With $R = 0.5$ Ω, $L = 0.5$ H and $C = 1$ F.

Worked Application Example 4.14

Solution Insertion of these parameters into the series differential Equation (4.33) shows that case (i) corresponds to $\omega_n = \sqrt{2}$ and $\zeta = 3/2$. The corresponding damping ratio is therefore $\zeta/\omega_n = 3/\sqrt{8} \approx 1.06$ so that the circuit response is overdamped and resonance cannot occur. The appropriate amplitude and phase response curves are those shown in Figs 4.15a and 4.16a.

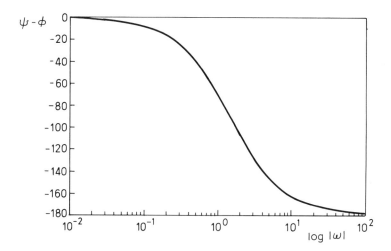

Fig. 4.18a The phase Bode plot for an overdamped system with $\omega_n = \sqrt{2}$ rad s^{-1} and $\zeta/\omega_n = 3/\sqrt{8}$.

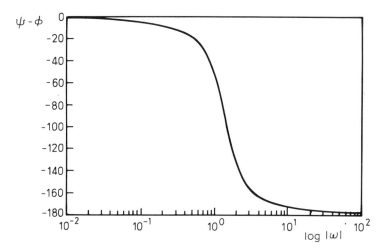

Fig. 4.18b The phase Bode plot for an underdamped system with $\omega_n = \sqrt{2}$ rad s^{-1} and $\zeta/\omega_n = 1/\sqrt{8}$.

For case (ii) a similar procedure shows that $\omega_n = \sqrt{2}$ and $\zeta = 1/2$, giving a damping ratio $\zeta/\omega_n = 1/\sqrt{8} \approx 0.35$. This is within the $1/\sqrt{2}$ limit and so this circuit will exhibit some degree of resonance, the maximum output amplitude being $2/\sqrt{7}$ V ≈ 0.756 V, corresponding to an input frequency of $\omega_{res} = \sqrt{(3/2)} \approx 1.225$ rad s^{-1}. Figs 4.15b and 4.16b illustrate the amplitude and phase curves for this particular resonant circuit.

It is common to display the amplitude and phase plots for dynamic systems of any order as **Bode diagrams**. These are plots of the amplitude/frequency relationship on log-log paper and the phase/frequency relationship on linear/log paper. The advantages of this are that it is possible to display a much wider range of frequencies on each plot; and, more importantly, the action of taking a logarithm of the data linearizes regions of the graph where a simple power law is a valid representation of the response. This means that it is now straightforward to study the asymptotic properties of the response for differing systems. Figs 4.17 and 4.18 display the same information as Figs 4.15 and 4.16, but in Bode plot form.

Bode plots are also known as **decibel plots**. They are used heavily for examining the practical frequency response of circuits and control systems. By measuring the slope of each of the linear regions it is possible to obtain immediate information about the order of the system and its overall dynamic structure.

The discussion of second-order differential equations provided in this chapter illustrates just how important and powerful a tool they provide for the analysis of dynamic systems. It should be stressed, however, that the discussion has been broadly restricted to linear differential equations with constant coefficients. This is due to two main facts:

1. It is usually possible to extract a good deal of meaningful information about a system by representing it by a second-order constant-coefficients model. When such a model is known to be an approximation the results are still valid over some operational range – determined by the individual ranges of validity of the specific approximations involved. Moreover, the methodology and interpretations derived for second-order systems can be extended readily to higher-order dynamic systems if necessary.

2. More general second-order (or higher) differential equations involving variable coefficients or nonlinearities can be extremely difficult to handle analytically. A multitude of advanced methods are available for the analysis of such equations, but generally they are not simple to understand or apply. Numerical methods can always be brought to bear on such, more realistic, simulations of the system, but the interpretation of the results is seldom as straightforward as for the simple second-order case.

By a higher-order system we mean one that can be modelled by an nth order linear differential equation with constant coefficients.

The final section of this chapter illustrates just how difficult it can be to incorporate a simple, but variable, physical effect with a differential model.

Second-order differential equations with variable coefficients

All of the previous discussion of second-order equations has hinged on the assumption that the coefficients of the differential terms are constant with respect to the independent variable. If this assumption is invalid, then it is impossible to write down the characteristic equation of the differential equation. The equation is still linear, but the techniques given above for obtaining the complementary solution break down.

One possible new approach is to attempt to build up a specific polynomial solution to the differential equation by using Taylor's theorem. This is possible because, at any given value of the independent variable, the differential equation relates the second derivative of the function to the first derivative and the current value of the function itself. If conditions are specified which fix these last two quantities at some given value of the independent variable, it is possible to use the differential equation to calculate a value for the second derivative as well. If the differential equation is differentiated once, however, it is possible to use the (now known) values of the first and second derivatives at some value of the independent variable to calculate the corresponding third derivative. The resultant set of derivative values can be inserted into a third-order Taylor series which gives an approximate form for the solution of the differential equation around the specified value of the independent variable. Similarly, a further differentiation can be carried out to obtain a value for the fourth derivative and, in fact, the procedure can be carried out arbitrarily often in theory, but often becomes cumbersome in practice for high-order derivatives. Despite this, it is sometimes possible to use a computer algorithm or to calculate general analytic formulae which enable a very accurate polynomial solution to be obtained for a wide operational range of the independent variable.

Effectively, the idea is to perform a polynomial expansion around the starting point of the solution of the differential equation. The polynomial will track the curve representing the true solution of the differential equation reasonably accurately for some range of the independent variable, but any finite approximation will eventually diverge from the true solution.

Application Example 4.15

For example, consider a series RLC circuit where the value of the resistor is increased linearly with time.

Suppose that we examine the properties of the specific circuit which is characterized by $R = (1.5 + 0.5\alpha t)$ Ω, $L = 0.5$ H, and $C = 1$ F, subject to a sinusoidal input of $\cos(2t)$ and initial conditions $V_C(t=0) = 1$ V and $I(t=0) [= dV_C/dt(t=0)] = 2$ A. For general values of α, the differential equation is

Resistance variations of this sort were discussed with respect to first-order systems in Example 4.5, where it was possible to obtain an analytic solution. Unfortunately, second-order systems require a much more complicated approach.

$$\frac{d^2V_C}{dt^2} + (3 + \alpha t)\frac{dV_C}{dt} + 2V_C = 2\cos(2t) \tag{4.71}$$

which collapses down to the overdamped case discussed in Example 4.13 when $\alpha = 0$. For positive values of α (increasing resistance) this equation will always be overdamped, but the damping factor will increase in magnitude with time.

Applying Leibnitz's theorem to Equation (4.71) term by term gives

Leibnitz's theorem (see Chapter T1) enables the nth-order differentiation of a product of two functions to be represented as a series of product terms with relative weightings determined by the binomial coefficients. In cases where one function is particularly simple (as here) the series has only a few nonzero terms.

$$\frac{d^{n+2}V_C}{dt^{n+2}} + (3 + \alpha t)\frac{d^{n+1}V_C}{dt^{n+1}} + (2 + n\alpha)\frac{d^nV_C}{dt^n} = 2^{n+1}\cos\left(2t + \frac{n\pi}{2}\right) \tag{4.72}$$

where every component of the equation has been differentiated n times and the extra term involving an $n\alpha$ weighting has arisen because of the product of functions of time contained within the second term of Equation (4.71). Since the conditions specified with the equation correspond to $t=0$, it is possible to set $t=0$ in Equation (4.72) and obtain

Recurrence relationships and difference equations can arise in discrete circuit analysis, discrete control theory, and the simulation of any sampled data/digitized system. Their basic properties are very closely related to those of the standard types of differential equations covered in this chapter.

$$\left.\frac{d^{n+2}V_C}{dt^{n+2}}\right|_{t=0} = -3\left.\frac{d^{n+1}V_C}{dt^{n+1}}\right|_{t=0} - (2 + n\alpha)\left.\frac{d^nV_C}{dt^n}\right|_{t=0} + 2^{n+1}\cos\left(\frac{n\pi}{2}\right) \tag{4.73}$$

which is a **recurrence relationship** between the derivatives of the function at $t=0$; it means that any derivative of the function at the origin ($t=0$) can be obtained in terms of the values of the two lower derivatives at $t=0$. The initial conditions for V_C and dV_C/dt alone are quite sufficient to specify precisely the entire sequence of derivatives.

For the particular example being considered here we have $V_C^{(0)}(t=0) = 1$ and $V_C^{(1)}(t=0) = 2$, so that we can obtain, step by step:

For more general time variations, or if more than one coefficient is time varying, it would be difficult to write down such a compact and general expression as (4.73).

$n = 0$: $V_C^{(2)}(t=0) = (-3)(2) - 2 + 2 = -6$
$n = 1$: $V_C^{(3)}(t=0) = (-3)(-6) - (2 + \alpha)(2) = 14 - 2\alpha$
$n = 2$: $V_C^{(4)}(t=0) = (-3)(14 - 2\alpha) - (2 + 2\alpha)(-6) - 8$
$\qquad = -38 + 18\alpha$
$n = 3$: $V_C^{(5)}(t=0) = (-3)(-38 + 18\alpha) - (2 + 3\alpha)(14 - 2\alpha)$
$\qquad = 86 - 92\alpha + 6\alpha^2$
$n = 4$: $V_C^{(6)}(t=0) = (-3)(86 - 92\alpha + 6\alpha^2) - (2 + 4\alpha)(-38 + 18\alpha) + 32$
$\qquad = -150 + 392\alpha - 90\alpha^2$

So that, in theory, two initial conditions and a second-order differential equation can be used to obtain all of the derivative information of a function at a given point on that function.

Recall that $x^{(n)}$ is an alternative (compact) notation for the nth derivative of a function with respect to some independent variable (often time, and sometimes understood from the context of the equation).

If a particular value is specified for α at the start of this process, every derivative will have a purely numerical value. This means that the process could be handled very readily by a computer program as an iterative routine – an algorithm which is designed to use the recurrence relationship and two input values of derivatives to generate a numerical value for the next derivative in the sequence.

The sixth-order approximation of Equation (4.75) does not really contain enough terms to examine the medium/long-term effects of the resistor variation – it only tracks the true solution to within a few percent for about the first second of operation of the circuit, diverging away rapidly for larger values of time.

and so on – for as many steps as you feel up to handling! If the process is halted at this stage, analytic expressions are available for the first six derivatives of the capacitor voltage at zero time. It is possible to insert the various derivative expressions into a sixth-order Taylor series expansion around $t = 0$, giving

$$V_C = 1 + 2t - \frac{6}{2!}t^2 + \frac{(14 - 2\alpha)}{3!}t^3 + \frac{(-38 + 18\alpha)}{4!}t^4$$
$$+ \frac{(86 - 92\alpha + 6\alpha^2)}{5!}t^5 + \frac{(-150 + 392\alpha - 90\alpha^2)}{6!}t^6 \qquad (4.74)$$

as a polynomial approximation to the behaviour of the solution of the differential equation. The validity of the approximation will decrease as t increases. The individual terms within Equation (4.74) can be expanded and regrouped to give

$$V_C = 1 + 2t - \frac{6}{2!}t^2 + \frac{14}{3!}t^3 - \frac{38}{4!}t^4 + \frac{86}{5!}t^5 - \frac{150}{6!}t^6$$
$$+ \alpha t^3 \left[-\frac{2}{3!} + \frac{18}{4!}t + \frac{(-92 + 6\alpha)}{5!}t^2 + \frac{(392 - 90\alpha)}{6!}t^3 \right] \qquad (4.75)$$

which shows that the solution of the differential equation can be partitioned into two series, one which is due to the time-independent coefficients of the differential equation and a second which augments the solution by adding the time-varying coefficient effects via an α-dependent function of t.

If an arbitrary number of terms are included in the Taylor expansion it can be shown (see Exercise 4.4) that the α-independent series is identical to the analytic result that would be obtained for the constant-coefficients differential equation ($\alpha = 0$). The remaining terms then correspond to a series which accurately reflects the additional, cumulative effect of the resistor variation on the value of the output.

Exercise 4.4 Consider the circuit characterized by the differential Equation (4.71) with the specified initial conditions and with $\alpha = 0$. Show that the solution is given by

$$V_C = 3.6 \exp(-t) - 2.5 \exp(-2t) - 0.1 \cos(2t) + 0.3 \sin(2t)$$

Insert the appropriate series expansions in this solution, including terms up to and including t^6, and gather the terms together to obtain a single, sixth-order polynomial approximation to the accurate solution.

Confirm that the resultant polynomial is the same as that obtained from Equation (4.75) by letting α tend to zero.

It is clear from the above example that generally it is much easier to cope with system models that can be represented by differential equations with constant coefficients!

Summary

Some of the main properties of the representation of dynamic systems by differential equations have been discussed. The role of linearity has been illustrated via the ability (within a general, driven, linear system) to partition the solution into two independent components: the complementary function (transient/natural response) and the particular integral (driven/forced/steady-state response). The magnitude of the transient response is governed directly by the difference between the initial conditions and the steady-state solution at $t = 0$ and can be eliminated completely if it is possible to arrange for a suitable start-up configuration of the system.

A small range of applications of first-order differential equations have been discussed, more general theoretical support being given in Chapter T4 (p. 156). Second-order equations form the basic model for the simulation and interpretation of a wide range of practical systems and have been discussed at some length.

For all types of equation the engineering importance of the concepts of impulse response, step response and frequency response has been stressed. Each type of response aims to extract information about a practical system in a different way. It is possible to attach a signal generator to a circuit input and examine the frequency response of that circuit by varying the input frequency. The resultant information can be used to attach numerical values to a model of the dynamics of the circuit. If the system of interest is a large engineering plant, however, in all probability it will be impossible to excite the system with a high-frequency input. In such circumstances the step or impulse response of the system may be a better way of extracting experimental information.

As often arises in process control engineering, for example.

The restricted number of types of differential equations that the tools discussed in this chapter enable us to solve have been shown to be amazingly useful in the solution and interpretation of practical examples. In particular, the forced, damped harmonic oscillator arises in a number of guises in a variety of apparently unrelated application areas and allows repeated use of the same powerful mathematical ideas.

An example has been given of a possible way to attack a differential equation with time-varying coefficients to obtain an approximate polynomial solution.

Finally, with regard to the general engineering applicability of the ideas discussed in this chapter, it should be said that, while the concepts and methods are very important for any analysis of dynamic systems, the techniques developed are aimed exclusively at systems with a single input (independent variable) and a single output (dependent variable). This has been perhaps the most important restriction of the whole text so far, and is one that we will now attempt to rectify by introducing the mathematical description of multivariable systems.

Further exercises

4.5 In an RL circuit the inductor has a non-linear current characteristic given by

$$L = \frac{L_0}{1 + \lambda^2 I^2} \quad \text{for some parameters } \lambda \text{ and } L_0$$

If a constant e.m.f. source, E, is switched in at time $t = 0$, show that the current/time relationship is given by

$$t = \frac{L_0}{1 + \lambda^2 I^2}\left[E\,\lambda \tan^{-1}(\lambda I) + \frac{R}{2}\ln|1 + \lambda^2 I^2| - R\ln\left|1 - \frac{IR}{E}\right| \right]$$

and show that this result becomes equivalent to that given by Equation 4.9 for the case of a linear inductor as λ is reduced to zero.

4.6 Find the transient and steady-state circuit response of the RL circuit modelled by the equation

$$L\,\frac{dI}{dt} + RI = E_0 \sin(\omega t)$$

where the voltage source is switched in at $t = 0$ and the initial current is zero.

4.7 A series RLC circuit with $R = 10\ \Omega$, $L = 1$ H and $C = 1/16$ F is driven by an ac voltage source of $E = 5.75 \cos(5t)$ V.

Find the time variation of the circuit current if $I(t = 0) = -19.92$ A and $I(t = 1) = 0.543$ A.

4.8 In Exercise 4.7, what is the natural frequency of the circuit? Can resonance occur?

4.9 Write down a second order differential equation governing the time variation of the charge on a capacitor in a series RLC circuit subject to an ac sinusoidal voltage source $E_0 \cos(\omega t)$.

Also, use Newton's laws of motion to write down a similar differential equation for the mechanical system where a sprung mass, m, is displaced from its equilibrium position by a distance x, and is subject to forces

$F_s = -kx$	A restoring force: k is the *spring constant*
$F_d = -r\dfrac{dx}{dt}$	A damping force: due to *viscous retarding* of the motion through the local medium (e.g. air).
$F_f = F_0 \cos(\omega t)$	A sinusoidal driving force of magnitude F_0

Draw analogies between the electrical and mechanical quantities in the two equations.

An Introduction to Multivariable Methods 5

Objectives

☐ To illustrate the fact that most practical engineering problems require the use of multivariable calculus.
☐ To introduce the idea of the partial derivatives of a multivariable function.
☐ To provide detailed examples of some of the basic applications of multivariable calculus within electronic engineering.
☐ To show that there are a variety of coordinate systems available for the analysis of multivariable problems, and to show how to switch between coordinate systems and employ the one that best suits the particular problem.

Multivariable problems in engineering

In Chapter 3 a number of examples were given of the way in which the physical parameters of a system can couple together. That chapter was concerned solely with the algebraic coupling of the many variables associated with any practical system: in general the variables will couple together in a dynamic fashion which requires the tools of multivariable calculus to be used.

This chapter will concentrate on an overview of some practical examples which illustrate the basic extensions to the concepts and techniques of the differential and integral calculus required to cope with multivariable effects. It will be necessary to stop short of techniques involving Lagrange multipliers, vector calculus, coupled differential equations, eigenvalue analysis and the normal modes of a dynamic multivariable system. Each of these further topics provides powerful analytical tools which have a wide range of engineering applications: further details on some of these topics are given by Jeffrey (1989) or more advanced mathematical texts.

Generally, multivariable problems will arise whenever some variable of interest, such as a system output or measurement, is dependent simultaneously on a number of independent variables, such as a set of system inputs and/or measurements of the current operational state of the system. This is usually expressed as $z = f(u, v, . . ., x, y)$, where the output, z, is determined by a function of the set of values for all inputs, $u, v, . . ., x, y$. The appropriate differential tool to use for such functions is partial differentiation. A range of types of problems involving multivariable functions and their differential properties will now be considered.

Applications of partial differentiation

The partial derivatives of a pre-specified function can be used to examine a number of problems where the important point of interest is the response of a system to some change in its multivariable inputs/operating conditions.

Precise tests performed on a particular type of resistor by the manufacturer have shown that the resistor is approximately linear and temperature invariant, having a

Lagrange multipliers are used in problems involving constrained minimization, as arise in finding the minimum energy state of a quantum electronic system, for example. Vector calculus forms the basic tools for most of electromagnetic theory and the analysis of fluid flow. Coupled differential equations arise in control theory and circuit analysis as representations of the differential coupling between internal subsystems via common components: eigenvalue methods and the analysis of normal modes provide an insight into the dynamic response of such systems.

The fact that many independent variables are related to only one dependent variable (output) is a reflection of the physical fact that a measurement of any one physical parameter of a system is in general dependent on a number of factors within the system.

Worked Application Example 5.1

This expression is obtained by
augmenting a linear *IV*
characteristic with an amount
(governed by the parameter *a*)
of cubic component centred
around I_0. The resistance is
given by the (current-
dependent) slope of the *IV*
characteristic. The temperature
dependence is governed
separately by the temperature
coefficient α. The overall
functional form is most
appropriate to the resistance
properties of thin filaments and
incandescent lamps.

See Chapter T5 for the
definition of the total
differential.

nominal resistance of 10 ohms over a reasonable range of operating conditions. If, in fact, the resistance is given more correctly by the expression

$$R(T,I) = 8.3(1 + \alpha T) + a(3I^2 - 6II_0 + 3I_0^2) \tag{5.1}$$

where the constants α, a and I_0 are characteristic of the resistor and T is measured in degrees centigrade, what will be the effect on R of simultaneous small changes in T and I?

For the specific values of $\alpha = 0.01$, $a = 0.1$, $I_0 = 3$ find the approximate change in resistance due to a change from the operating conditions $T = 20$ °C and $I = 5$ A to $T = 25$ °C and $I = 5.5$ A.

Solution For small changes ΔT and ΔI away for some given set of operating conditions T and I it is possible to use the approximate form of the expression for the **total differential** of a function $z = f(u, v, \ldots, x, y)$:

$$dz = \frac{\partial f}{\partial u} du + \frac{\partial f}{\partial v} dv + \ldots + \frac{\partial f}{\partial x} dx + \frac{\partial f}{\partial y} dy \tag{5.2}$$

where the infinitesimal displacements are replaced by small errors, Δx, etc. In this case,

$$\Delta R \approx 8.3\alpha(\Delta T) + a(6I - 6I_0)(\Delta I)$$

where the coefficients of the small changes are the appropriate partial derivatives of the original resistance function.

For the specified resistor parameters and operating conditions the change in resistance is

$$\Delta R \approx (8.3)(0.01)(5) + 6\,(0.1)(2)(0.5) = 1.015 \text{ ohms}$$

In many applications the value of an output may depend on the value of a range of internal parameters and variables of the system, which themselves depend on some other single parameter, such as time. In such a case the **chain rule** of partial differentiation proves useful.

Worked Application Example 5.2

In the previous example the temperature and current are varied deliberately with time via the laws $T = (20 + 0.15t)$ °C and $I = (5 + \sin t)$ amps. Find the rate of change of the value of the resistance of the circuit element with time.

Solution The chain rule for this two-variable problem is:

$$\frac{dR}{dt} = \frac{\partial R}{\partial T} \frac{dT}{dt} + \frac{\partial R}{\partial I} \frac{dI}{dt} \tag{5.3}$$

and the partial derivatives have already been established to be

$$\frac{\partial R}{\partial T} = 8.3\alpha \quad \text{and} \quad \frac{\partial R}{\partial I} = a(6I - 6I_0)$$

Therefore,

$$\frac{dR}{dt} = (8.3\alpha)(0.15) + a(6I - 6I_0)(\cos t)$$
$$= 1.245\alpha + 6a(5 - I_0 + \sin t)\,(\cos t)$$

The previous problem can also be solved by substituting the t-dependent functions for T and I directly into the expression (5.1), giving R as an explicit function of t which can be differentiated immediately. The advantages of keeping the multivariable form are that the differentiation of R is split up into a number of simpler differentiations and, more importantly, it is possible to keep track of the variables which are internal to the problem: T and I. The question is not concerned directly with the values of these variables: they are assumed to be important only in that they affect the circuit element of interest. In practical problems, however, the steady increase in temperature may well eventually cause some other circuit component or connection to fail: it is often necessary to ensure that all important circuit parameters remain within nominally desirable operational ranges. The step of expressing R directly in terms of t loses the explicit information about the time dependence of the temperature: it is better to retain the multivariable viewpoint and gain insight into the simultaneous behaviour of many of the circuit variables.

One particular situation where partial derivatives prove useful is when a particle is moving under the influence of a force or field along some planar path.

In control system applications the representation of a system as an output which is determined directly by the dynamic properties of the system and some specific input is often known as the **transfer function** approach, or **classical control theory. Modern control theory** is concerned with the simultaneous study of the internal variables of the system in addition to the input and output functions: this is called the **state space** representation of a system.

The motion of a particle in a plane is specified by a general implicit function $f(x, y) = 0$. Show that it is possible to calculate d^2y/dx^2 via the expression

$$\frac{d^2y}{dx^2} = \frac{-f_x^2 f_{yy} + 2f_x f_y f_{xy} - f_y^2 f_{xx}}{f_y^3} \tag{5.4}$$

Worked Application Example 5.3

Solution If it is possible to rearrange the functional relationship in an explicit form the second derivative can be evaluated directly: if not, it can often be obtained using implicit differentiation (see Chapter T1, p. 115). This case is completely general, however, and neither technique can be used.

Viewing the function as merely one constraint curve within a larger surface given by $z = f(x, y)$, it is possible to evaluate the partial derivatives of the surface along the points on the curve. It can be shown (see Chapter T5) that in such a case

$$\frac{dy}{dx} = -\frac{f_x}{f_y} \tag{5.5}$$

The concept of operators and the derivation of this expression are discussed in Chapter T5.

To obtain higher derivatives of the l.h.s. it is necessary to apply the operator d/dx, but the r.h.s. is a ratio of functions of two variables and cannot be subjected directly to ordinary differentiation. It is necessary to replace the ordinary differentiation operator by the **total differentiation operator**:

$$\frac{d}{dx} = \frac{\partial}{\partial x} + \frac{dy}{dx}\frac{\partial}{\partial y} \tag{5.6}$$

Effectively, this supplies the general conversion formula from ordinary to partial differentiation when the two variables are not truly independent. Equation (5.5) becomes

$$\frac{d}{dx}\left[\frac{dy}{dx}\right] = \left[\frac{\partial}{\partial x} - \frac{f_x}{f_y}\frac{\partial}{\partial y}\right]\left[-\frac{f_x}{f_y}\right] \tag{5.7}$$

So that the operator equivalence of Equation (5.6) has been applied to both sides of Equation (5.5). Also, the general operator (5.6) has been made specific for this problem by using (5.5) to fix the value of dy/dx within the operator.

The evaluation of this expression involves taking the partial derivatives of a ratio of multivariable functions: the ratio rule of differentiation must be employed, giving

$$\frac{d}{dx}\left[\frac{dy}{dx}\right] = \left[\frac{-f_y f_{xx} + f_x f_{xy}}{f_y^2} - \frac{f_x[-f_y f_{xy} + f_x f_{yy}]}{f_y^3}\right]$$

$$\Rightarrow \quad \frac{d^2 y}{dx^2} = \frac{-f_x^2 f_{yy} + 2f_x f_y f_{xy} - f_y^2 f_{xx}}{f_y^3}$$

as required.

Exercise 5.1 A charged particle moving solely under the influence of a constant magnetic field describes a circle in the XY-plane defined by the equation

$$x^2 + y^2 = a^2$$

Evaluate $d^2 y/dx^2$ for this planar curve (i) by repeated implicit differentiation of the function, and (ii) by evaluating the first- and second-order partial derivatives and using the general result obtained in the previous example.

As a further example of the use of basic formulae involving partial derivatives, the technique of changing the variables in which a function is represented will be illustrated.

A common problem in field theory, and multivariable applications in general, involves relating a series of function and gradient measurements to a series of corresponding measurements (or theoretical predictions) expressed in a different coordinate system. Such a problem will arise whenever the natural coordinate system for establishing the mathematical model does not match the practical coordinate system used by the measuring device.

Such a difference in coordinate systems is usually dictated by design limitations: analytical study of the magnetic field of the Earth is best suited to a spherical coordinate system, but it is difficult to orientate all ground and satellite measurements of field and field gradients along a common spherical coordinate system.

Worked Application Example 5.4

Measurements of field can be made with a fluxmeter, and field gradients can be obtained with a flux gradiometer if required. Measurements of the Earth's magnetic field are used in archaeological pre-excavation analysis and underground surveying for pipes or mineral deposits.

See Carter (1986) or Lorrain and Corson (1978) for details of the theory of electrostatics and dipoles.

Measurements of electric field are made in Cartesian coordinate system at the point $(1, 2, \sqrt{2})$. The three measured field components at the point are found to be given accurately by

$$\mathbf{E} = \begin{bmatrix} \dfrac{3}{16\sqrt{2}} \\[2mm] \dfrac{3}{16\sqrt{2}} \\[2mm] \dfrac{1}{16} \end{bmatrix} \ \text{V m}^{-1}$$

Find the derivatives of the electrostatic potential at this point in the spherical polar coordinate system. Are the potential gradients compatible with those produced at the point by a point dipole of dipole moment $4\pi\epsilon_0$ C m positioned at the origin and pointing along the z-axis?

Solution The components of electric field measured at a point in Cartesian coordinates are related to the electrostatic potential at that point by

$$E_x = -\frac{\partial V}{\partial x} \qquad E_y = -\frac{\partial V}{\partial y} \qquad \text{and} \qquad E_z = -\frac{\partial V}{\partial z}$$

so that the field measurements are equivalent to a set of measurements of the Cartesian partial derivatives of the scalar function $V(x,y,z)$.

The spherical coordinate system is related to the Cartesian system by the equations

$$x = r \sin \theta \cos \phi$$
$$y = r \sin \theta \sin \phi$$
$$z = r \cos \theta$$

and to relate the gradient measurements in the two coordinate systems it is necessary to evaluate the **Jacobian** matrix for the transformation:

$$\frac{\partial(x,y,z)}{\partial(r,\theta,\phi)} = \begin{bmatrix} \sin \theta \cos \phi & \sin \theta \sin \phi & \cos \theta \\ r \cos \theta \cos \phi & r \cos \theta \sin \phi & -r \sin \theta \\ -r \sin \theta \sin \phi & r \sin \theta \cos \phi & 0 \end{bmatrix}$$

See Chapter T5 for a discussion of the Jacobian of a transformation.

which transforms a vector of partial derivatives in the XYZ coordinate system to a vector of derivatives in the $R\Theta\Phi$ system. The particular point of interest, $(1, 1, \sqrt{2})$, in Cartesian coordinates is the point $(2, \pi/4, \pi/4)$ in the spherical system. At this point the transformation matrix gives a specific set of gradients in the new coordinate system:

$$\begin{bmatrix} \dfrac{\partial V}{\partial r} \\[2mm] \dfrac{\partial V}{\partial \theta} \\[2mm] \dfrac{\partial V}{\partial \phi} \end{bmatrix} = \begin{bmatrix} 1/2 & 1/2 & 1/\sqrt{2} \\ 1 & 1 & -\sqrt{2} \\ -1 & 1 & 0 \end{bmatrix} \begin{bmatrix} -\dfrac{3}{16\sqrt{2}} \\[2mm] -\dfrac{3}{16\sqrt{2}} \\[2mm] -\dfrac{1}{16} \end{bmatrix}$$

$$\Rightarrow \quad \frac{\partial V}{\partial r} = -\frac{1}{4\sqrt{2}} \qquad \frac{\partial V}{\partial \theta} = -\frac{1}{4\sqrt{2}} \qquad \text{and} \qquad \frac{\partial V}{\partial \phi} = 0$$

at the point of measurement.

A point dipole of dipole moment, p, at the origin and pointing in the Z-direction produces an electrostatic potential

See Carter (1986) or Lorrain and Corson (1978).

$$V(r,\theta,\phi) = \frac{p \cos \theta}{4\pi\epsilon_0 \, r^2}$$

in spherical coordinates. Since p is given to be $4\pi\epsilon_0$ the partial derivatives of this are

$$\frac{\partial V}{\partial r} = -\frac{2 \cos \theta}{r^3} \qquad \frac{\partial V}{\partial \theta} = -\frac{\sin \theta}{r^2} \qquad \text{and} \qquad \frac{\partial V}{\partial \phi} = 0$$

which match the measurements at the point $(2, \pi/4, \pi/4)$ precisely! The measurements are consistent with a dipole at the origin.

These measurements cannot identify the source of the field: they can only indicate whether certain forms of charge distribution are consistent with the measured field. With many measurements it becomes possible to be more precise!

Multivariable polynomial expansions

In a number of applications information may be available about some physical variable and a number of its derivatives at a point in space, the objective usually being to build up a picture of the approximate behaviour of the variable in some region around the point at which experimental measurements have been made. Alternatively, a mathematical model of the expected functional behaviour of a system may have been derived, but the solution may require a great deal of computational effort to evaluate: in such a case it can be adequate to work with a multivariable polynomial approximation to the exact function at any point.

There is no mathematical difference between the idea of a function $f(x,y,z)$ in space and that of a function $g(R,L,C)$ in a simple circuit: it is common to think of a set of n values for any system variables as representing a point in an n-dimensional **state space**, in much the same way that IV characteristics can be viewed as curves in a plane.

Consider a simple single-loop RL circuit with perfect elements and a constant voltage source of E volts. In Chapter 4 (p. 59) it was shown that the time variation of the loop current of the circuit is

$$I(E,R,L,t) = \frac{E}{R}\left[1 - \exp\left[-\frac{Rt}{L}\right]\right] \tag{5.8}$$

If it is required to undertake a numerical study of the properties of this current response as any of the variables $\{E,R,L,t\}$ are varied simultaneously, the exponential function can become a computational burden. The evaluation of any mathematical function on a computer takes far longer than the basic operations of addition or multiplication: if that function evaluation takes place within an iterative loop it can become the limiting factor in the program execution speed. One popular solution to the problem is to break up the function into a number of ranges, and within each range replace the full function by a simple polynomial approximation, which can be evaluated much more rapidly.

If E is accurately a constant 5 volts and interest is centred about the circuit properties at a time $t = 2$ seconds, construct a quadratic approximation to the current response of Equation (5.8) around the values of $R = 2$ ohms and $L = 3$ henrys.

With no assumptions, it is possible to build a quadratic Taylor expansion in all four variables: these particular constraints serve to keep the example at a level that can be interpreted readily.

The evaluation of these partial derivatives is tedious, but it is well worth working through the details to ensure that you gain some practice.

Solution Using the information about E and t, it is necessary to build a second-order Taylor approximation to the function

$$I(R,L) = \frac{5}{R}\left[1 - \exp\left[-\frac{2R}{L}\right]\right] \tag{5.9}$$

around the point $R = 2$, $L = 3$. The required partial derivatives are

$$I_R = -\frac{5}{R^2} + \left[\frac{10}{RL} + \frac{5}{R^2}\right]\exp\left[-\frac{2R}{L}\right]$$

$$I_L = -\frac{10}{L^2}\exp\left[-\frac{2R}{L}\right]$$

$$I_{RR} = \frac{10}{R^3} - \left[\frac{20}{RL^2} + \frac{20}{R^2L} + \frac{10}{R^3}\right]\exp\left[-\frac{2R}{L}\right]$$

$$I_{LL} = \left[\frac{20}{L^3} - \frac{20R}{L^4}\right]\exp\left[-\frac{2R}{L}\right]$$

$$I_{RL} = \frac{20}{L^3}\exp\left[-\frac{2R}{L}\right]$$

so that at the specified set of circuit element values,

$I(2,3) = 1.841$	$I_R(2,3) = -0.481$	$I_L(2,3) = -0.293$
$I_{RR}(2,3) = 0.188$	$I_{LL}(2,3) = 0.065$	$I_{RL}(2,3) = 0.195$

and the desired second-order Taylor expansion is

$$\begin{aligned}I(R,L) \approx\ & 1.841 - 0.481(R-2) - 0.293(L-3) \\ & + 0.094(R-2)^2 + 0.195(R-2)(L-3) + 0.033(L-3)^2\end{aligned} \tag{5.10}$$

The accuracy of the above approximate representation can be checked at a few randomly chosen points, as in the following table.

R	L	Exact function (5.9)	Quadratic fit (5.10)	Percentage error
1.5	2.5	2.3294	2.3085	-0.90
2.8	2.8	1.5440	1.5451	0.07
2.7	3.7	1.4216	1.4570	2.49

Such an approach can give only a crude picture of the quality of the quadratic fit: more generally it is possible to establish analytic limits or to evaluate the errors over a coarse mesh of points around the expansion point. Such an approach shows that the approximation is relatively good: for R in the interval [1,3] and L in [2,4] the error will be no more than about 7% in magnitude, and will be much less than that value for most points within the region.

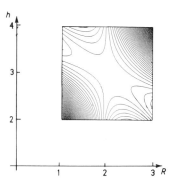

A contour plot illustrating the variation of percentage error of the quadratic approximation in a region around the expansion point $R = 2$, $L = 3$.

Multivariable optimization

The need to find the maxima/minima of multivariable functions arises surprisingly often in practical engineering applications. The whole topic of system identification hinges around finding the best mathematical functional representation of a system that is consistent with a series of experimental measurements of a number of outputs of the system. In its simplest form, such identification corresponds to finding the best (least squares) straight line through a set of data points drawn on graph paper: even this simplest case amounts at an optimization of the two parameters which specify the X-axis intercept and slope of the line that achieve a best fit to the data.

One key application of minimization techniques arises in the justification of the maximum power transfer theorem for a general RLC circuit with an ac source.

So that the best fit is obtained by finding the overall minimum of some two-variable function which describes the error associated with a given line. If the data is particularly noisy or ill defined, many false minima may exist.

Using Thévenin equivalent circuit techniques, any network of sources and resistive/reactive circuit elements can be reduced to a single equivalent load being driven by a single equivalent source. A great deal of information can be obtained from the simple one-loop equivalent circuit.

In such a circuit, if the resistive and reactive characteristics of the source are known, determine those of the load that will lead to the maximum power dissipation in the load.

Solution   In any ac circuit the instantaneous current can be represented in phasor form as

$$I = \frac{E}{R + jX}$$

where E is the source voltage phasor and $Z = R + jX$ is the impedance of the circuit.

If a general load is driven by an ac source of known internal resistance, inductance and capacitance at a particular frequency the current phasor is

$$I = \frac{E}{R_s + R_l + j(X_s + X_l)} \tag{5.11}$$

where the subscripts distinguish the source and load characteristics.

The power phasor for the load is

$$S_l = V_l I^* = I Z_l I^* = \frac{|E|^2 (R_l + jX_l)}{(R_s + R_l)^2 + (X_s + X_l)^2}$$

Worked Application Example 5.6

This theorem was proved in Chapter 1 for the purely resistive case.

See Chapter 2 for an introduction to phasor methods. Boctor (1987) gives many examples of phasor methods.

The reactive contribution to the impedance arises from the circuit energy storage elements: the inductors and capacitors.

In a purely resistive circuit the instantaneous power is VI: for more general cases, in phasor form the complex power is the product of the complex voltage and the complex conjugate of the complex current (see Boctor, 1987, for details).

and since the reactive components do not dissipate power, but only store and release energy, the question amounts to finding the values of R_l and X_l that will maximize the real part of this function: the power dissipation in the load resistor.

For a given ac voltage source being driven at a fixed frequency E, ω, R_s and X_s are constants and the power transferred to the load resistor is a function of the load resistance and reactance:

$$P(R_l, X_l) = \frac{|E|^2 R_l}{(R_s + R_l)^2 + (X_s + X_l)^2} \tag{5.12}$$

It is necessary to establish the stationary points of this function and examine whether they correspond to maxima, minima or saddle points. The first partial derivatives are

$$\frac{\partial P}{\partial R_l} = \frac{|E|^2 [R_s^2 - R_l^2 + (X_s + X_l)^2]}{[(R_s + R_l)^2 + (X_s + X_l)^2]^2}$$

$$\text{and} \quad \frac{\partial P}{\partial X_l} = -\frac{2|E|^2 R_l (X_s + X_l)}{[(R_s + R_l)^2 + (X_s + X_l)^2]^2}$$

For a nonzero value of R_l these two partial derivatives can be simultaneously zero only when $X_l = -X_s$ and when $R_l = R_s$. Therefore there is a single stationary point of the function which occurs when the load impedance is the complex conjugate of the source impedance:

$$Z_l = R_s - jX_s \quad \text{if} \quad Z_s = R_s + jX_s \tag{5.13}$$

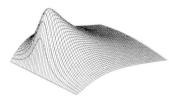

In general, it is necessary to calculate all three of the second-order partial derivatives of the power function and examine the sign of a specific quadratic function of these derivatives (see Chapter T5 p. 175) to establish the nature of the stationary point. In this case it can be argued that the power dissipated is always positive and tends to zero for very small values of the load resistance and very large values of load impedance: since there is only one stationary point it must be an overall maximum.

Physically, the result means that the maximum power is transferred between the source and load portions of a circuit network when the resistances of the two portions balance perfectly and the reactances cancel perfectly. In effect, the source and load reactances are equal in magnitude but 180° out of phase with each other: as energy is released by the reactive elements of the source it is taken up by those of the load, and vice versa. The result is a circuit that is reactance free overall: the additional criterion for maximum power transfer then collapses to the same as for the purely resistance case discussed in Chapter 1 (p. 6).

It can be shown that the resonance condition (see Chapter 4) for an RLC circuit is achieved when the conditions of Equation (5.13) are satisfied. Maximum power transfer is obtained when the total circuit impedance is a minimum and the loop current is a maximum: which is the condition for the resonance of the current response.

Exercise 5.2 Evaluate the three second-order partial derivatives for the above problem and verify analytically that the stationary point is indeed a maximum.

Exercise 5.3 In Example 2.6 the expression

$$\mathbf{r}_\mu - \mathbf{r}_\lambda = \begin{bmatrix} 4 \\ -11 \\ -6 \end{bmatrix} + \begin{bmatrix} 5\mu - 10\lambda \\ 8\mu - 6\lambda \\ \mu + \lambda \end{bmatrix}$$

was obtained as representing the possible vectors between two aircraft on different flight paths. By considering the modulus of this vector as a function of λ and μ find the distance of closest possible approach of the aircraft.

It is possible to consider either the modulus of the vector or the square of the modulus: when the former is a minimum the latter will also be. The use of the square of the modulus will be easier in practice.

Multiple integrals

There are a large number of physical situations where the need for multiple integrals arises. In particular, in electrostatic applications it is common to describe the line charge of electrons in a thin wire, surface charge on a charged conductor, and the volume charge within a region of a dielectric with line, surface and volume charge densities. In general, these charge densities are variable functions of position on the line, surface, or in space and yield a total charge only when integrated over an appropriate region.

A surface charge density varies according to the curvature of the surface, with very high charge densities at a sharp point. This accumulation of charge at a point leads to the phenomenon of corona discharge.

A charged disc of radius a with uniform surface charge density ρ_1 C m^{-2} is positioned in the XY-plane and centred on the origin. Calculate the magnitude of the force between this disc and a line charge of uniform density, ρ_2 C m^{-1} spread along a section of the Z-axis from $z = d - b/2$ to $z = d + b/2$, where $d > b/2$.

Show that as the distance, d, between the two charge distributions is increased, the force tends towards that between two point charges $\rho_1 \pi a^2$ C and $\rho_2 b$ C, a distance d apart.

Worked Application Example 5.7

This example arises in the investigation of the effect of a circular charged plate with a small central hole as an **electron beam accelerator.**

Solution Clearly, the total charge on the disc and line segment are $\rho_1 \pi a^2$ and $\rho_2 b$ respectively. The overall force between the two distributions is given by the vector sum of the directed forces between all infinitesimal charge area elements on the disc and all infinitesimal line charge elements on the line. The direction and magnitude of these force contributions will vary according to the position of the elements on the line and disc: it is necessary to find the integrated force.

The symmetry of the problem is such that it is natural to choose to work in the cylindrical polar coordinate system. Then the charges associated with the infinitesimal elements are

element of line: $\rho_2 \, dz$ element of disc: $\rho_1 \, r \, dr \, d\theta$

so that the magnitude of the force between these two elements is

$$\frac{(\rho_1 \, r \, dr \, d\theta)(\rho_2 \, dz)}{4\pi\epsilon_0 \, (r^2 + z^2)}$$

This force is directed between the two elements and can be partitioned up into two vector components

$$\frac{(\rho_1 \, r \, dr \, d\theta)(\rho_2 \, dz)}{4\pi\epsilon_0 \, (r^2 + z^2)} \sin \alpha \qquad \text{in the direction of the Z-axis}$$

and

$$\frac{(\rho_1 \, r \, dr \, d\theta)(\rho_2 \, dz)}{4\pi\epsilon_0 \, (r^2 + z^2)} \cos \alpha \qquad \text{radially out (perpendicular to the Z-axis)}$$

where $\sin \alpha = z/(r^2 + z^2)^{1/2}$ and $\cos \alpha = r/(r^2 + z^2)^{1/2}$.

The total force in the direction of the Z-axis is given by the multiple integral obtained by summing the Z-components of all possible force interactions between the charge distributions:

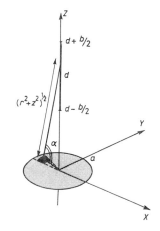

99

$$F = \frac{\rho_1 \rho_2}{4\pi\epsilon_0} \int_0^{2\pi} d\theta \int_0^a dr \int_{d-b/2}^{d+b/2} dz \, \frac{zr}{[r^2 + z^2]^{3/2}} \tag{5.14}$$

The radial force can be argued to be zero because of the symmetry of the problem: for every charge element on one side of the line charge there is a corresponding charge element of equal magnitude 180° around the disc. Hence, Equation (5.14) defines the magnitude of the total force between the charge distributions.

To evaluate the multiple integral it is possible to carry out the angular integration independently of the other two variables, producing a multiplying factor of 2π. The remaining integrations with respect to r and z can be carried out in either order, exploiting the fact that

The angular integration is said to decouple from the other variables.

It is possible to solve this by substitution, but it is always worth while checking whether the integral is a disguised version of a standard form.

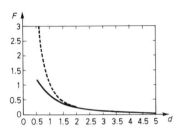

The form of the exact force relationship (solid line) and the approximate force (dashed line) for the case of $a = b = 1$. When d is more than a few times the linear dimensions of the charge distributions their particular geometrical structure becomes relatively unimportant and to a good approximation they can be treated as point charges.

$$\frac{d}{dx}\left[\frac{1}{[a^2 + x^2]^{1/2}}\right] = -\frac{x}{[a^2 + x^2]^{3/2}}$$

Carrying out the z integration first (and treating r as a constant) leads to

$$F = \frac{2\pi\rho_1\rho_2}{4\pi\epsilon_0} \int_0^a r\, dr \left[\frac{-1}{[r^2 + z^2]^{1/2}}\right]_{d-b/2}^{d+b/2}$$

$$= \frac{2\pi\rho_1\rho_2}{4\pi\epsilon_0} \int_0^a dr \left[\frac{-r}{[r^2 + (d+b/2)^2]^{1/2}} + \frac{r}{[r^2 + (d-b/2)^2]^{1/2}}\right]$$

which are two ordinary single-variable integrals. These can be integrated directly to give

$$F = \frac{2\pi\rho_1\rho_2}{4\pi\epsilon_0}\left[-[r^2 + (d+b/2)^2]^{1/2} + [r^2 + (d-b/2)^2]^{1/2}\right]_0^a$$

$$= \frac{2\pi\rho_1\rho_2}{4\pi\epsilon_0}\left[-[a^2 + (d+b/2)^2]^{1/2} + [a^2 + (d-b/2)^2]^{1/2} + (d+b/2) - (d-b/2)\right]$$

$$\tag{5.15}$$

This is the exact solution of the problem in terms of all of the specific parameters of the system.

When d is large relative to the dimensions of both charge distributions it is possible to obtain a simpler approximation to this exact force by expanding the square-root terms using the binomial expansion:

$$[a^2 + (d+b/2)^2]^{1/2} = (d+b/2)\left[1 + \frac{a^2}{(d+b/2)^2}\right]^{1/2}$$

$$\approx (d+b/2) + \frac{a^2}{2(d+b/2)}$$

and

It is necessary to perform these expansions and rearrange the expression for the force before considering the limiting case. As a and b become arbitrarily small relative to d, all of the terms in the full expression cancel: it is necessary to retain the first set of higher-order terms that do not cancel each other out.

$$[a^2 + (d-b/2)^2]^{1/2} = (d-b/2)\left[1 + \frac{a^2}{(d-b/2)^2}\right]^{1/2}$$

$$\approx (d-b/2) + \frac{a^2}{2(d-b/2)}$$

These expressions can be substituted directly into the exact Equation (5.15), leading to

$$F \approx \frac{2\pi\rho_1\rho_2}{4\pi\epsilon_0}\left[-\frac{a^2}{2(d+b/2)} + \frac{a^2}{2(d-b/2)}\right] = \frac{\pi a^2 \rho_1 \, b\rho_2}{4\pi\epsilon_0(d^2 - b^2/4)}$$

$$\approx \frac{(\pi a^2 \rho_1)(b\rho_2)}{4\pi\epsilon_0 \, d^2} \qquad \text{for } d \gg b$$

so that when a/d and b/d are both small the force approximates to that between two point charges of density $\rho_1 \pi a^2$ and $\rho_2 b$ a distance d apart.

To evaluate the force between two surface charge distributions requires the evaluation of a four-variable multiple integral, and the calculation of the electron–electron forces due to the interaction of two volume distributions of charge around two atoms requires the evaluation of six-dimensional integrals. Because of this it is very often necessary to use a symmetry argument such as that employed in the previous example to remove the need to calculate the radial force. The evaluation of six simultaneous integrals is a task which is usually turned over to a computer program: if any symmetry can be exploited to decrease the processing time required, so much the better.

In the full theory of the properties of the solid state it is usual to extend the basic concepts of symmetry to include the much more powerful tools of group theory which can be used to classify and simplify the description of solids.

In a cathode ray tube (CRT) a highly collimated electron beam is accelerated towards a phosphor-coated screen which absorbs the energy of the electrons and releases it as energy in the visible wavelengths. With the impact of each electron a brief spot of light is produced at the point of impact, but due to physical limitations in the collimation of the beam and in the natural properties of the phosphor coating there will always be a spread of radiated energy: the spot will be somewhat diffuse.

Worked Application Example 5.8

If the CRT is mapped as an XY-plane the spread of each spot can be described by the **luminescence density function**:

$$l(x, y) = \exp(-x^2 - y^2) \tag{5.16}$$

To all practical purposes the screen can be viewed as being infinite in size relative to the width of an individual spot: calculate the total luminance associated with a single spot.

Solution   The function described by Equation (5.16) is the **two-dimensional Gaussian** function and occurs in a number of practical applications. In this case the total luminance is given by the double integral

$$L = \int_{-\infty}^{\infty} dx \int_{-\infty}^{\infty} dy \exp(-x^2 - y^2) \tag{5.17}$$

In this form it is difficult to see how to proceed. Although the integral decouples into the product of two identical one-variable integrals:

$$L = \int_{-\infty}^{\infty} \exp(-x^2)\, dx \int_{-\infty}^{\infty} \exp(-y^2)\, dy$$

The two integrals in this product are exactly the same; despite the fact that one is being integrated with respect to x and the other with respect to y. These are dummy variables of integration.

it is still not obvious how these integrals could be approached. The solution lies in the fact that the problem is being formulated in the wrong coordinate system: polar coordinates are more appropriate to the symmetry of the problem.

Evaluation of the Jacobian determinant for the conversion of integrals from Cartesian coordinates to polar shows that

$$dx\, dy = r\, dr\, d\theta$$

In polar coordinates the luminance integral takes the form

$$L = \int_{0}^{2\pi} d\theta \int_{0}^{\infty} dr\, r \exp(-r^2)$$

where the limits have been chosen to scan out the whole of the plane of the screen. The angular integration produces a factor of 2π, and the radial integration can be carried out to give

This transformation would have caused problems if the limits had not been infinite: although the change of coordinates simplifies the integrand it is requiring that a square be the area of integration in polar coordinates. Because the limits are infinite and the function tends rapidly to zero this does not matter. If the limits were finite the transformation would introduce a difficult boundary of integration: in such a case it is probably easier to carry out a numerical integration!

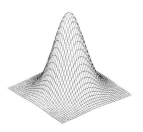

The luminance density function of the bright spot produced on a CRT screen

$$L = 2\pi \left[-\frac{\exp(-r^2)}{2} \right]_0^\infty = \pi$$

as the total brightness of the spot.

As a final example of the techniques of multiple integration it is worth illustrating a useful option when a coordinate system does not exist that is suitable for the specified problem. Why not design the coordinate system to suit the integral?

Worked Application Example 5.9

The **epicycloids** are a family of curves that are obtained by rotating a small circle around the outside edge of a large one and keeping track of the locus of any one point on the outer circle. Likewise the **hypercycloids** are obtained by rotating a small circle within a larger one. The **astroid** is the specific hypercycloid that has four cusps.

A uniform surface distribution of charge of unit density is spread out over a region defined by the **astroid**:

$$x^{2/3} + y^{2/3} = a^{2/3} \tag{5.18}$$

which is a closed curve with four cusps at the coordinate axes. Find the total amount of charge in the region.

Solution The total charge can be expressed as an integral in Cartesian coordinates:

$$Q = \int_{-a}^{a} dx \int_{-(a^{2/3} - x^{2/3})^{3/2}}^{(a^{2/3} - x^{2/3})^{3/2}} dy \tag{5.19}$$

so that as x is varied from $-a$ to a, the upper and lower limits of the y integration are unpleasant functions of x. This boundary is no better when viewed in polar coordinates.

The problem with integrals such as this is that although the integrand could hardly be easier (unity!) the boundary is difficult: it is generally better to try to obtain an equivalent integral with a simple boundary, no matter how difficult the integrand becomes. In this case the best approach is to define a new coordinate system by the equations:

At worst it will be possible to use numerical integration on the transformed integral: it is difficult to perform a numerical integration over a strange boundary.

$$x = r\cos^3\theta \quad \text{and} \quad y = r\sin^3\theta \tag{5.20}$$

which have been chosen so that when inserted into Equation (5.18) the equation for the astroid in the new coordinate system is

Unlike the ordinary coordinate systems which have been used before, this transformation does not preserve distances between points and the shape of curves: it scales the original coordinate system in an angle-dependent fashion. In this particular case the transformation is designed so that in the new coordinate system the boundary looks like a circle.

$$(r\cos^3\theta)^{2/3} + (r\sin^3\theta)^{2/3} = a^{2/3}$$
$$\Rightarrow \quad r^{2/3}\cos^2\theta + r^{2/3}\sin^2\theta = a^{2/3}$$
$$\Rightarrow \quad r = a \quad \text{(defining } r \geqslant 0)$$

which is the polar equation of a circle of radius a. In this **pseudo-polar** coordinate system the boundary of the region of integration is trivial, but it is necessary to evaluate the Jacobian of the transformation:

Imagine drawing the original curve on a piece of rubber of uniform thickness and then stretching it to fit the line of the curve onto a circular frame: the stretched piece of rubber would now exhibit a non-uniform density. The Jacobian expresses the extent to which an area of the surface has been stretched.

$$\left| \frac{\partial(x,y)}{\partial(r,\theta)} \right| = \left| \begin{array}{cc} \cos^3\theta & -3\,r\cos^2\theta\sin\theta \\ \sin^3\theta & 3\,r\sin^2\theta\cos\theta \end{array} \right| = 3\,r\sin^2\theta\cos^2\theta$$

Using these results, the original integral is equivalent to

$$Q = \int_0^{2\pi} d\theta \int_0^a dr \; 3r\sin^2\theta\cos^2\theta \tag{5.21}$$

which partitions neatly into two one-variable integrals which are easily evaluated by the normal techniques.

Exercise 5.4 Show that the value of the integral in Equation (5.21) is $3a^2\pi/8$.

Summary

Most practical engineering problems are multivariable. The reason that this can often be ignored is that by examining the effect of only one parameter on a system an ordinary one-variable function will be obtained. More realistically, however, the coupling between the inputs to a system will be important and a full model will need to examine the simultaneous effect of variations in independent system variables.

This chapter has given a brief review of some of the applications of partial differentiation, multivariable optimization and multiple integrals. Little space has been given to mathematical practice examples: the emphasis has been on indicating a few of the situations in which the ordinary calculus is insufficient to provide a realistic practical description of the system.

The equations describing a multivariable system are usually much harder to manipulate than those of a corresponding single-variable problem, but the effort is nearly always rewarded: the increased insight into the internal structure of a practical system can be considerable. When combined with the theory of differential equations the multivariable calculus forms the basic toolkit for all of dynamic control and circuit theory; and when combined with vector methods it enables the manipulation of the most powerful equations of electromagnetic theory and fluid flow.

Overall, the techniques outlined in this chapter and Chapter T5 may be thought of as representing the beginning of realistic applied mathematical methods.

Stroud (1986) contains a range of examples which illustrate the purely mathematical techniques associated with these methods.

Further Exercises

5.5 In Cartesian coordinates the potential due to an ideal point dipole of dipole moment p positioned at the origin and pointing in the Z direction is given by

$$V(x,y,z) = \frac{p}{4\pi\epsilon_0} \frac{z}{[x^2 + y^2 + z^2]^{3/2}}$$

Calculate the corresponding electric field (in Cartesian coordinates) at all points in space.

5.6 Calculate a linear approximation to the changes in the dipole potential of Exercise 5.5 in the region of the point $(1,4,8)$.

5.7 The potential due to a point charge Q at the point (a,b) in the XY plane is given by

$$V(x,y) = \frac{Q}{4\pi\epsilon_0} \frac{1}{[(x-a)^2 + (y-b)^2]^{1/2}}$$

Consider the total potential due to two positive point charges, Q_1 at the point $(1,2)$ and Q_2 at $(4,4)$. Show that a turning point of this potential will arise when

$$Q_1(x-1)[(x-4)^2 + (y-4)^2]^{3/2} = -Q_2(x-4)[(x-1)^2 + (y-2)^2]^{3/2}$$

and

$$Q_1(y-2)[(x-4)^2 + (y-4)^2]^{3/2} = -Q_2(y-4)[(x-1)^2 + (y-2)^2]^{3/2}$$

By taking the ratio of these equations, show that the turning point must lie on the line $3y - 2x = 4$: the line joining the charges.

Show that this turning point occurs when

$$\left[\frac{y-4}{y-2}\right]^2 = \left[\frac{-x-4}{x-1}\right]^2 = \frac{Q_2}{Q_1}$$

5.8 A surface charge density given by

$$\rho(x,y) = x^2 + y^2 + xy \qquad \text{C m}^{-2}$$

is spread over a triangular area bounded by the three lines $y - x - 1 = 0$, $y + 1 = 0$, and $x - 1 = 0$ (units in metres). Establish the amount of charge contained in the area.

5.9 In a cylindrical fluorescent tube of length 2 m and radius 2 cm the density of ionized charge carriers is given by

$$\rho(r,\theta,z) = A \cosh(100 \, r^2 + z) \qquad \text{m}^{-3}$$

where r and z are measured in metres and A is a constant dependent on the particular gas used in the tube. The coordinate system is positioned at the origin at the centre of the tube with the Z-axis pointing along its length.

Calculate the total number of charge carriers in the tube.

A Mathematical Toolkit for Electronic Engineers

PART TWO

This part of the book will list many of the mathematical definitions, formulae, identities, techniques and 'tricks' that form the basic theoretical survival kit of the electronic engineer. Some examples and derivations are given but, in the main, the intention is to supply a reasonably compact summary of the definitions and ideas that are basic to applied mathematical methods. Lists and tables of standard results are enclosed, but bear in mind that memorizing tables of results is a poor second to developing an understanding of how to obtain those results from first principles! The material is arranged throughout the five chapters of this Toolkit in such a fashion that it corresponds broadly to that required for each chapter in Part One.

In a text of this size only a brief overview is possible and few derivations or proofs are given. Often, conditions such as continuity and differentiability of functions are assumed without being stated. Also, the material corresponds only broadly to that contained in a first-year undergraduate course: certainly, at some stage it will be necessary to consult other mathematical textbooks for more information.

More detailed lists and derivations are available in Jeffrey (1989), which is a superb overall rigorous mathematical reference text; and Stroud (1982) is an excellent source of illustrative worked examples, together with detailed explanations of the steps involved in the solutions. Glenn and Littler (1984) is a useful and readable dictionary of common mathematical terminology; while Gradshteyn and Ryzhik (1980) provide a hugely detailed compilation of more mathematical formulae and integrals than any practising engineer can conceivably require in a working lifetime!

Summary of basic notation

$[a, b]$	a closed interval of a continuous variable
(a, b)	an open interval of a continuous variable
$[a, b)$ and $(a, b]$	semi-open intervals of a continuous variable
$\{\ \}$	used to specify the elements of a set or sequence
$\in$	is an element of the set *or* is in the interval
$\notin$	is not an element of the set *or* is not in the interval
$\cup \quad \cap \quad \setminus$	set operations of union, intersection and complement
$\subseteq$	is a subset of
$= \ \neq$	is equal to, is not equal to
$\approx$	is approximately equal to
$\equiv$	is identically equal to *or* is equivalent to
$< \ \leqslant$	less than, less than or equal to
$> \ \geqslant$	greater than, greater than or equal to
$\Rightarrow \ \Leftarrow \ \therefore$	implies, is implied, therefore
$\Leftrightarrow$ *or* iff	implies and is implied by *or* if and only if
$+ \ - \ \times \ /$	addition, subtraction, multiplication, division
∞	infinity
Lim $\quad \rightarrow$	limit, tends towards

$\Sigma \quad \int \quad \Pi$	summation, integration, product
$n!$	n factorial: $n(n-1)(n-2) \ldots 1$
$\begin{bmatrix} n \\ i \end{bmatrix} \quad {}^nC_i \quad {}_nC_i$	alternative notations for binomial coefficients
${}^nP_i \quad {}_nP_i$	permutation coefficients
$\Delta x \quad \mathrm{d}x$	finite increment, infinitesimal increment
$\dfrac{\mathrm{d}x}{\mathrm{d}t} \quad \dot{x} \quad x^{(1)}$	first derivative of x with respect to t
$\dfrac{\mathrm{d}^2x}{\mathrm{d}t^2} \quad \ddot{x} \quad x^{(2)}$	second derivative of x with respect to t
$\dfrac{\partial y}{\partial x} \quad \dfrac{\partial^2 y}{\partial x^2} \quad f_x \quad f_{xy}$	partial derivatives of a multivariable function
(a_x, a_y, a_z)	coordinates of a point
$\mathbf{a} \begin{bmatrix} a_x \\ a_y \\ a_z \end{bmatrix} \quad \overrightarrow{OA}$	vector quantity
$\mathbf{a.b}$	scalar product of two vectors
$\mathbf{a \wedge b}$	vector product of two vectors
$[\mathbf{a, b, c}]$	vector triple product
$|\mathbf{a}|$	modulus or length of a vector
$\|\mathbf{a}\|$	norm of an n-dimensional vector
$\perp$	is perpendicular to
$\mathbf{i} \quad \mathbf{j} \quad \mathbf{k}$	Cartesian basis vectors
$\alpha \quad \beta \quad \gamma$	direction angles
$l \quad m \quad n$	direction cosines ($= \cos \alpha, \cos \beta, \cos \gamma$)
$\exp \ln \log_{10}$	exponential, natural logarithm, base 10 logarithm
$\cos \sin \tan$ $\sec \operatorname{cosec} \cotan$	trigonometric, or circular, functions
$\cos^{-1} \sin^{-1} \tan^{-1}$ $\arccos \arcsin$	inverse trigonometric functions
$\sinh \cosh \tanh$	hyperbolic functions
$\sinh^{-1} \operatorname{arcsinh}$	inverse hyperbolic functions
$\omega \quad f$	angular frequency, frequency
$z = a + jb = Ae^{j\theta}$	complex number
Re	real part of a complex number
Im	imaginary part of a complex number
$z^* = a - jb = Ae^{-j\theta}$	complex conjugate of the complex number $a + jb$
$|a|$	absolute value *or* modulus of a complex number
δ_{il}	the *kronecker delta*, defined by: $\qquad \delta_{il} = 0$ if $i \neq l$ $\qquad \delta_{il} = 1$ if $i = l$
r.h.s.	right hand side of an equation
l.h.s.	left hand side of an equation
KVL	Kirchhoff's Voltage Law
KCL	Kirchhoff's Current Law

Definitions, Formulae and General Information

Functions

A **function** is a mathematical relationship between an **independent variable**, x, and a **dependent variable**, y, such that specification of any value of x yields a resultant value of y via the function definition. For example,

$$y = x^2 + 3$$
and $y = \sin(x)$

are valid functions. It is common to express a general functional relationship between the variables x and y as the **explicit** equation $y = f(x)$. The variable x is referred to as the **argument** of the function. Often x is defined as a **continuous variable** over some **interval**, say $[x_0, x_1]$, but if x can take on only values from a discrete **set** of numbers, $\{x_0, x_1, x_2, ..., x_n\}$, then a **discrete function** will be more appropriate. In the former case, if the value of the function jumps suddenly from one value to another at one or more points within the interval the function is said to be **discontinuous** at those points.

With the above definition of a function it is quite acceptable for the same value of y to correspond to different values of x, so that $\sin(\pi/2) = \sin(5\pi/2) = 1$, for example. However, it is not valid for many values of y to correspond to a single value of x. This means that the equation of a circle:

$$y^2 = c^2 - x^2$$

is not a function. Since the equation can be written as

$$y = +\sqrt{(c^2 - x^2)}$$
and $y = -\sqrt{(c^2 - x^2)}$

it is, in fact, a double function – it has two branches corresponding to the upper and lower semicircles respectively. By extending the idea of functions to include **many-valued functions** (a number of ordinary function branches defined by a single equation) a very wide range of physical relationships can be represented as functions.

It is often desirable to define an **inverse function**, f^{-1}, that has the effect of reversing $y = f(x)$ to become $x = f^{-1}(y)$. An inverse function can only be defined if f is one-to-one. For example, ln and exp form a pair of inverse functions.

An **implicit** function is one where it is more convenient (or perhaps necessary) to express the functional relationship as $f(x, y) = 0$. For example,

$$\exp(xy) - y - x = 0$$

is an implicit function.

An important further type of function arises when a relationship between variables x and y is expressed in **parametric form**. In this description the functional forms of both variables are generated by the variation of a third variable: a parameter. For example,

More generally, it is possible to think of a function of a number of independent variables: $y = f(u, v, . . ., y, z)$. Multivariable functions such as this are introduced in Chapter T5.

Given the functional relationship $y = f(x)$, the set of values from which x can be drawn (continuous or discrete) is called the **domain** of the function. The values of y which the function produces define the **range** of the function. See Jeffrey (1989) for more detail.

A function which does always produce a different value of y for each value of x is described as being **one-to-one**.

Naturally enough, the application of a function and its inverse in sequence has no overall effect. For example, $\exp[\ln(x)] = x$.

Recall that a function expressed in the form $y = f(x)$ is said to be in explicit form. This particular equation cannot be put into an explicit form.

The parameter might correspond to distance travelled along a curve (arc length), time or some other variable of practical interest.

With the introduction of inverse, implicit and parametric functions it may seem that there is little difference between the dependent and independent variables. However, equations describing practical systems usually have a clear-cut causal relationship between a system input (independent variable) and a system response/output (dependent variable) so that it is useful to retain the idea that changes in the value of one variable have a direct effect on the values of another.

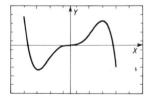

An even function with respect to the origin.

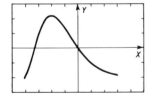

An odd function with respect to the origin.

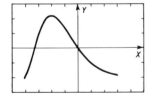

A function which is neither even, nor odd, with respect to the origin.

$$x = t + \exp t$$
$$y = t^2$$

are the parametric equations of a curve in the XY-plane. It is not always possible to solve two equations of this form to remove the parameter t and express the relationship in explicit or implicit form.

An equation or function involving a number of unknown variables (say $x, y, z, \ldots$) is **algebraic** if the variables appear only in the form of polynomials. The equation or function is also said to be **linear** if each variable appears only with a power of zero (a constant) or one. Hence, the equation

$$x + y^2 + z^3 = 1$$

is algebraic, while

$$x^2 + \sin y = 2$$

is not. Likewise,

$$2x + 4y + 6\dot{z} = 3$$

is linear and algebraic, while the equation

$$xy + \cos z = 0$$

is neither linear nor algebraic. Equations in which all of the variables appear in a linear fashion are considerably easier to solve than those involving any nonlinear terms and many of the basic mathematical methods are defined around an assumption of linearity in their fundamental equations. Also, the concept of linearity can be extended to equations which involve differential terms in addition to ordinary functions of the variables. Such **linear differential equations** obey the **principle of superposition**: the full solution of the equation can be constructed from a weighted sum of simpler solutions. This superposition principle forms the basis, explicitly or implicitly, of a large part of fundamental mathematical methods across the whole range of the applied sciences. Nonlinear equations do not obey the superposition principle and are considerably more difficult to solve: correspondingly, linear models tend to be used wherever they will provide an adequate model of the system of interest. Chapters 3 and 4, and the corresponding Chapters T3 and T4, cover the solution of linear algebraic equations and differential equations respectively.

Finally within this overview of functions and their properties, a function which is symmetric when reflected in the Y-axis is described as being an **even** function with respect to the origin: such a function must satisfy the relationship $f(x) = f(-x)$ for all values of the variable x. Likewise, a function which is antisymmetric under reflection in the Y-axis is called an **odd** function with respect to the origin and satisfies $f(-x) = -f(x)$. In general, a function is neither even nor odd, but it is always possible to partition an arbitrary function into an even component and an odd component:

$$f(x) = \underbrace{\frac{f(x) + f(-x)}{2}}_{\text{even component}} + \underbrace{\frac{f(x) - f(-x)}{2}}_{\text{odd component}}$$

By shifting the origin with a change of variables it is possible to extend this result to show that a function can always be expressed as the sum of two components which are odd and even with respect to any value of the independent variable.

The rules for combining purely even and odd functions by multiplication are the same as those for positive and negative numbers:

even × even ⇒ even
even × odd ⇒ odd
odd × odd ⇒ even

Trigonometric functions and formulae

The **trigonometric** functions sine and cosine can be defined algebraically (as opposed to geometrically) as:

$$\sin \alpha = \frac{\exp(j\alpha) - \exp(-j\alpha)}{2j}$$

$$\cos \alpha = \frac{\exp(j\alpha) + \exp(-j\alpha)}{2}$$

Other trigonometric functions can be defined in terms of these two:

$$\tan \alpha = \frac{\sin \alpha}{\cos \alpha} \qquad \cot \alpha = \frac{\cos \alpha}{\sin \alpha}$$

$$\sec \alpha = \frac{1}{\cos \alpha} \qquad \operatorname{cosec} \alpha = \frac{1}{\sin \alpha}$$

and a series of formulae can be shown to be valid for these functions:

$$\cos^2 \alpha + \sin^2 \alpha = 1$$

$$1 + \tan^2 \alpha = \sec^2 \alpha$$

$$1 + \cot^2 \alpha = \operatorname{cosec}^2 \alpha$$

$$\sin(\alpha \pm \beta) = \sin \alpha \cos \beta \pm \cos \alpha \sin \beta$$

$$\cos(\alpha \pm \beta) = \cos \alpha \cos \beta \mp \sin \alpha \sin \beta$$

$$\tan(\alpha \pm \beta) = \frac{\tan \alpha \pm \tan \beta}{1 \mp \tan \alpha \tan \beta}$$

$$\cos(2\alpha) = \cos^2 \alpha - \sin^2 \alpha$$

$$= 2 \cos^2 \alpha - 1$$

$$= 1 - 2 \sin^2 \alpha$$

$$\sin(2\alpha) = 2 \sin \alpha \cos \alpha$$

$$\tan(2\alpha) = \frac{2 \tan \alpha}{1 - \tan^2 \alpha}$$

$$2 \sin \alpha \cos \beta = \sin(\alpha + \beta) + \sin(\alpha - \beta)$$

$$2 \cos \alpha \cos \beta = \cos(\alpha + \beta) + \cos(\alpha - \beta)$$

$$2 \sin \alpha \sin \beta = -\cos(\alpha + \beta) + \cos(\alpha - \beta)$$

$$\sin \alpha + \sin \beta = 2 \sin \frac{(\alpha + \beta)}{2} \cos \frac{(\alpha - \beta)}{2}$$

$$\sin \alpha - \sin \beta = 2 \cos \frac{(\alpha + \beta)}{2} \sin \frac{(\alpha - \beta)}{2}$$

$$\cos \alpha + \cos \beta = 2 \cos \frac{(\alpha + \beta)}{2} \cos \frac{(\alpha - \beta)}{2}$$

$$\cos \alpha - \cos \beta = -2 \sin \frac{(\alpha + \beta)}{2} \sin \frac{(\alpha - \beta)}{2}$$

For example, x^3 and $\sin x$ are odd functions with respect to the origin, while $x^3 \sin x$ is even. Note that in these rules even functions correspond to positive numbers and odd functions to negative numbers (not, confusingly, to even and odd numbers!): the rules merely reflect whether or not sign changes occur when the number or function is squared.

The trigonometric functions are also known as the **circular** functions.

See the section on complex numbers in Chapter T2 for more information on these definitions.

The addition formulae for trigonometric functions.

The double-angle formulae for trigonometric functions.

The product formulae for trigonometric functions.

A useful result is the formula

$$A \cos \theta + B \sin \theta = R \cos(\theta - \alpha).$$

where $R = \sqrt{(A^2 + B^2)}$ and α satisfies $\cos \alpha = \dfrac{A}{R}$ and $\sin \alpha = \dfrac{B}{R}$

which expresses a weighted sum of two sinusoidal functions as a resultant, phase-shifted sinusoidal function.

Inverse trigonometric functions

The trigonometric functions are many-to-one in that an infinite set of values of the function argument (independent variable) can correspond to a given function value (dependent variable). Thus, it is impossible to talk about an inverse trigonometric function unless it is defined to be valid for only one particular branch of the trigonometric function in question. The most common way of doing this is to define a **principal branch** of the function, over which the function and its inverse are one-to-one, and conventionally choose the angle produced by the inverse function to correspond to the interval specified by that branch. The common inverse functions and their corresponding **principal values** are:

$$\theta = \arcsin x = \sin^{-1} x \qquad \theta \in [-\pi/2, \pi/2]$$
$$\theta = \arccos x = \cos^{-1} x \qquad \theta \in [0, \pi]$$
$$\theta = \arctan x = \tan^{-1} x \qquad \theta \in [-\pi/2, \pi/2]$$

If x is outside the range $[-1,1]$ or is complex, these inverse functions are still defined, but will not return a real value of θ: see the sections below on hyperbolic functions and complex numbers.

The first two of these functions will only produce real values of θ if $x \in [-1, 1]$, the second is valid for any value of x.

Some integral and derivative expressions involving inverse trigonometric functions will be given shortly.

Hyperbolic functions

The **hyperbolic** functions sinh and cosh are defined in a very similar fashion to the trigonometric functions as:

For graphs and a detailed discussion of these functions see Jeffrey (1989).

$$\sinh x = \frac{\exp(x) - \exp(-x)}{2}$$

$$\cosh x = \frac{\exp(x) + \exp(-x)}{2}$$

and, as with sin and cos, other hyperbolic functions can be defined by:

$$\tanh x = \frac{\sinh x}{\cosh x} \qquad \coth x = \frac{\cosh x}{\sinh x}$$

$$\mathrm{sech}\, x = \frac{1}{\cosh x} \qquad \mathrm{cosech}\, x = \frac{1}{\sinh x}$$

These functions clearly have a strong relationship with the trigonometric functions, and a similar series of identities and formulae can be shown to be valid for these functions:

$$\cosh^2 x - \sinh^2 x = 1$$
$$1 - \tanh^2 x = \mathrm{sech}^2 x$$
$$\coth^2 x - 1 = \mathrm{cosech}^2 x$$
$$\sinh(x \pm y) = \sinh x \cosh y \pm \cosh x \sinh y$$
$$\cosh(x \pm y) = \cosh x \cosh y \pm \sinh x \sinh y$$

and other expressions that are very similar in form to those listed for the trigonometric functions. Rather than list all of these expressions it is worth describing the relationship between hyperbolic and trigonometric functions, so that one set of formulae can be obtained directly from the other.

Directly from the definitions, it is possible to state that:

$$\sin(jx) = j \sinh x$$
$$\text{and } \cos(jx) = \cosh x$$

Thus, it can be seen that the hyperbolic functions are just a compact notation for extending the definitions of sin and cos to include a complex argument.

so that starting, for example, with the trigonometric identity:

$$\cos(2\alpha) = \cos^2 \alpha - \sin^2 \alpha$$

it is possible to set $\alpha = jx$, giving

$$\cos(2jx) = \cos^2(jx) - \sin^2(jx)$$
$$\Rightarrow \quad \cosh(2x) = \cosh^2 x - [j \sinh x]^2$$
$$= \cosh^2 x + \sinh^2 x$$

Using this approach it is possible to convert any formula involving trigonometric functions into a related version for the hyperbolic functions.

Inverse hyperbolic functions

The inverses of the hyperbolic functions are defined by

$$x = \text{arcsinh } y = \sinh^{-1} y \qquad \text{for all } x$$
$$x = \text{arccosh } y = \cosh^{-1} y \qquad \text{for } x \geqslant 0$$
$$x = \text{arctanh } y = \tanh^{-1} y \qquad \text{for all } x$$

If $\cosh x$ is restricted to values of x such that $x \geqslant 0$ then the hyperbolic functions are one-to-one and their inverse functions are well defined.

Summation of finite series: combinations and permutations

A number of finite series can arise in a variety of applications. It is useful to be able to recognize and sum the commonest:

Arithmetic progression: $$\sum_{i=1}^{n} [a + (i-1)d] = \frac{n[2a + (n-1)d]}{2}$$

Geometric progression: $$\sum_{i=1}^{n} a R^{i-1} = \frac{a[1 - R^n]}{[1 - R]} \qquad R \neq 1$$

The sum of an infinite geometric progression will be discussed shortly.

Binomial expansion: (integer n) $$\sum_{i=0}^{n} \frac{n!}{i! (n-i)!} a^{n-i} b^i = (a + b)^n$$

When n is not an integer the binomial expansion becomes an infinite series, as is discussed below.

The weighting factors of the binomial expansion, the **binomial coefficients**, appear in a number of notations in different texts:

$$\frac{n!}{i! (n-i)!} \equiv \begin{bmatrix} n \\ i \end{bmatrix} \equiv {}^n C_i \equiv {}_n C_i$$

and they are usefully represented in **Pascal's triangle**:

Binomial coefficients are also known as **combinatorial coefficients** and occur in statistical applications.

```
                  1
               1     1
            1     2     1
         1     3     3     1
       1     4     6     4     1
     1     5    10    10     5     1
   1     6    15    20    15     6     1
               etc.
```

which is constructed by taking any element as being the sum of the two elements immediately above and to either side of it.

The binomial coefficient ^nC_i gives the number of ways of arranging i indistinguishable objects in n positions, or choosing any i objects out of a set of n indistinguishable objects. When the objects are distinguishable the theory of permutations is employed instead.

Given n distinguishable objects labelled by the numbers 1, ..., n, it is possible to **permute** (interchange) the elements a pair at a time. It can be shown that any rearrangement of the objects can be achieved by applying a sequence of simple permutations (single interchanges) to the objects in the starting order 1, 2, 3, ..., n. If an odd number of interchanges are required to obtain the final, desired ordering of objects the overall arrangement is called an **odd permutation**. Similarly, an **even permutation** can be achieved with an even number of interchanges. For example, for the three objects in the set $\{1,2,3\}$,

$$\{1,2,3\} \qquad \{2,3,1\} \qquad \text{and } \{3,1,2\}$$

are even permutations, while

$$\{1,3,2\} \qquad \{2,1,3\} \qquad \text{and } \{3,2,1\}$$

are odd permutations.

Given a set of n distinguishable objects, there are $n!$ permutations of those objects. Given a set of n distinguishable objects, there are

$$\frac{n!}{(n-i)!} \equiv {^nP_i} \equiv {_nP_i}$$

permutations of any i objects taken from this set.

Note that the number of combinations is related to the number of permutations by $^nP_i = i! \, ^nC_i$: when the i objects are indistinguishable $i!$ of the permutations have the same combinatorial structure.

Limits and limiting processes

For discrete sequences of numbers the idea of a limit is fairly straightforward: if a sequence of numbers x_i approach arbitrarily close to some limiting value, l, as the sequence counter, i, is increased, l is said to be the limit of the sequence. For example, the series

$$\frac{1}{1}, \quad \frac{1}{2}, \quad \frac{1}{3}, \quad \frac{1}{4}, \quad \frac{1}{5}, \quad \frac{1}{6}, \quad ... \qquad \text{has a limiting value of zero}$$

while the sequence

$$1, 2, 3, 4, 5, 6 \, ... \qquad \text{has no limit.}$$

For functions of continuous variables the mathematical idea of a limit is usually expressed in a similar form: if a function, $f(x)$, can be made arbitrarily near to some numerical value, say l, by choosing a value of x sufficiently near to some numerical value, say a, then the limit of the function as x **tends to** a is given by l:

See Jeffrey (1989) for a detailed discussion of the concept of limit and a more rigorous definition than is given here.

$$\underset{x \to a}{\text{Lim}} \quad f(x) = l$$

The infinite series expansions of a number of common functions are listed later in this chapter.

The concept of limit allows the numerical treatment of functions that seem intractable at first. For example, using the infinite series expansion for $\sin(x)$ it is possible to show that

Similarly, the limit of $[1 - \cos(x)]/x$, as x tends to zero, is zero.

$$\underset{x \to 0}{\text{Lim}} \left[\frac{\sin(x)}{x} \right] = \underset{x \to 0}{\text{Lim}} \left[\frac{x - x^3/3! + ...}{x} \right] = \underset{x \to 0}{\text{Lim}} \left[1 - x^2/3! + ... \right]$$

so that carrying out the limiting process it is clear that the limiting value of $\sin(x)/x$ at

$x = 0$ is unity. A more general technique for obtaining the limit of the ratio of two functions is l'Hôpital's rule, discussed later in this chapter.

Differentiation

Given a function which relates two continuous variables, $y = f(x)$, it is possible to define the **ordinary derivative** of y with respect to x as the limiting value of the ratio of the small change in y produced by a small change in x:

$$\frac{dy}{dx} = \underset{\Delta x \to 0}{\text{Lim}} \left[\frac{\Delta y}{\Delta x} \right] = \underset{\Delta x \to 0}{\text{Lim}} \left[\frac{f(x + \Delta x) - f(x)}{\Delta x} \right]$$

As an example of a first principles application of this definition, consider differentiating the function $y = \sin x$ with respect to x:

$$\frac{dy}{dx} = \underset{\Delta x \to 0}{\text{Lim}} \left[\frac{\sin(x + \Delta x) - \sin x}{\Delta x} \right] = \underset{\Delta x \to 0}{\text{Lim}} \left[\frac{\sin x[\cos(\Delta x) - 1] + \cos x \sin(\Delta x)}{\Delta x} \right]$$

It has already been shown that the limiting value of $\sin(\Delta x)/\Delta x$ as Δx tends to zero is unity. Similarly, using the infinite series expansion of $\cos(\Delta x)$ it is easy to show that the corresponding limit of $[\cos(\Delta x) - 1]/\Delta x$ is zero. Hence, the overall limit leads to a result of $dy/dx = \cos x$.

If the function is continuous and the same limiting value is obtained for both positive and negative increments for all values of x in the domain the function is said to be **differentiable**.

The following table lists a set of the most common analytic derivatives.

Function	Derivative
x^n	$n\,x^{n-1}$
$\ln x$	x^{-1}
$\sin(a\theta)$	$a\cos(a\theta)$
$\cos(a\theta)$	$-a\sin(a\theta)$
$\tan(a\theta)$	$a\sec^2(a\theta)$
$\sin^{-1}\left[\dfrac{x}{a}\right]$	$\dfrac{1}{\sqrt{a^2 - x^2}}$
$\cos^{-1}\left[\dfrac{x}{a}\right]$	$\dfrac{-1}{\sqrt{a^2 - x^2}}$
$\tan^{-1}\left[\dfrac{x}{a}\right]$	$\dfrac{a}{a^2 + x^2}$
$\sinh(ax)$	$a\cosh(ax)$
$\cosh(ax)$	$a\sinh(ax)$
$\tanh(ax)$	$a\,\text{sech}^2(ax)$
$\sinh^{-1}\left[\dfrac{x}{a}\right]$	$\dfrac{1}{\sqrt{a^2 + x^2}}$
$\cosh^{-1}\left[\dfrac{x}{x}\right]$	$\dfrac{\pm 1}{\sqrt{x^2 - a^2}}$
$\tanh^{-1}\left[\dfrac{x}{a}\right]$	$\dfrac{a}{a^2 - x^2}$

Another way of viewing a discontinuous function is as a function which possesses more than one limit at a particular value of independent variable: at a discontinuity different limiting values are obtained when the discontinuity is approached from different directions.

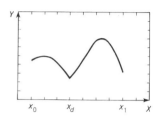

A function which is continuous over the domain $[x_0, x_1]$ and differentiable everywhere within [i.e. in the interval (x_0, x_1)] the domain except at the point x_d. The differentiability criterion cannot be extended to the end points: no information is given about the behaviour of the function beyond the ends of the domain.

Provided that $n \neq 0$.

$|x| \leqslant a$.

$|x| > a$. Choose the positive sign if $\cosh^{-1}(x/a)$ is positive, else use the negative sign.

$x^2 < a^2$

These 'standard' results need not necessarily be committed to memory: it is more important to note the relationships between the trigonometric and hyperbolic results, and to consider all of these results as being a basic set from which to derive more complicated derivatives using a set of differentiation rules:

$$\frac{d}{dx}(a u + b v) = a\frac{du}{dx} + b\frac{dv}{dx}$$

$$\frac{d}{dx}(uv) = u\frac{dv}{dx} + v\frac{du}{dx}$$

$$\frac{d}{dx}\left(\frac{u}{v}\right) = \frac{\left[v\frac{du}{dx} - u\frac{dv}{dx}\right]}{v^2}$$

$$\frac{df}{dz}\frac{dz}{dx} = \frac{df}{dx}$$

For example, it easy to use the ratio rule with $u = 1$ and $v = \cos(ax)$ to show that the derivative of $\sec(ax)$ is given by

$$\frac{d}{dx}\left[\frac{1}{\cos(ax)}\right] = \frac{0 - (-a\sin(ax))}{\cos^2(ax)} = a\sec(ax)\tan(ax)$$

When differentiation is being carried out with respect to time, t, it is common to employ the shorthand notation:

$$\frac{df}{dt} = \dot{f} \qquad \frac{d^2f}{dt^2} = \ddot{f}$$

Repeated differentiation – Leibnitz's theorem

In certain applications, it can be useful to write down the nth derivative of a given function – for any value of n. While this is very difficult for a totally general function there are several specific types for which it is straightforward. It is easy to verify that:

$$\frac{d^n}{dx^n}[\exp(ax)] = a^n\exp(ax)$$

$$\frac{d^{2n}}{dx^{2n}}[\sinh(ax)] = a^{2n}\sinh(ax)$$

$$\frac{d^{2n}}{dx^{2n}}[\cosh(ax)] = a^{2n}\cosh(ax)$$

and with a little more thought it can be seen that:

$$\frac{d^n}{dx^n}[\sin(ax)] = a^n\sin(ax + n\pi/2)$$

and $$\frac{d^n}{dx^n}[\cos(ax)] = a^n\cos(ax + n\pi/2)$$

so that the nth derivatives of these simple functions can be readily written down in a compact and general form. It is also possible to express the nth derivative of a product of two functions in terms of the derivatives of the individual functions by using **Leibnitz's theorem:**

$$(uv)^{(n)} = u\,v^{(n)} + {}^nC_1\,u^{(1)}\,v^{(n-1)} + \ldots + {}^nC_r\,u^{(r)}\,v^{(n-r)}$$
$$+ \ldots + {}^nC_{n-1}\,u^{(n-1)}\,v^{(1)} + u^{(n)}\,v$$

where the notation $f^{(r)}$ has been introduced as a convenient (compact) notation for the rth derivative of the function, f. This theorem is of most use when one of the functions is particularly simple, so that it will have zero derivatives for most of the terms. For example, consider $u = x^2$ and $v = \exp x$. Then

$$v^{(n)} = \exp x \qquad u^{(1)} = 2x \qquad u^{(2)} = 2 \qquad u^{(n)} = 0 \qquad \text{if } n > 2$$

so that these derivatives can be substituted directly into the Leibnitz expansion to give:

$$(x^2 \exp x)^{(n)} = x^2 \exp x + 2n \, x \exp x + n(n-1) \exp x$$

as the general expression for the nth derivative of $x^2 \exp x$.

The theorem can be proved by noting that $(uv)^{(1)} = u \, v^{(1)} + u^{(1)} \, v$, then that $(uv)^{(2)} = u \, v^{(2)} + 2 \, u^{(1)} \, v^{(1)} + u^{(2)} \, v$, and proceeding with a **proof by induction** – see Jeffrey (1989).

Parametric and implicit differentiation

If the variables x and y are expressed in parametric form as $x = x(t)$ and $y = y(t)$, then it is possible to obtain dy/dx by rearranging the chain rule:

$$\frac{dy}{dx} = \frac{dy}{dt} \bigg/ \frac{dx}{dt}$$

Since dy/dt and dx/dt are functions of t, this will give dy/dx in terms of t. Higher-order derivatives can be obtained by using the expression:

$$\frac{d^2 y}{dx^2} = \frac{d}{dx}\left[\frac{dy}{dx}\right] = \frac{dt}{dx} \frac{d}{dt}\left[\frac{dy}{dx}\right]$$

Similarly, the chain rule is the way to obtain dy/dx if the variables are related by an implicit equation: $f(x, y) = 0$. For example, consider

$$x^5 + 4xy^3 - 3y^5 - 2 = 0$$

and differentiate throughout the equation with respect to x, taking account of the fact that y does (implicitly) depend on x:

$$5x^4 + 4y^3 + 12xy^2 \frac{dy}{dx} - 15y^4 \frac{dy}{dx} = 0$$

$$\Rightarrow \frac{dy}{dx} = \frac{5x^4 + 4y^3}{15y^4 - 12xy^2}$$

Since y is implicitly a function of x, it is necessary to treat terms such as xy^3 as a product of functions of x when differentiating with respect to x.

Rolle's theorem, the mean value theorem, L'Hôpital's rule

Rolle's theorem is the (geometrically obvious) statement that a continuous function $y = f(x)$, defined on the interval $[x_0, x_1]$ and differentiable at all internal points of this interval, which has $f(x_0) = f(x_1)$, must have at least one value of x in (x_0, x_1), say $x = \xi$, where the gradient of the function is zero.

The **mean value theorem** is rather more general: again assuming a continuous and differentiable function, if the function values at the end points of the domain are $f(x_0)$ and $f(x_1)$ there must be at least one point in (x_0, x_1), say ξ, where the gradient of the function satisfies

$$\frac{dy}{dx}\bigg|_{x=\xi} = \frac{f(x_1) - f(x_0)}{x_1 - x_0}$$

so that at such a point the tangent to the curve is parallel to the line joining the end points of the function.

These theorems have a number of uses in providing more specific results in a number of situations: they can be used to place a limit on the quality of a finite polynomial approximation to a function (see the following section) and they can be

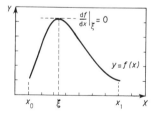

An illustration of Rolle's theorem: the curve must have at least one maximum or minimum, and possibly arbitrarily many.

115

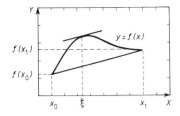

The mean value theorem. Rolle's theorem is merely a special case of the mean value theorem, corresponding to the case when $f(x_0) = f(x_1)$. The theorems are, in fact, equivalent and, given one, the other can be proved immediately.

It is being assumed implicitly that the function is 'well behaved' (continuous and differentiable an arbitrary number of times at x_0) so that all of the necessary derivatives are obtainable.

In a broad sense, the ideas of linear dependence (see Chapters T2 and T3) of vectors can be extended to functions: the functions $1, x, x^2, \ldots$ are all independent.

Some examples of such infinite series expansions of functions are given shortly.

A function which is subject to rapid changes in its value or which alters its behaviour drastically over a small range of x is likely to need a high-order polynomial expansion to represent it well within a range of values of x.

This upper bound can be obtained from the Lagrange remainder – see Jeffrey (1989).

used to prove **L'Hôpital's rule** for obtaining the limit of the ratio of two functions which both tend to zero or infinity: if two functions f and g are both zero (or both infinite) at $x = a$, then

$$\lim_{x \to a} \frac{f(x)}{g(x)} = \lim_{x \to a} \left[\frac{df/dx}{dg/dx} \right]$$

provided that the second limit exists. If the limit still does not exist the rule can be applied again, leading to the ratio of two second derivatives. The process can be repeated until a well-defined answer is obtained. For example, consider the ratio $(1 - \cos x)/x^2$:

$$\lim_{x \to 0} \left[\frac{1 - \cos x}{x^2} \right] = \lim_{x \to 0} \left[\frac{\sin x}{2x} \right] = \lim_{x \to 0} \left[\frac{\cos x}{2} \right] = \frac{1}{2}$$

Maclaurin and Taylor expansions

Taylor's theorem states that it is normally possible to express a given function $f(x)$ as an infinite power series expansion of the form:

$$f(x) = f(x_0) + (x - x_0) \frac{df}{dx}(x_0) + \frac{(x - x_0)^2}{2!} \frac{d^2 f}{dx^2}(x_0) + \ldots$$
$$\ldots + \frac{(x - x_0)^r}{r!} \frac{d^r f}{dx^r}(x_0) + \ldots$$

This is known as the **Taylor series expansion** around the point x_0. The series can be thought of as an expansion to higher derivatives of the linear expression discussed above with regard to the mean value theorem. Indeed, if the Taylor series is truncated after the linear term in $(x - x_0)$ the resulting expression is similar in form to the mean value theorem.

The aim of the Taylor series is to use derivative information about a function at one particular value of the independent variable, x_0, to build up a picture of how that function will behave for some different value of the independent variable, x. The proof of the infinite expansion is given by Jeffrey (1989) and for our purposes it is sufficient to argue that the Taylor series, truncated to exclude terms beyond $(x - x_0)^n$, can be thought of as an nth-order polynomial approximation to the function in the region of x_0. Each component of the polynomial involves a term $(x - x_0)^i$, so that the components are independent functions for different values of i. The choice of the coefficients of the series as $(x - x_0)^i/(i!)$ ensures that the approximation matches the function, and all of the specified derivative values, perfectly at the point $x = x_0$. Increasing the order of the series expansion will improve the general accuracy of the approximation.

If the function is given in analytic form, then it may be possible to obtain arbitrarily high derivatives for the function and obtain an **infinite power series expansion** of the function, which can be thought of as being an exact representation of the function in some pre-specified range of validity. More generally, the derivative information might correspond to a series of experimental measurements, in which case the series can only represent a finite polynomial approximation which will be reasonably accurate in some region of x_0. The specific degree of accuracy and the 'size' of the region of validity depend on the order of the approximation employed and particular nature of the function involved – but it is possible to obtain an upper bound on the error involved in a given Taylor expansion and it is generally possible to reduce this bound by making further derivative measurements and increasing the order of the approximation.

The Taylor series expansion can be expressed in several similar forms. For example,

$$f(b+a) = f(a) + b\frac{\mathrm{d}f}{\mathrm{d}x}(a) + \frac{b^2}{2!}\frac{\mathrm{d}^2f}{\mathrm{d}x^2}(a) + \dots + \frac{b^r}{r!}\frac{\mathrm{d}^rf}{\mathrm{d}x^r}(a) + \dots$$

is a totally equivalent form, and the particular special case:

$$f(x) = f(0) + x\frac{\mathrm{d}f}{\mathrm{d}x}(0) + \frac{x^2}{2!}\frac{\mathrm{d}^2f}{\mathrm{d}x^2}(0) + \dots + \frac{x^r}{r!}\frac{\mathrm{d}^rf}{\mathrm{d}x^r}(0) + \dots$$

where the expansion is performed around the point $x=0$, is called the **Maclaurin series** of the function f.

Examples and applications of Taylor and Maclaurin expansions are given in Chapter 1 (p. 7), and some Taylor series expansions of common functions are given below.

Infinite series expansions

The Taylor/Maclaurin series approach can be applied to most analytic functions to give a power series expansion. Some common series are:

$$(1+x)^n = 1 + nx + \frac{n(n-1)}{2!}x^2 + \dots + \frac{n(n-1)\dots(n-r+1)}{r!}x^r + \dots$$

The Binomial Theorem

This series is infinite when n is not a positive integer, in which case it is valid for $|x| < 1$. For the special case of $n = -1, x = -R$ $(0 < R < 1)$, this gives the sum of an infinite geometric progression as:

$$\frac{a}{1-R} = a[1 + R + R^2 + R^3 + \dots + R^r + \dots]$$

The series

$$\ln(1+x) = x - \frac{x^2}{2} + \frac{x^3}{3} - \dots + (-1)^{r+1}\frac{x^r}{r} + \dots$$

is valid for $-1 < x \leqslant 1$

and the following series are valid for all values of x:

$$\exp(x) = 1 + x + \frac{x^2}{2!} + \frac{x^3}{3!} + \dots + \frac{x^r}{r!} + \dots$$

$$\cos(x) = 1 - \frac{x^2}{2!} + \frac{x^4}{4!} - \dots + (-1)^r\frac{x^{2r}}{(2r)!} + \dots$$

$$\sin(x) = x - \frac{x^3}{3!} + \frac{x^5}{5!} - \dots + (-1)^r\frac{x^{2r+1}}{(2r+1)!} + \dots$$

$$\cosh(x) = 1 + \frac{x^2}{2!} + \frac{x^4}{4!} + \dots + \frac{x^{2r}}{(2r)!} + \dots$$

$$\sinh(x) = x + \frac{x^3}{3!} + \frac{x^5}{5!} + \dots + \frac{x^{2r+1}}{(2r+1)!} + \dots$$

$$\frac{\sin(x)}{x} = 1 - \frac{x^2}{3!} + \frac{x^4}{5!} - \dots + (-1)^r\frac{x^{2r}}{(2r+1)!} + \dots$$

These four expansions can all be derived from the series for $\exp(x)$ by combining it with the definitions of sin, cos, sinh and cosh given above and employing complex numbers (see Chapter T2) where necessary.

This final expansion is perfectly valid for all x, despite the fact that $\sin(x)/x$ requires the evaluation of a limit at $x = 0$. All that has been done is to divide every term of the $\sin(x)$ series by x.

Integration

Integration can be thought of as the inverse operation to differentiation. Geometrically, a **definite integral** can be thought of as the limit of a sum of vertical strips below a function curve between pre-specified limits:

The function $f(x)$ in this expression is known as the **integrand**.

$$\int_{x_0}^{x_1} f(x)\, dx = \lim_{n \to \infty} \left[d \sum_{i=0}^{n-1} f(x_0 + id) \right]$$

where the summation represents an approximation to the area contained under that portion of the curve and the integral gives an exact measure of that area, provided that the limit exists. In this expression there are n vertical strips, each of width d. The limit must be taken in such a fashion that as the number of strips is increased the width of the strips decreases correspondingly: the constraint $nd = (x_1 - x_0)$ must be satisfied. This definition of area means that areas above the X-axis contribute to the integral with a positive sign, while areas below the X-axis are negative contributions. Similarly, reversing the limits on a definite integral has the effect of reversing the sign of the integral.

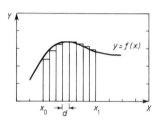

An **indefinite integral** arises when the limits of the integrals are completely unspecified. In such a case the result of the integration is not a numerical value, corresponding to a specific area, but is another function $g(x)$, corresponding to the way in which the area will vary as a function of its position under the curve. The new function $g(x)$ will satisfy $dg/dx = f(x)$. For example,

C is the so-called **constant of integration**. Its appearance will be justified shortly.

$$I = \int x^n\, dx = \frac{x^{n+1}}{n+1} + C$$

There is a major difficulty with this expression. Integration can be thought of as the limit of a summation process, as defined above, where the dx factor specifies the variable over which the function is being summed: but if the summation is being carried out over the variable x, how can there be any x dependence on the r.h.s.? The answer lies in the fact that the above expression is a poor shorthand for the truth: it can be written more correctly as

The main point of this is that the variable appearing as a counter in a summation, or as the variable of integration in an integral, is nothing more than a label: it is used to keep track of the elements of the summation or the current value of the integration variable. In this sense the x appearing within the indefinite integral and the x appearing within the integrated function are not really the same variable.

$$I = \int_a^x u^n\, du = \left[\frac{u^{n+1}}{n+1} \right]_a^x = \frac{x^{n+1}}{n+1} - \frac{a^{n+1}}{n+1} = \frac{x^{n+1}}{n+1} + C$$

where u is a **dummy variable of integration** and a is any number. This can now be seen to be a definite integral with an arbitrary lower limit and a variable upper limit. Insertion of the limits shows that the result is identical to that given previously: except that now the arbitrary constant can be seen to arise from the fact that no information has been given about where the integration process should start from. The result of an indefinite integration must always be to produce a family of solution functions that can be shifted to any vertical position by adjustment of this arbitrary constant of integration.

In a definite integral the arbitrary constant appears twice (once for each limit) with opposite signs, leading to a zero contribution overall.

The integral of a function over an infinite interval can be evaluated, provided that the limiting process defined above returns a finite value for the integral as the length of the integration range is increased without limit. Under similar conditions, it is valid for an integral to encompass a point where the function itself becomes infinite. In the latter case, however, or when the function being integrated involves any discontinuity in value or in gradient, it is necessary to break the integration interval up into regions and treat the overall integral as a sum of integrals over the sub-intervals defined by the discontinuities in the function.

A finite area can be obtained under an infinite interval of a function provided that the function tends to zero 'fast enough' in some mathematical sense.

'Standard' integrals and useful methods

The previous table of derivatives of a range of functions can be used in reverse to obtain the integrals of a wide range of functions. In general, however, the process of integration is rather more difficult than that of differentiation. It is more important to understand the available techniques for the manipulation of complicated integrals than to know a few restricted forms by heart.

Integration obeys the basic additive law of **linearity**:

$$\int [a\,f(x) + b\,g(x)]\,\mathrm{d}x = a\int f(x)\,\mathrm{d}x + b\int g(x)\,\mathrm{d}x$$

but the analogues of the differentiation rules for products, ratios and function of a function are rather more complicated. The differentiation product rule

$$\frac{\mathrm{d}}{\mathrm{d}x}(uv) = u\frac{\mathrm{d}v}{\mathrm{d}x} + v\frac{\mathrm{d}u}{\mathrm{d}x}$$

can be integrated term-by-term and rearranged to give

$$\int u\frac{\mathrm{d}v}{\mathrm{d}x}\,\mathrm{d}x = u\,v - \int v\frac{\mathrm{d}u}{\mathrm{d}x}\,\mathrm{d}x$$

This expression defines the approach of **integration by parts** for the integration of the product of two functions.

Integration by substitution is a powerful technique which is based upon the idea of changing the variable of integration for some new variable, related to the original by an invertible functional relationship. Jeffrey (1989) develops the approach in its most powerful form but a common special case is given by:

$$\int f(x)\,\mathrm{d}x = \int f[g(u)]\frac{\mathrm{d}g}{\mathrm{d}u}\,\mathrm{d}u$$

where the relationship between the variables u and x is given by $x = g(u)$ and the integral equation can be justified from the function-of-a-function rule of differentiation. The main art of this technique is choosing a change of variable which will result in some simplification in the form of the integrand. There are no absolute rules, but the following substitutions are often helpful:

If factors of this form appear anywhere within the integrand	Try the substitution
$ax + b$	$ax + b = u$
$\sqrt{(ax + b)}$	$ax + b = u^2$
$\sqrt{(a^2 - x^2)}$	$x = a\sin u \qquad u \in [-\pi/2, \pi/2]$
$\sqrt{(a^2 + x^2)}$	$x = a\tan u \qquad u \in [-\pi/2, \pi/2]$
	or $x = a\sinh u$
$a^2 + x^2$	$x = a\tan u \qquad u \in [-\pi/2, \pi/2]$
$\sqrt{(x^2 - a^2)}$	$x = a\cosh u \qquad u > 0$
$\sqrt{\left(\dfrac{a - x}{a + x}\right)}$	$x = a\cos(2u)$
Any rational function involving any combination of trigonometric functions	$t = \tan(x/2)$ $\Rightarrow \quad \sin x = \dfrac{2t}{1 + t^2}$

This technique is illustrated in Chapter 1.

There is no standard integration formula for the ratio of two general functions. The differentiation ratio formula is, in fact, equivalent to the product rule. In integral form the product rule remains useful while the ratio rule becomes cumbersome and is little used.

Many of these substitutions can also be used to handle the more awkward 'standard' integrals: the advantage of this approach is that it is also useful when the integral is not standard.

These factors can appear anywhere within the integrand: as part of a ratio of functions, for example, or as the argument of another function, such as $\cos(3x + 2)$.

This is the **half-angle substitution**. It has the property of transforming a general ratio of circular functions into the ratio of algebraic polynomials in the new variable t.

119

If factors of this form appear anywhere within the integrand	Try the substitution
	$\cos x = \dfrac{1 - t^2}{1 + t^2}$ $\tan x = \dfrac{2t}{1 - t^2}$ and $dx = \dfrac{2\,dt}{1 + t^2}$
Any rational function involving any combination of hyperbolic functions	$t = \tanh(x/2)$ $\Rightarrow \sinh x = \dfrac{2t}{1 - t^2}$ $\cosh x = \dfrac{1 + t^2}{1 - t^2}$ $\tanh x = \dfrac{2t}{1 + t^2}$ and $dx = \dfrac{2\,dt}{1 - t^2}$

The various relationships between the trigonometric functions and t can be proved using the double-angle formulae for trigonometric functions and can be conveniently summarized in the Pythagorean triangle:

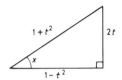

This substitution is clearly very similar to the previous trigonometric version. It can be derived from the hyperbolic double-angle formulae or can be proved directly from the trigonometric version.

These substitutions give some likely substitutions to try: often it is a matter of experiment to obtain a useful simplification, and it is sometimes necessary to perform a sequence of substitutions. If a definite integral is involved, it is essential to keep a careful track of the changes in the values and order of the limits of the function with each substitution. If the integral is indefinite it is usually necessary to re-express the final function in terms of the original variable.

When changing the variable of integration in the above fashion it is often useful to **complete the square** if any quadratic factors appear within the integrand:

$$a x^2 + b x + c \equiv a \left[\left[x + \frac{b}{2a} \right]^2 + \left[\frac{c}{a} - \frac{b^2}{4a^2} \right] \right]$$

For example, $3x^2 + 6x + 7 = 3(x + 1)^2 + 4 = 3[u^2 + 4/3]$ where $u = x + 1$. This enables the above substitutions to be used on a much wider range of functions.

Some particularly useful special rules that can be justified by substitution are:

Substitute $u = g(x)$.

$$\int f[g(x)]\frac{dg}{dx}\, dx = \int f(u)\, du$$

In both of these substitute $u = f(x)$.

$$\int [f(x)]^n\, \frac{df}{dx}\, dx = \frac{1}{n + 1}\, [f(x)]^{n+1}$$

$$\int \frac{df/dx}{f(x)}\, dx = \ln |f(x)|$$

Several of these substitutions result in a transformed integrand which has the form of a ratio of finite polynomials in the new variable. Integrals of such a form can be handled using the technique of **partial fractions**. This approach considers a general ratio of two polynomials:

$$\frac{P(x)}{Q(x)} = \frac{a_0 + a_1 x + a_2 x^2 + \ldots + a_m x^m}{b_0 + b_1 x + b_2 x^2 + \ldots + b_n x^n}$$

If $m \geqslant n$ it is necessary first to divide the polynomials to obtain

$$\frac{P(x)}{Q(x)} = M(x) + \frac{R(x)}{Q(x)}$$

Or, equivalently, $P(x) = M(x) Q(x) + R(x)$. $M(x)$ is an order $m - n$ polynomial which corresponds to how many 'times' $Q(x)$ may be divided into $P(x)$. $R(x)$ is a remainder polynomial whose order is at most $n - 1$.

After such a division the polynomial $M(x)$ is in a form suitable for direct integration. The partial fractions approach concentrates on the remaining ratio of polynomials, where the order of the numerator is less than that of the denominator. Given such a ratio, the denominator polynomial can be expressed as a product of a number of basic factors, say $f_i(x)$, which must all be of the form:

$(ax + b)$	a linear factor
$(ax + b)^n$	a power of a linear factor
$(a x^2 + b x + c)$	a quadratic factor
or $(a x^2 + b x + c)^n$	a power of a quadratic factor

The partial fractions approach expresses the original polynomial ratio as a sum of terms involving the reciprocals of these factors. The difficult part is finding the appropriate numerators which ensure that the original ratio and the sum of simpler ratios are identically equal.

The following rules define the forms of the new terms which must be included in the new expansion for each factor of the denominator in the original expression.

One common technique is the **cover-up rule**. This is a rule which is useful if the factor structure of the denominator is particularly simple but can fail in the general case. It will not be used here.

For each factor	Include terms of the form
$(a x + b)$	$\dfrac{A}{a x + b}$
$(a x + b)^k$	$\dfrac{A}{ax + b} + \dfrac{B}{(ax + b)^2} + \ldots + \dfrac{N}{(ax + b)^k}$
$(a x^2 + b x + c)^k$	$\dfrac{A x + B}{(a x^2 + b x + c)}$
$(a x^2 + b x + c)^k$	$\dfrac{Ax + B}{(ax^2 + bx + c)} + \dfrac{Cx + D}{(ax^2 + bx + c)^2} + \ldots + \dfrac{Mx + N}{(ax^2 + bx + c)^k}$

In the table, A, B, C, ... are pure numbers. In full, the final expansion will look something like

$$\frac{R(x)}{Q(x)} \equiv \sum_{\substack{\text{linear} \\ \text{factors}}} \frac{A_i}{f_i(x)} + \sum_{\substack{\text{quadratic} \\ \text{factors}}} \frac{B_j x + C_j}{f_j(x)} + \text{similar power terms}$$

If $Q(x)$ is of order n there will be n unknown coefficients, A_i, etc., on the r.h.s. of this identity. There are a number of ways to evaluate them, the best approach in general being:
1. Multiply both sides by $Q(x)$: this will produce an identity between two polynomials of order $n - 1$. It is usually worth writing out this step in full.
2. Obtain relationships between the unknown coefficients on the r.h.s. and the known coefficients of $P(x)$ on the l.h.s.
3. Solve these relationships for the values of the unknown coefficients.

The first step is straightforward: the second and third can be extremely difficult if not handled carefully. Common approaches are to insert n particular, distinct values of x in both sides of the equation, or to expand both sides fully into polynomials of order $n - 1$ and compare the coefficients of x^i for $i \in [0, n-1]$. Both of these approaches

The point of this first step is to put the relationship in a form that is identically valid for all x: the ratio form is undefined whenever x takes on a value that is a root of the polynomial $Q(x)$. Note that, strictly, the identity is between two polynomials of order $n - 1$ even when the order of $R(x)$ is less than $n - 1$: in such a case the higher-order coefficients of $R(x)$ are considered to be zero.

See Chapter 3 for a discussion of such problems. Generally, these are difficult to work with on paper for $n > 3$, so it is desirable to avoid such a set of equations if possible.

This process is, in fact, equivalent to the cover-up rule.

result in n simultaneous algebraic equations in the n unknown coefficients, which then require further effort to obtain a full solution.

A good approach is to use particular values of x which cause many of the linear factors in the r.h.s. to vanish: choose x to be a root of $Q(x)$. This will produce simpler equations for some of the unknown coefficients. The problem is that, in all but the simplest cases, the quadratic factors will still cause problems: there are not enough simple linear factors to give n equations in the unknown coefficients.

The most useful approach for the quadratic factors is to calculate a complex root of any quadratic factor and set x to be that complex root on both sides of the identity. Some manipulation of complex numbers will be required but, after simplification, it is then possible to compare separately the real and imaginary parts of the equation (see Chapter T2, p. 132 for details) to obtain two pieces of information about the coefficients at once.

In general it is necessary to combine a little of all of the above approaches: the aim is to produce a set of relationships between the unknown coefficients that will require as little effort as possible to solve for specific numerical values.

To illustrate the process in full, consider the integrand

$$f(x) = \frac{2x^5 + x^4 + 3x^3 + x^2 + x + 1}{x^3 + x}$$

To reduce this to a suitable form for a partial fraction expansion it is necessary to divide out the denominator from the numerator: i.e. find the constants a,b,c,d,e,f, such that

$$f(x) = \frac{(x^3 + x)(a x^2 + b x + c) + (dx^2 + e x + f)}{x^3 + x}$$

Comparing coefficients of decreasing powers of x leads to $a = 2$, $b = 1$, etc., so that it is possible to write

$$f(x) = (2x^2 + x + 1) + \frac{1}{x^3 + x}$$

The polynomial component can be integrated as it stands. The partial fraction expansion of the ratio term is given by

$$\frac{1}{x^3 + x} \equiv \frac{1}{x(x^2 + 1)} \equiv \frac{A}{x} + \frac{Bx + C}{x^2 + 1}$$

so that multiplying throughout by the factors of the denominator

$$\Rightarrow 1 \equiv A(x^2 + 1) + (Bx + C)x$$

and $x = 0$ $\Rightarrow$ $1 \equiv A$
while $x = j$ $\Rightarrow$ $1 \equiv (Bj + C)j \equiv -B + Cj$

This is valid because the relationship involved here is more than an equation, it is an algebraic identity between the two polynomials. The point is to find values of the coefficients which mean that the two sides will be the same whatever the value of x: nowhere has it been specified that x needs to be real!

and comparing real and imaginary parts

gives $B \equiv -1$ and $C \equiv 0$

Therefore, in full, the original integrand can be written as

$$f(x) = (2x^2 + x + 1) + \frac{1}{x} - \frac{x}{x^2 + 1}$$

which is now in a form suitable for term-by-term integration.

Perhaps the most neglected technique of integration is the exploitation of any symmetry, or more correctly antisymmetry, within the integrand over the interval of integration. It has been shown above that any function can be partitioned into an even and an odd component with respect to the midpoint of any interval. It is easy to see that if an integral is taken of an even function over an interval extending the same distance either side of its line of symmetry then:

$$\int_a^b E(x)\,dx = 2\int_{(a+b)/2}^b E(x)dx$$

where the function $E(x)$ is even with respect to $(a+b)/2$, the midpoint of $[a, b]$: the areas under each half of the function curve are identical.

Likewise, if the overall integrand is an odd function with respect to $(a+b)/2$,

$$\int_a^b O(x)\,dx = 0$$

since the areas on each side of the central line are equal in magnitude but opposite in sign.

Using these results it is easy to see that

$$\int_{-1.3}^{1.3} x^{28} \cosh x \sin^{17} x\,dx = 0$$

whereas it would take some courage to attempt to solve this integral using integration by parts, for example.

Other important techniques of integration exist; the use of a reduction formula, for example. See Jeffrey (1989) for a more detailed description.

Nothing is free! The use of a complex number gives two separate equations simultaneously, but nothing further would be gained by setting x to be the complex conjugate of this particular complex root and working through a similar analysis: all possible information about that root has already been obtained.

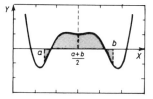

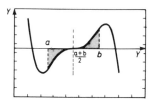

T2 Vectors and Complex Numbers

Vector algebra

The most common basic definition of a **vector** is as a mathematical entity which possesses both a **magnitude** and a **direction**. This definition is extremely useful for the interpretation of some of the operations and geometrical effects associated with vectors, but, in fact, it lacks generality in that it involves an automatic restriction of the concept of a vector to that of an object existing in a three-dimensional world. It is useful to develop vector ideas initially in a three-dimensional Cartesian coordinate system, but it should be kept in mind that the results obtained are much more general than they might seem at first.

Vectors: definitions and algebra

In three-dimensional space a vector can be thought of as a **directed line** joining two points in space. The vector will be specified uniquely by the relative positions of the two points in question. If the two points, say A and B, have coordinates (a_x, a_y, a_z) and (b_x, b_y, b_z) relative to some pre-specified set of Cartesian axes XYZ, then it is possible to specify the vector from A to B in terms of the three differences in each of the coordinates of the two points. A knowledge of these three difference values is equivalent to measuring the direction and length of the line between the points. It is usual to write

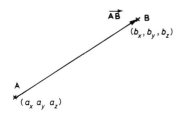

$$\vec{AB} = \begin{bmatrix} b_x - a_x \\ b_y - a_y \\ b_z - a_z \end{bmatrix}$$

where the l.h.s. defines the vector from A to B and the r.h.s. is known as a **column vector**. It has three elements which are merely the differences between the X, Y and Z coordinates respectively of the two points. These elements are known as the **components** of the vector. In particular, when one point is at the origin, O, of the coordinate system,

It is often convenient to choose the origin to be at one of the points of interest. This can always be achieved by a simple change of coordinates or shift of origin. It is also common to use the notation **a**, **b**, etc., as a shorthand notation for any vectors.

The positive square root is being assumed in this definition.

A unit vector contains information about a direction in three-dimensional space.

$$\vec{OA} = \begin{bmatrix} a_x \\ a_y \\ a_z \end{bmatrix} = \mathbf{a}$$

so that the vector from the origin to a point is given by the coordinates of that point written in a column. The notation **a** is usually used for such vectors. The magnitude of a vector corresponds to the (always positive) distance btween the points. By repeated application of Pythagoras' theorem, the magnitude of the vector from A to B can be seen to be

$$|\vec{AB}| = [(b_x - a_x)^2 + (b_y - a_y)^2 + (b_z - a_z)^2]^{1/2}$$

A vector with a magnitude of one is called a **unit vector**. Unit vectors are usually denoted by a 'hat': **â**. A unit vector can be obtained from any particular vector by dividing the vector in question by its magnitude.

One advantage of writing vector information like this is that it is possible to establish a number of compact, basic algebraic rules for the manipulation of vector quantities: the same algebraic laws apply for the manipulation of each of the coordinates in three-dimensional space, but in vector form they are gathered together to form new rules for the multivariable vector quantities. For example, for any vectors.

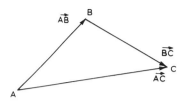

$$\text{or} \quad \begin{aligned} \overrightarrow{OA} + \overrightarrow{AB} &= \overrightarrow{OB} \\ \overrightarrow{AB} + \overrightarrow{BC} &= \overrightarrow{AC} \end{aligned}$$

$$|\mathbf{a}| = a \geqslant 0 \qquad \text{for any vector } \mathbf{a}$$

$$\mathbf{a} = \mathbf{b} \quad \Leftrightarrow \quad \left. \begin{aligned} a_x &= b_x \\ a_y &= b_y \\ a_z &= b_z \end{aligned} \right\} \quad \begin{aligned} &\text{all three must hold} \\ &\text{simultaneously} \end{aligned}$$

Two vectors are equal if and only if all of their respective components are equal. It is worth commenting that no distinction is being made regarding the absolute position in space of these vectors: they are sometimes described as **free** vectors. In some circumstances (such as forces exerting moments around a pivot, for example) it may be more appropriate to employ **bound** vectors, which are restrained to some particular position in space.

$$\mathbf{a} - \mathbf{b} = \mathbf{a} + (-\mathbf{b})$$

The negative of a vector is the equal and opposite vector: the vector with the same magnitude but reverse direction.

$$\begin{aligned} \mathbf{0} + \mathbf{a} &= \mathbf{a} \\ \mathbf{a} + \mathbf{b} &= \mathbf{b} + \mathbf{a} \qquad && \textbf{commutative law } \text{(addition)} \\ \mathbf{a} + (\mathbf{b} + \mathbf{c}) &= (\mathbf{a} + \mathbf{b}) + \mathbf{c} \qquad && \textbf{associative law } \text{(addition)} \end{aligned}$$

$$\lambda(\mathbf{a}) = \lambda\mathbf{a} = \begin{bmatrix} \lambda a_x \\ \lambda a_y \\ \lambda a_z \end{bmatrix}$$

$$\begin{aligned} \lambda(\mu\mathbf{a}) &= (\lambda\mu)\mathbf{a} = \lambda\mu\mathbf{a} \qquad && \textbf{associative law } \text{(scalar multiplication)} \\ (\lambda + \mu)\mathbf{a} &= \lambda\mathbf{a} + \mu\mathbf{a} \qquad && \textbf{distributive law } \text{(scalar multiplication)} \\ \lambda(\mathbf{a} + \mathbf{b}) &= \lambda\mathbf{a} + \lambda\mathbf{b} \qquad && \textbf{distributive law } \text{(vector multiplication)} \\ 0\mathbf{a} &= \mathbf{0} = \lambda\mathbf{0} \end{aligned}$$

These laws provide the basic rules for manipulating vectors: each can be associated with a particular geometrical interpretation.

Linear independence and basis vectors

Given any two vectors, **a** and **b**, it is possible to find a plane which contains the two vectors. If these two vectors are not parallel, they define the plane uniquely: such vectors are said to be **independent**. Two independent vectors **span** the plane that they define in the sense that any other vector within the plane, **c**, can be expressed as some linear combination of **a** and **b**:

$$\mathbf{c} = \lambda\mathbf{a} + \mu\mathbf{b}$$

for some pair of numbers λ and μ; provided that **a** and **b** are independent. The three vectors **a**, **b** and **c** are said to form a **linearly dependent set**. Similarly, any three vectors that are not coplanar span the whole of three-dimensional space and any other vector can be written as a linear combination of the three independent vectors.

The formal definition of linear dependence is that a set of n vectors $\{\mathbf{a}_i\}$ are linearly dependent if the equation

The triangle law of addition. This follows immediately from the definitions. The **triangle inequality** is the, geometrically obvious, statement that for any two vectors **a** and **b** the inequality $|\mathbf{a} + \mathbf{b}| \leqslant |\mathbf{a}| + |\mathbf{b}|$ must hold, with equality if and only if all vectors are parallel.

With the introduction of negative vectors it is possible to state the triangle inequality in the alternative form: $|\mathbf{a} - \mathbf{b}| \geqslant |\mathbf{a}| - |\mathbf{b}|$.

The zero vector has zero magnitude and its direction is undefined.

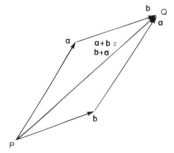

For example, the commutative law corresponds to the two paths around the illustrated parallelogram from the point P to the point Q.

Unless otherwise stated, it is being assumed that the vector has only three components.

The l.h.s. of this equation is called a general linear combination of the *n* vectors a_j. The numbers λ_i are the coefficients of the linear combination. This test for linear dependence is valid for vectors with any number of components.

Geometrically, this means that any three vectors which lie in a plane are dependent, since $c = \lambda a + \mu b \Rightarrow \lambda a + \mu b - c = 0$. Similarly, any four vectors in three-dimensional space are linearly dependent.

The order of the vectors is important when specifying a triad: the vectors: $\{j, i, k\}$ correspond to a left-handed triad. See Jeffrey (1989). A practical set of right-handed vectors are $\{v, B, F\}$, which describe the direction of the force (F) acting on a charged particle moving with a given velocity (v) in a magnetic field (B). See Compton (1986).

Any three independent (not necessarily orthogonal) vectors can be used to define a basis: it is often convenient to exploit this fact and choose the basis to suit the geometry of the practical problem of interest.

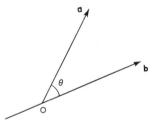

a and *b* are magnitudes and are always positive. Therefore, $a.b$ is positive if $\theta < \pi/2$ and is negative if $\pi/2 < \theta \leqslant \pi$. The scalar product is also known as the **dot product** of two vectors.

This shows how to evaluate the dot product of two vectors expressed in component form. The scalar result will be identical to that obtained by

$$\sum_{i=1}^{n} \lambda_i a_i = 0$$

can be satisfied with a set of numerical coefficients $\{\lambda_i\}$ that are not all zero. If the only solution to this equation is the **trivial solution** $\lambda_i = 0$ for all λ_i, then the vectors are linearly independent.

A set of three independent vectors will span three-dimensional space and are said to form a **basis** for that space. As mentioned above, any other vector in the space can be expressed as a linear combination of these three **basis vectors**. The most commonly used basis vectors are the set

$$i = \begin{bmatrix} 1 \\ 0 \\ 0 \end{bmatrix} \qquad j = \begin{bmatrix} 0 \\ 1 \\ 0 \end{bmatrix} \qquad k = \begin{bmatrix} 0 \\ 0 \\ 1 \end{bmatrix}$$

which are a set of unit vectors pointing along the three coordinate axes. Each of these vectors is **orthogonal** to the other two.

This basis set is often described as forming a **right-handed triad** of orthogonal vectors. The word 'triad' is used because three vectors are involved, and it is described as right-handed because the vector j can be obtained from the vector i by a clockwise rotation of $\pi/2$ around an axis pointing in the direction of k: as with turning a right-handed screw.

In terms of this basis a general vector, a, can be written as

$$a = \begin{bmatrix} a_x \\ a_y \\ a_z \end{bmatrix} = a_x i + a_y j + a_z k$$

Products of vectors

Two basic forms of product are defined for vectors. The **scalar product** of two vectors a and b is given by

$$a.b = a\,b\cos\theta$$

where θ is the angle between the vectors. In terms of this definition it is clear that

$$
\begin{aligned}
a.b &= b.a \\
a.(b + c) &= a.b + a.c \\
\lambda(a.b) &= (\lambda a).b = a.(\lambda b) = \lambda a.b \\
a.a &= a^2 \\
a.b &= 0 \Leftrightarrow a \perp b \text{ (provided that neither } a \text{ nor } b \text{ are } 0)
\end{aligned}
$$

Clearly, the basis vectors i, j and k satisfy the relationships

$$i.j = j.j = k.k = 1$$
and $i.j = j.k = k.i = 0$

since they are unit vectors and make angles of $\pi/2$ with each other.

If a and b are written in the forms

$$a = a_x i + a_y j + a_z k$$
and $b = b_x i + b_y j + b_z k$

then

$$
\begin{aligned}
a.b &= [a_x i + a_y j + a_z k].[b_x i + b_y j + b_z k] \\
&= a_x b_x + a_y b_y + a_z b_z
\end{aligned}
$$

using the previous results.

The scalar product is sometimes written in terms of the product of a **row vector** and a **column vector**

$$\mathbf{a}^{\mathrm{T}} \mathbf{b} = [a_x \quad a_y \quad a_z] \begin{bmatrix} b_x \\ b_y \\ b_z \end{bmatrix} = a_x b_x + a_y b_y + a_z b_z$$

where the notation $\mathbf{a}^{\mathrm{T}}$ is used to signify that the elements of the vector should be written in a row, as a **transpose** of the column vector. The product is obtained by multiplying the corresponding components of each vector in pairs and summing over all of the components.

One of the major uses of the scalar products is that it enables information to be gained about the component of a vector quantity which acts along any pre-specified direction. If the vector quantity of interest is **a**, and a direction is given by $\hat{\mathbf{b}}$ then the **projection** (or component) of **a** along a line in the direction of $\hat{\mathbf{b}}$ is given by

$$\mathbf{a}.\hat{\mathbf{b}} = a \cos \theta$$

In this sense, it is clear that the numerical coefficients associated with a vector expressed in terms of the **i**, **j**, **k** basis vectors merely correspond to the projections of that vector onto each of the chosen basis vectors. If a different basis is chosen, the numerical values of the components will change correspondingly.

The second basic way of multiplying two vectors is the **vector product**, defined by the expression

$$\mathbf{c} = \mathbf{a} \wedge \mathbf{b}$$

where $\wedge$ denotes the operation of vector product. The magnitude of **c** is defined to be

$$|\mathbf{c}| = a b \sin \theta$$

where θ is the angle between **a** and **b** (as before). The direction of **c** is defined as being given by the unit vector $\hat{\mathbf{n}}$ which is orthogonal to the plane defined by **a** and **b** and which forms a right-handed triad with the vectors **a** and **b**.

Therefore, just as the scalar product of two vectors always produces a scalar result, the vector product is an operation between two vectors that will always produce another vector. As usual, it is easy to verify the basic algebraic rules for non-zero vectors **a**, **b** and **c**:

$$
\begin{aligned}
\mathbf{a} \wedge \mathbf{b} &= -\mathbf{b} \wedge \mathbf{a} \\
\mathbf{a} \wedge (\mathbf{b} + \mathbf{c}) &= \mathbf{a} \wedge \mathbf{b} + \mathbf{a} \wedge \mathbf{c} \\
\lambda(\mathbf{a} \wedge \mathbf{b}) &= (\lambda \mathbf{a}) \wedge \mathbf{b} = \mathbf{a} \wedge (\lambda \mathbf{b}) \\
\mathbf{a} \wedge \mathbf{b} = 0 \quad &\Leftrightarrow \quad \theta = 0 \text{ or } \theta = \pi
\end{aligned}
$$

provided neither a nor b are zero.

For the standard Cartesian basis vectors **i**, **j** and **k** in particular,

$$
\begin{aligned}
\mathbf{i} \wedge \mathbf{i} = \mathbf{j} \wedge \mathbf{j} &= \mathbf{k} \wedge \mathbf{k} = 0 \\
\mathbf{i} \wedge \mathbf{j} = \mathbf{k} \qquad &\mathbf{j} \wedge \mathbf{i} = -\mathbf{k} \\
\mathbf{j} \wedge \mathbf{k} = \mathbf{i} \qquad &\mathbf{k} \wedge \mathbf{j} = -\mathbf{i} \\
\mathbf{k} \wedge \mathbf{i} = \mathbf{j} \qquad &\mathbf{i} \wedge \mathbf{k} = -\mathbf{j}
\end{aligned}
$$

These results can be used to show that the vector product of the general vectors

$$\mathbf{a} = a_x \mathbf{i} + a_y \mathbf{j} + a_z \mathbf{k}$$
and $\mathbf{b} = b_x \mathbf{i} + b_y \mathbf{j} + b_z \mathbf{k}$

expressed in component form is

evaluating $ab \cos \theta$ for the two vectors.

The scalar product is, in fact, a special case of a mathematical operation known as the **inner product**.

The distinction between row and column vectors is not critical in geometrical applications. The details of this interpretation are more important for linking the theory of vectors with that of matrices, as discussed in Chapter T3. In fact, a row vector can be viewed as being a 1×3 matrix, and a column vector as being a 3×1 matrix.

This is a generalization of the idea of component. The components of a vector referred to previously have reflected the extent to which a general vector contains contributions from the basis vectors **i**, **j** and **k**: more generally it is possible to think of the degree to which any vector is contained within the vector of interest.

The vector product is also known as the **cross product** and is sometimes written in the notation $\mathbf{a} \times \mathbf{b}$.

Equivalently, the magnitude of the vector **c** can be seen to be defined as the area of the parallelogram defined by **a** and **b**.

The vector product is a **non-commutative** operation.

127

$$\mathbf{a} \wedge \mathbf{b} = (a_y b_z - a_z b_y)\mathbf{i} + (a_z b_x - a_x b_z)\mathbf{j} + (a_x b_y - a_y b_x)\mathbf{k}$$

This cumbersome expression can be written more effectively in a compact form which can be multiplied out using the standard rules of **determinants**:

$$\mathbf{a} \wedge \mathbf{b} = \begin{vmatrix} \mathbf{i} & \mathbf{j} & \mathbf{k} \\ a_x & a_y & a_z \\ b_x & b_y & b_z \end{vmatrix}$$

which greatly eases the practical evaluation of vector products.

The theory of determinants is discussed in Chapter T3 with regard to matrices and sets of linear equations.

The scalar and vector product provide the basic multiplicative tools for use with vectors, but more complex products can be constructed readily. The two most common products are the scalar triple product and the vector triple product.

The **scalar triple product** has the form

$$\mathbf{a}.(\mathbf{b} \wedge \mathbf{c}) = a_x(b_y c_z - b_z c_y) + a_y(b_z c_x - b_x c_z) + a_z(b_x c_y - b_y c_x)$$

or, in determinantal form,

$$\mathbf{a}.(\mathbf{b} \wedge \mathbf{c}) = \begin{vmatrix} a_x & a_y & a_z \\ b_x & b_y & b_z \\ c_x & c_y & c_z \end{vmatrix}$$

The scalar triple product is sometimes written in the compact notation [**a**, **b**, **c**].

It is clear that

$$\mathbf{a}.(\mathbf{b} \wedge \mathbf{c}) = (\mathbf{a} \wedge \mathbf{b}).\mathbf{c} = \mathbf{b}.(\mathbf{c} \wedge \mathbf{a}) = (\mathbf{b} \wedge \mathbf{c}).\mathbf{a} = \mathbf{c}.(\mathbf{a} \wedge \mathbf{b}) = (\mathbf{c} \wedge \mathbf{a}).\mathbf{b}$$

These six objects arise from the three positive permutations of the three vectors (**a**, **b**, **c**) combined with two possible positions for the . and ∧. Products such as **b**.(**a** ∧ **c**) are negative permutations of the vectors and satisfy **b**.(**a** ∧ **c**) = − **a**. (**b** ∧ **c**).

Also, the scalar triple product can be written as

$$\mathbf{a}.(\mathbf{b} \wedge \mathbf{c}) = a \cos \phi \, (bc \sin \theta)$$

where θ is the angle between **b** and **c** and ϕ is the angle between **a** and **b** ∧ **c**. Considering the parallelepiped defined by the three vectors, the base area of the parallelepiped is given by the magnitude of the vector product **b** ∧ **c**, $bc \sin\theta$, while the height is given by the projection of **a** on the unit normal to the plane of **b** and **c**, $a \cos\phi$. Therefore, the volume of the parallelepiped is given by the product of these two quantities: the scalar product **a**.(**b** ∧ **c**).

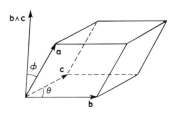

The second important type of multiple product, the **vector triple product**, is the vector, **d**, obtained from three other vectors by

$$\mathbf{d} = \mathbf{a} \wedge (\mathbf{b} \wedge \mathbf{c})$$

When such an expression occurs in vector calculations, it is possible (fortunately) to simplify it somewhat. It can be argued that the vector **d** can be expressed in terms of some linear combination of the vectors **b** and **c**:

$$\mathbf{d} = \mathbf{a} \wedge (\mathbf{b} \wedge \mathbf{c}) = \lambda \mathbf{b} + \mu \mathbf{c}$$

Having established this, taking the scalar product of both sides with the vector **a** gives

$$(\mathbf{a} \wedge (\mathbf{b} \wedge \mathbf{c})).\mathbf{a} = 0 = \lambda \mathbf{b}.\mathbf{a} + \mu \mathbf{c}.\mathbf{a}$$

since the l.h.s. involves two dependent (identical!) vectors in the scalar triple product. This provides a single constraint on the two parameters λ and μ, which can be satisfied by setting $\lambda = \kappa\, \mathbf{c}.\mathbf{a}$ and $\mu = -\kappa\, \mathbf{b}.\mathbf{a}$ for some new parameter κ. Therefore,

$$\mathbf{d} = \mathbf{a} \wedge (\mathbf{b} \wedge \mathbf{c}) = \kappa[(\mathbf{c}.\mathbf{a})\mathbf{b} - (\mathbf{b}.\mathbf{a})\mathbf{c}]$$

By comparing both sides in full component form it follows that $\kappa = 1$, so that in general

$$\mathbf{d} = \mathbf{a} \wedge (\mathbf{b} \wedge \mathbf{c}) = [(\mathbf{c}.\mathbf{a})\mathbf{b} - (\mathbf{b}.\mathbf{a})\mathbf{c}]$$

Since **b** ∧ **c** is perpendicular to the plane of **b** and **c**, all vectors perpendicular to **b** ∧ **c** can be drawn correspondingly in the plane spanned by **b** and **c**. But, by definition, **d** = **a** ∧ (**b** ∧ **c**) is perpendicular to **b** ∧ **c**. Therefore, since **d** can lie in the plane for which **b** and **c** form a basis, it must be possible to find numbers λ and μ such that **d** = λ**b** + μ**c**.

A number of proofs will be found in texts involving ways of obtaining $\kappa = 1$ by looking

similarly,

$$\mathbf{d} = (\mathbf{a} \wedge \mathbf{b}) \wedge \mathbf{c} = [(\mathbf{c}.\mathbf{a})\mathbf{b} - (\mathbf{c}.\mathbf{b})\mathbf{a}]$$

Note that this means that in general

$$\mathbf{a} \wedge (\mathbf{b} \wedge \mathbf{c}) \neq (\mathbf{a} \wedge \mathbf{b}) \wedge \mathbf{c}$$

More complicated products (involving four or more vectors) can be divided into smaller sub-products and simplified using the results given above.

It is worth commenting that only products have been defined for vectors: no form of vector division has been defined or discussed. In practice, it is usually necessary to employ a series of carefully chosen multiplication operations (scalar and vector) to handle expressions involving unwanted vectors: they cannot be divided out; they must be eliminated by multiplying them by factors which will make them vanish or simplify.

at special cases of this relationship. Some of the alternative proofs are valid, but a few are not totally rigorous. In general, if you are uncertain about the steps or 'tricks' involved in vector proofs, it is often possible to fall back on the technique of carrying out the operations explicitly and comparing the components of each side of the equation. The method may be long-winded, but it is infallible if carried out carefully.

Vector geometry

In the same way that the function $x(t)$ specifies the behaviour of a variable x with respect to a parameter t, the position of a point in space may vary with respect to some parameter. In the three-dimensional case a knowledge is required of the parameter dependence of the three elements of the coordinates $(x(t), y(t), z(t))$ of a general point, P, in the Cartesian coordinate system. Similarly,

$$\mathbf{r}(t) = \overrightarrow{OP} = \begin{bmatrix} x(t) \\ y(t) \\ z(t) \end{bmatrix}$$

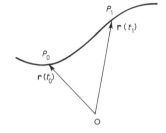

is used to describe a variable vector whose components are completely specified at any given value of the parameter t. This concept of a variable vector can be used with some basic geometrical ideas of Cartesian geometry (line, plane, curve, surface) to build up a powerful structure of tools known as **vector geometry**.

It has been stated above that a unit vector specifies a direction in three-dimensional space. An alternative way of describing the direction of a line segment in Cartesian coordinates is by giving values for the **direction cosines** of the line. These are the cosines of the angles that the line makes with each of the three coordinates axes. In fact, a direction is specified by two measurements, so that one of the direction cosines is redundant. Since the unit vector can be denoted by

For well-behaved functions (continuous and differentiable) the vector will define a curve as the parameter is varied. A curve has only one degree of freedom: only one parameter is required to generate it.

$$\begin{bmatrix} l \\ m \\ n \end{bmatrix} = \begin{bmatrix} \cos \alpha \\ \cos \beta \\ \cos \gamma \end{bmatrix}$$

it follows that the three direction cosines must satisfy the constraint equation

$$\cos^2\alpha + \cos^2\beta + \cos^2\gamma = 1$$

Note that the Cartesian direction cosines simply correspond to the components of the unit vector in the direction of interest.

In a similar fashion it is possible to re-examine many of the concepts of coordinate geometry in vector form. The Cartesian equation of a line, for example, is

$$\frac{x - a_x}{l} = \frac{y - a_y}{m} = \frac{z - a_z}{n}$$

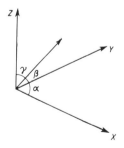

where the line passes through the point (a_x, a_y, a_z) and points in the direction given by the direction cosines l, m and n. In this equation each term is equal to its neighbours, so let them all be equal to some variable parameter, say μ, The equalities can then be viewed one at a time in terms of μ:

The denominators need not be specified as direction cosines, since it is always possible to multiply through by an appropriate scaling factor and ensure that the sum of the squares of the scaled denominators is unity.

These are the parametric equations of a line. The single parameter corresponds to the single degree of freedom of a line.

$$x = a_x + \mu\, l$$
$$y = a_y + \mu\, m$$
$$z = a_z + \mu\, n$$

or $\quad \mathbf{r} = \mathbf{a} + \mu\, \hat{\mathbf{d}}$

in a compact vector form. This equation can be generalized to

$$\mathbf{r} = \mathbf{a} + \lambda\, \mathbf{d}$$

since μ is merely a parameter: the new parameter, λ, can absorb any scale factor associated with the vector $\mathbf{d}$. This equation gives the vector equation of a line through the point given by the vector $\mathbf{a}$ and pointing in the direction of a vector $\mathbf{d}$. Specification of a particular value of the parameter λ determines a corresponding point on the line.

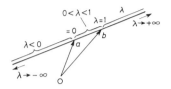

A line is often specified by the fact that it passes through two points, A and B. In this case the vector $\mathbf{b} - \mathbf{a}$ gives the direction of the line and the appropriate vector equation is

$$\mathbf{r} = \mathbf{a} + \lambda(\mathbf{b} - \mathbf{a}) = (1 - \lambda)\mathbf{a} + \lambda\,\mathbf{b}$$

This is known as the **ratio formula** or **section theorem**. The result is valid not only when the ratio is positive (the point of division is internal to the segment AB), but also when it is negative (the point is external to the segment AB). In particular, when $m = n = 1$ it is possible to see that the position vector of the point which bisects the segment is $(\mathbf{a} + \mathbf{b})/2$. Likewise, the two points of trisection are given by $(2\mathbf{a} + \mathbf{b})/3$ and $(\mathbf{a} + 2\mathbf{b})/3$.

A useful corollary to this equation is the result that the position vector of a point which divides the line segment AB in the ratio $m{:}n$ is given by

$$\mathbf{r} = \frac{n\mathbf{a} + m\mathbf{b}}{m + n}$$

The general Cartesian equation of a plane is given by

$$\frac{x}{a} + \frac{y}{b} + \frac{z}{c} = 1$$

Two position vectors (points) are required to define a line (one degree of freedom). Three position vectors (points) are needed to define a plane (two degrees of freedom).

where the plane intercepts the coordinate axes at $x = a$, $y = b$ and $z = c$. Therefore, the end points of the three vectors $a\mathbf{i}$, $b\mathbf{j}$ and $c\mathbf{k}$ from the origin define the plane. Two vectors which lie in (span, form a basis for) the plane are therefore $b\mathbf{j} - a\mathbf{i}$ and $c\mathbf{k} - a\mathbf{i}$. Thus, it is possible to use the position vector $a\mathbf{i}$ to define a specific point in the plane and a linear combination of the vectors $b\mathbf{j} - a\mathbf{i}$ and $c\mathbf{k} - a\mathbf{i}$ to specify any point in the plane relative to $a\mathbf{i}$:

$$\mathbf{r} = \begin{bmatrix} a \\ 0 \\ 0 \end{bmatrix} + \lambda \begin{bmatrix} -a \\ b \\ 0 \end{bmatrix} + \mu \begin{bmatrix} -a \\ 0 \\ c \end{bmatrix}$$

In general, given the position vectors of any three points, A, B and C, it is possible to write the vector equation of the plane containing the points in the form

$$\mathbf{r} = \mathbf{a} + \lambda(\mathbf{b} - \mathbf{a}) + \mu(\mathbf{c} - \mathbf{a}) = (1 - \lambda - \mu)\mathbf{a} + \lambda\mathbf{b} + \mu\mathbf{c}$$

If the normal is not known it can always be calculated. For example, if three points within the plane are given at vectors $\mathbf{a}$, $\mathbf{b}$ and $\mathbf{c}$, the vector product of the vectors $\mathbf{b} - \mathbf{a}$ and $\mathbf{c} - \mathbf{a}$ (which lie in the plane) yields a normal vector.

A more compact vector equation for a plane can be obtained by using the fact that any vector which is in a plane must (by definition) be orthogonal to the normal, $\mathbf{n}$, to that plane. If the direction of the normal is known, together with the position vector of any point, say $\mathbf{a}$, in the plane, then it must follow that

$$(\mathbf{r} - \mathbf{a}).\mathbf{n} = 0$$

This form represents the two degrees of freedom of the plane as a single (implicit) constraint on the three variables in the general vector $\mathbf{r}$ instead of the explicit expression in terms of two variable parameters given above.

for the position vector, $\mathbf{r}$, of any point in the plane. Equivalently, this can be written as

$$\mathbf{r}.\mathbf{n} = \mathbf{a}.\mathbf{n} \qquad \text{or} \qquad \mathbf{r}.\mathbf{n} = s$$

for some scalar $s = \mathbf{a}.\mathbf{n}$. If the unit normal is used, the expression

$$\mathbf{r}.\hat{\mathbf{n}} = s$$

is the **normal form** of the vector equation of a plane.

Differentiation of a vector: space curves

In general, the variation of the components of a vector with respect to some parameter t will be more complicated than the linear case discussed above. The position vector

$$\mathbf{r}(t) = \overrightarrow{OP} = \begin{bmatrix} x(t) \\ y(t) \\ z(t) \end{bmatrix}$$

for any functions $x(t)$, $y(t)$ and $z(t)$ will represent a **space curve** in three-dimensional space. For example, the variable vector

$$\mathbf{r}(t) = \begin{bmatrix} \cos t \\ \sin t \\ 0 \end{bmatrix}$$

represents the position vectors of all points on a unit circle in the XY-plane.

Whenever a vector varies with respect to some parameter it is valid to evaluate the derivative of that variable vector. Define $\Delta\mathbf{r}$ as the vector difference between the vector at parameter values t and $t + \Delta t$:

$$\Delta\mathbf{r} = \mathbf{r}(t + \Delta t) - \mathbf{r}(t)$$

then $$\frac{d\mathbf{r}}{dt} = \lim_{\Delta t \to 0} \frac{\Delta\mathbf{r}}{\Delta t} = \lim_{\Delta t \to 0} \frac{\mathbf{r}(t + \Delta t) - \mathbf{r}(t)}{\Delta t}$$

Since it is possible to eliminate the parameter t to obtain $x^2 + y^2 = 1$.

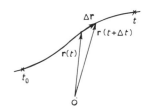

Therefore, differentiating a variable vector leads to a vector which is a tangent vector to the space curve described by the original vector.

Viewed in component form vector differentiation reduces to:

$$\frac{d\mathbf{r}(t)}{dt} = \frac{d}{dt} \begin{bmatrix} x(t) \\ y(t) \\ z(t) \end{bmatrix} = \begin{bmatrix} dx/dt \\ dy/dt \\ dz/dt \end{bmatrix}$$

so that it is straightforward to differentiate a vector: merely differentiate the components individually. Because of this, all of the usual rules of differentiation can be readily derived for vectors. For vectors $\mathbf{f}$ and $\mathbf{g}$ which vary with respect to some parameter t the appropriate rules are:

$$\frac{d}{dt}(\mathbf{f} + \mathbf{g}) = \frac{d\mathbf{f}}{dt} + \frac{d\mathbf{g}}{dt}$$

$$\frac{d}{dt}(\phi\mathbf{f}) = \frac{d\phi}{dt}\mathbf{f} + \phi\frac{d\mathbf{f}}{dt}$$

$$\frac{d}{dt}(\mathbf{f}.\mathbf{g}) = \frac{d\mathbf{f}}{dt}.\mathbf{g} + \mathbf{f}.\frac{d\mathbf{g}}{dt}$$

$$\frac{d}{dt}(\mathbf{f}\wedge\mathbf{g}) = \frac{d\mathbf{f}}{dt}\wedge\mathbf{g} + \mathbf{f}\wedge\frac{d\mathbf{g}}{dt}$$

and $$\frac{d\mathbf{f}}{du} = \frac{dt}{du}\frac{d\mathbf{f}}{dt}$$

It is also possible to evaluate properties of the curve such as its curvature and torsion and define an associated orthogonal triad of axes which move along the curve itself.

One special case occurs when $|\mathbf{r}|$ is a constant (spherical motion). In this case $d\mathbf{r}/dt$ is perpendicular to $\mathbf{r}$ at all times.

For some scalar function $\varphi(t)$.

There are three product rules for differentiation.

This is useful when the vector variation is expressed in terms of some parameter which is not that of practical interest: it corresponds to the ordinary chain rule of differentiation.

Arc length

Arc length is a measure of the distance along a space curve between any two points on the curve. Defining a finite difference vector $\Delta\mathbf{r}$ as above, it is easy to see that the length (modulus) of $\Delta\mathbf{r}$ is

$$\Delta s = |\Delta \mathbf{r}| = [(\Delta x)^2 + (\Delta y)^2 + (\Delta z)^2]^{1/2}$$

so that
$$\frac{ds}{dt} = \lim_{\Delta t \to 0}\left[\left[\frac{\Delta x}{\Delta t}\right]^2 + \left[\frac{\Delta y}{\Delta t}\right]^2 + \left[\frac{\Delta z}{\Delta t}\right]^2\right]^{1/2}$$

$$= \left[\left[\frac{dx}{dt}\right]^2 + \left[\frac{dy}{dt}\right]^2 + \left[\frac{dz}{dt}\right]^2\right]^{1/2}$$

This expression gives the derivative of the arc length, s, as a function of t. To obtain a measurable arc length it is necessary to integrate this between two limits:

$$\text{arc length} = \int_{t_0}^{t_1}\left[\left[\frac{dx}{dt}\right]^2 + \left[\frac{dy}{dt}\right]^2 + \left[\frac{dz}{dt}\right]^2\right]^{1/2} dt$$

n-dimensional vectors

The geometrical ideas developed above are easy to visualize if the vectors have only two (planar geometry) or three (space geometry) components. Surprisingly, however, most of the concepts are transferable to n-dimensional space. The ideas of line, length and arc length can all be generalized to cope with the situation when the vector has n components, as can the operations of scalar product and projection. It is also possible to operate on such vectors with matrices, as discussed in Chapter T3 (p. 146). The details will not be pursued here.

Complex numbers

Equations involving complex numbers carry twice the amount of information that is available if the variables are restricted to be real: any relationship between the complex variables must be valid for both real and imaginary parts. This is a valuable property that is exploited in many applications where two important characteristics (such as amplitude and phase) can be represented compactly in a single complex variable. The application of this result is usually described as **equating real and imaginary parts**.

Complex numbers are often defined as an **ordered pair** of real numbers x_1 and y_1. They originally arose from a mathematical requirement that all polynomial equations of order n should have n roots, despite the fact that even simple quadratic equations, such as $x^2 + 1 = 0$, exist which clearly have no real roots. Complex numbers can be written in the form $z_1 = (x_1, y_1)$, $x_1 + jy_1$ or $r_1 \exp(j\theta_1)$ where the **imaginary number** j has the property that $j^2 = -1$.

If $z_1 = x_1 + jy_1$ and $z_2 = x_2 + jy_2$ are complex numbers, then the basic algebraic rules appropriate to their manipulation may be summarized as:

$$z_1 = z_2 \Leftrightarrow x_1 = x_2 \text{ and } y_1 = y_2$$
$$z_1 \pm z_2 = (x_1 \pm x_2) + j(y_1 \pm y_2)$$
$$z_1 z_2 = (x_1 x_2 - y_1 y_2) + j(x_1 y_2 + y_1 x_2)$$
$$z_1^* = x_1 - jy_1 \quad \text{the \textbf{complex conjugate} of } z_1$$
$$|z_1| = \text{modulus}(z_1) = (z_1 z_1^*)^{1/2} = (x_1^2 + y_1^2)^{1/2}$$
$$z_1/z_2 = z_1 z_2^*/z_2 z_2^* = [(x_1 x_2 + y_1 y_2) + j(y_1 x_2 - x_1 y_2)]/(x_2^2 + y_2^2)$$

The complex number z_1 can be represented as a point (x_1, y_1) on a Cartesian plane. Such a picture, with the Y-axis representing the imaginary component, is known as an **Argand diagram**. A complex number z_1 and its complex conjugate z_1^* appear on an Argand diagram as a pair of points at the same X-coordinate, but positioned equally above and below the X-axis.

Polar form of complex numbers – De Moivre's theorem

If the Argand plane is viewed in polar coordinates the position of the point corresponding to z_1 is equally well represented by (r_1, θ_1). Clearly,

$$z_1 = x_1 + jy_1 = r_1 \cos \theta_1 + j r_1 \sin \theta_1$$

where r_1 is the **modulus** of the complex number and θ_1 is its **argument**. This is known as the **polar** form of the complex number. It is sometimes convenient to consider the complex number as defining a vector of length r_1 from the origin to the number, making an angle θ_1 with the X-axis.

The X and Y components of this vector are thus $r_1 \cos \theta_1$ and $r_1 \sin \theta_1$ respectively.

Complex numbers obey all of the algebraic rules of the real numbers and, in particular, familiar power series expansions of functions can also be expressed in terms of complex numbers. Real series expansions which involve a range of convergence will similarly converge when used with a complex argument provided that the complex number lies within an area of convergence in the complex plane. For example,

$$\exp z = e^z = \sum_{n=0}^{\infty} \frac{z^n}{n!} = 1 + z + \frac{z^2}{2!} + \dots \qquad \text{for all } z$$

whereas

$$(1 - z)^{-1} = \sum_{n=0}^{\infty} z^n = 1 + z + z^2 + z^3 + \dots \qquad |z| < 1$$

In particular, putting $z = j\theta$ in the first series and partitioning the expansion into real and imaginary parts leads to the result

$$\exp(j\theta) = \cos \theta + j \sin \theta$$

using the standard series expansions for $\sin \theta$ and $\cos \theta$. Thus,

$$z_1 = x_1 + jy_1 = r_1(\cos \theta_1 + j \sin \theta_1) = r_1 e^{j\theta_1}$$

This is the **exponential** form of a complex number.
  Since

$$z_1^* = x_1 - jy_1 = r_1(\cos \theta_1 - j \sin \theta_1) = r_1 e^{-j\theta_1}$$

it follows that

$$\cos \theta_1 = [e^{j\theta_1} + e^{-j\theta_1}]/2$$
and $\sin \theta_1 = [e^{j\theta_1} - e^{-j\theta_1}]/2j$

In fact, these expressions are often taken as definitions of the trigonometric functions.
  In exponential form complex multiplication and division simplify considerably:

These results are particularly useful for partitioning a complicated product/ratio of individual complex numbers into real and imaginary parts.

$$z_1 z_2 = [r_1 e^{j\theta_1}][r_2 e^{j\theta_2}] = r_1 r_2 e^{j(\theta_1 + \theta_2)}$$
$$z_1/z_2 = [r_1 e^{j\theta_1}]/[r_2 e^{j\theta_2}] = (r_1/r_2) e^{j(\theta_1 - \theta_2)}$$

so that it is only necessary to multiply (divide) the moduli of the numbers and to add (subtract) their arguments. The evaluation of powers and roots is also greatly eased, but when calculating roots it is necessary to take into account the fact that

$$e^{j\theta} = e^{(j\theta + 2\pi j)} = e^{(j\theta + 2k\pi j)} \qquad \text{if } k \text{ is an integer}$$
$$\therefore \quad z^n = r^n e^{jn\theta}$$
but $z^{1/n} = r^{1/n} e^{j(\theta + 2k\pi)/n} \qquad k = \dots -2, -1, 0, 1, 2\dots$

As k cycles through the integers, n distinct roots of the original complex number are generated. These n roots lie on a circle of radius $r^{1/n}$ centred on the origin in the complex plane and are evenly spaced around the circle, starting at an angle of θ/n and at regular angular intervals of $2\pi/n$.

De Moivre's theorem is the statement that

$$(\cos\theta + j\sin\theta)^n = e^{(j\theta)n} = e^{j(n\theta)} = \cos(n\theta) + j\sin(n\theta)$$

and is extremely useful for obtaining multiple-angle formulae for sines and cosines. For example:

$$\cos(4\theta) + j\sin(4\theta) = (\cos\theta + j\sin\theta)^4$$
$$= \cos^4\theta + 4j\sin\theta\cos^3\theta - 6\sin^2\theta\cos^2\theta - 4j\sin^3\theta\cos\theta + \sin^4\theta$$

So that, equating real and imaginary parts and rearranging slightly,

$$\cos(4\theta) = 1 - 8\cos^2\theta + 8\cos^4\theta$$
$$\text{and } \sin(4\theta) = 4\cos\theta\sin\theta\,(\cos^2\theta - \sin^2\theta)$$

It is possible to obtain similar expansions for powers of trigonometric functions in terms of multiple angles. For example:

$$\cos^3\theta = [(e^{j\theta} + e^{-j\theta})/2]^3 = (e^{3j\theta} + 3e^{j\theta} + 3e^{-j\theta} + e^{-3j\theta})/8$$
$$= \tfrac{3}{4}\cos\theta + \tfrac{1}{4}\cos 3\theta$$

Summation of series and evaluation of integrals using complex numbers

To sum series involving $\cos(r\theta)$ (or $\sin(r\theta)$) it is often convenient to consider the series as being just the real (or imaginary) part of a more general series in $\exp(jr\theta)$. For example, to sum the infinite series

$$\sum_{r=0}^{\infty} \frac{\cos(r\theta)}{2^r}$$

instead consider the series

$$\sum_{r=0}^{\infty} \frac{e^{jr\theta}}{2^r} = \sum_{r=0}^{\infty} \left[\frac{e^{j\theta}}{2}\right]^r = \sum_{r=0}^{\infty} z^r = (1 - z)^{-1}$$

where $z = \tfrac{1}{2}e^{j\theta}$ and the infinite geometric progression converges since $|z| < 1$. The original series will be given by the real part of $1/(1 - \tfrac{1}{2}e^{j\theta})$, which can be obtained simply by multiplying above and below by the complex conjugate of the denominator.

The general procedure with summing such series is:

1. Replace any trigonometric terms by complex exponentials and consider the more general complex summation.
2. Group together all terms which are r-dependent and express the dependence on r in as simple a fashion as possible. Pass any r-independent component out through the summation sign.
3. Try to recognize the summation over r as one that has already been encountered, or perhaps a modified version of a familiar summation.
4. If 3 fails, replace the terms on which r operates by a temporary variable (such as z in the example above) and try again. The sort of series that might occur in recognizable form are the arithmetic, geometric and binomial series, or the series expansion of common functions, such as $\exp z$. Also, it is often possible to sum slightly modified versions of such series directly (those multiplied by factors, or differentiated, for example).

A similar technique can be used to simplify the evaluation of integrals of the form

$$I = \int \exp(ax)\cos(nx)\,dx$$

which arise in practical circuit analysis, for example. The integral can be written as the real part of the complex integral

$$\int \exp(ax) \exp(jnx) \, dx = \int \exp[(a+jn)x] \, dx$$

which can be integrated directly to give

$$I = \text{Re}\left[\frac{\exp[(a+jn)x]}{(a+jn)}\right] = \frac{\exp(ax)\,[a\cos(nx) + n\sin(nx)]}{a^2 + n^2}$$

by multiplying above and below by $(a - jn)$. Considering the corresponding imaginary component gives

$$\int \exp(ax) \sin(nx) \, dx = \frac{\exp(ax)\,[a\sin(nx) - n\cos(nx)]}{a^2 + n^2}$$

The general theory of complex integration (also known as **contour integration**) is rather more complicated than this might indicate. It is safest to view this as a worthwhile trick for simplifying difficult integrals that involve trigonometric components in the integrand. This particular integral is useful for the analysis of an ac circuit: see Example 4.6.

T3 Linear Equations, Determinants and Matrices

The mathematical definitions, tools and methods used within the subjects of simultaneous equations, determinants and matrices are reviewed in this chapter. These three subject areas are grouped together in this chapter because, to a good extent, they represent different ways of attacking the same type of problem. For example, it will be seen that it is possible to solve a set of equations by direct manipulation of the equations, by using determinants, or by expressing the equations in a matrix form. However, despite the close relationship between these particular subjects, from the points of view of ease of application and interpretation each approach has specific advantages and disadvantages which make it worthwhile to consider their properties separately.

In particular, the theory of matrices is by far the most powerful and flexible of the three approaches and allows the straightforward solution of complicated problems which would be nearly impossible to solve when expressed as linear equations.

Linear simultaneous equations

Chapter T1 contains definitions of the meanings of the words algebraic and linear in this context.

A linear, algebraic equation in n unknowns x_i ($i = 1, ..., n$) has the form

$$a_1 x_1 + a_2 x_2 + ... + a_n x_n = k$$

where the a_i ($i = 1, ..., n$) and k are numbers, or functions of some variable parameter not already included in the equation. Such an equation represents a single **constraint** on the n unknown variables and reduces the **degrees of freedom** of this set of unknowns by one. Hence, it seems reasonable to expect that, in general, a set of n such **simultaneous equations** in n unknown variables should lead to a unique set of values for the n variables which satisfy all of the given equations. A number of methods will now be presented which can be used to find such a solution, if one exists. In general the approaches will be illustrated with three unknown variables, but the methods can be extended readily to any number of variables.

For example, the variables might correspond to the measured states of a system and the coefficients of the equation might be functions of time. Although the coefficients of the equation may change with time, the equation is still linear in the n unknown variables at any given time.

Gaussian elimination algorithm

The solution of a set of three simultaneous linear algebraic equations of the form

$$a_{11} x + a_{12} y + a_{13} z = k_1$$
$$a_{21} x + a_{22} y + a_{23} z = k_2$$
$$a_{31} x + a_{32} y + a_{33} z = k_3$$

involves obtaining values for the unknowns, x, y and z, in terms of the known coefficients a_{ij} and k_i. If all of the k_i are zero the equations are described as being **homogeneous**, else they are **non-homogeneous**. The linearity of the entire set of equations means that a number of systematic approaches can be used to manipulate the equations, and one of the most popular is the **Gaussian elimination algorithm**.

An algorithm may be described as a systematic set of rules and operations (such as found in a computer program) that can be applied rigidly in sequence in order to obtain some desired result. In this case the key step is always to add or subtract just the right amount of equation i to remove the leading variable from equation $i + 1$.

The Gaussian elimination approach involves a step-by-step removal of the leading variable from a decreasing number of equations in turn, until only one variable is left in the nth equation. For the case of three equations, this is achieved by first of all adding a factor of $-(a_{21}/a_{11})$ times the first equation to the second equation, and a factor of $-(a_{31}/a_{11})$ times the first equation to the third equation. The removal of the first variable produces an intermediate set of modified equations of the form:

$$
\begin{aligned}
a_{11}x \quad + \quad a_{12}y \quad + \quad a_{13}z \quad &= \quad k_1 \\
[a_{22}-a_{21}a_{12}/a_{11}]y + [a_{23}-a_{21}a_{13}/a_{11}]z &= [k_2-k_1 a_{21}/a_{11}] \\
[a_{32}-a_{31}a_{12}/a_{11}]y + [a_{33}-a_{31}a_{13}/a_{11}]z &= [k_3-k_1 a_{31}/a_{11}]
\end{aligned}
$$

It is now possible to remove the y variable from the third equation by repeating the process and adding a factor of $-[a_{32}-a_{31}a_{12}/a_{11}]/[a_{22}-a_{21}a_{12}/a_{11}]$ times the second equation to the third. The final equations take on an **upper triangular form**:

$$
\begin{aligned}
a_{11}x + a_{12}y + a_{13}z &= k_1 \\
A_{22}y + A_{23}z &= K_2 \\
A_{33}z &= K_3
\end{aligned}
$$

For more then three equations the procedure is identical: remove the first variable from $n-1$ of the equations, the second from $n-2$, etc.

where the capital letters indicate those coefficients which have been changed from their initial values by one or more of the manipulations. Having obtained this hierarchically structured set of equations it is possible to obtain the value of z immediately as $z = K_3/A_{33}$ and carry out a series of **back-substitutions**, using the, now known, value of z in the second equation to obtain

$$
y = \frac{K_2 - A_{23}z}{A_{22}}
$$

and then use both of the known values of y and z in the first equation to obtain x from

$$
x = \frac{k_1 - a_{12}y - a_{13}z}{a_{11}}
$$

so that, in general, the full solution of the equations will have been obtained. The systematic nature of the operations at each stage make this a particularly straightforward algorithm to implement on a digital computer.

Problems can arise with the above steps: a number of divisions must be carried out during each part of the algorithm, and it is quite possible for it to be necessary to divide by zero: fortunately, it is often possible to reorder the equations if this occurs. However, it must be pointed out that the equations are not actually guaranteed to have a solution: as will be discussed shortly, such difficulties may merely reflect a lack of any unique solution.

In summary, the general Gaussian elimination algorithm for n simultaneous linear equations involves two stages:
1. Reduction of the set of equations to upper triangular form by removing the first variable from $(n-1)$ of the equations, and then the second variable from $(n-2)$, etc., until (if possible) the nth equation contains only one variable.
2. Back-substitution of the value of the nth variable in the $(n-1)$th equation to obtain the value of the $(n-1)$th variable, and then substitution of both of these variables in the $(n-2)$th equation to obtain one more variable value, etc., until all equations have been used and all n values of the variables have been established.

Division by zero can sometimes be avoided by reordering the equations, but may reflect a problem within the equations themselves, as is discussed in the next section.

The approach needs numerical examples to be understood clearly, and a number of illustrative application examples are given in Chapter 3.

The order of the set of equations is irrelevant, and so you are quite free to reorder them at any stage in the algorithm so as to take advantage of any zeros that might already appear in appropriate positions or to move zeros that are in undesirable positions. One simple way in which Gaussian elimination can be improved slightly is by employing **pivoting** – an approach which continually performs a systematic reordering of the equations so that when a division is carried out, the division is by the largest number available. This tends to increase the computational accuracy of the process by reducing the rounding errors associated with the finite precision of digital computers.

Insufficient and contradictory equations

When working through the Gaussian elimination algorithm for a set of n linear equations in n unknowns three distinct types of behaviour can occur:

1. It may be that the set can be solved to obtain a unique solution without difficulty.
2. It may happen that two or more equations turn out to be multiples of each other or, equivalently, a complete equation collapses to the form $0 = 0$. If this happens the equations do not contain enough information to obtain a single unique solution: the equations are said to form an **insufficient set** and will give rise to an infinite family of solutions.
3. Two or more equations may reduce to a subset that are clearly incompatible with each other, such as $x + y = 2$ and $2x + 2y = 5$ or, equivalently, a contradiction such as $0 = 1$ may be obtained. In this case the equations are said to be **contradictory** and there is no possible set of values for the unknowns that satisfies the entire set of equations.

Geometrical interpretation of linear equations

It is worth while trying to visualize exactly why some sets of equations have no solution, some one and some an infinity.

Consider again a general set of three linear equations:

$$a_{11}\, x + a_{12}\, y + a_{13}\, z = k_1$$
$$a_{21}\, x + a_{22}\, y + a_{23}\, z = k_2$$
$$a_{31}\, x + a_{32}\, y + a_{33}\, z = k_3$$

It is quite possible to rewrite the equations in a totally equivalent vector form:

$$(a_{11},\ a_{12},\ a_{13}) \begin{bmatrix} x \\ y \\ z \end{bmatrix} = k_1$$

$$(a_{21},\ a_{22},\ a_{23}) \begin{bmatrix} x \\ y \\ z \end{bmatrix} = k_2$$

and

$$(a_{31},\ a_{32},\ a_{33}) \begin{bmatrix} x \\ y \\ z \end{bmatrix} = k_3$$

This is an alternative way of viewing the three previous equations, where the unknown variables have been gathered into a single three-variable column vector. Similarly, the numerical coefficients of the equations are held in three third-order row vectors. If we denote the three known row vectors by $\mathbf{a}_i^T$ ($i = 1,2,3$) and the unknown variables vector by $\mathbf{v}$ then we have

$$\mathbf{a}_1^T\mathbf{v} = k_1$$
$$\mathbf{a}_2^T\mathbf{v} = k_2$$
$$\mathbf{a}_3^T\mathbf{v} = k_3$$

as a compact way of writing the three equations. Each equation can be viewed as representing a plane in three-dimensional Cartesian space (see Chapter 2, p. 23 and Chapter T2, p. 130) and the direction of each plane is given by the vector $(a_{i1}, a_{i2}, a_{i3}) = \mathbf{a}_i^T$. It is not too difficult to convince oneself that any two non-parallel planes will intersect somewhere in space and to see that those points which are common to both planes will lie along a line of intersection. In terms of the equations, this line is composed of the infinite set of answers which are obtained as the parameterized solution to any chosen pair of equations.

The relationship of the third equation and its associated plane to the first two is the critical factor: if (and only if) the three planes point in different directions is there a single point of intersection of the planes. The coordinates of the intersection point in Cartesian space provide the unique solution of the equations. Hence, these equations will have a unique solution for the unknown variables if and only if the three vectors $\mathbf{a}_i^T$ ($i = 1, 2, 3$) form a linearly independent set. If this is not the case then the equations are either insufficient or contradictory, depending on the detailed behaviour of the three numbers that appear on the right of the equations. If the vectors do happen to form a dependent set then, by definition, it is possible to write

$$\sum_{i=1}^{3} c_i \mathbf{a}_i^T = 0$$

for some set of numbers $\{c_i\}$. If it is also possible to write

$$\sum_{i=1}^{3} c_i k_i = 0$$

where k_i ($i = 1, 2, 3$) are the numbers on the r.h.s. of the equations, for the same set of values $\{c_i\}$, then the equations are insufficient. If it is not possible, then the equations are contradictory.

Geometrically, an infinite number of solutions will be obtained if the three planes intersect along a single line or if all three planes are superimposed perfectly. The case of contradictory equations arises when the three planes intersect in such a fashion so as to produce three separate and parallel lines of intersection between any two of the planes at a time, or when any two of the planes are parallel but separate: in either case no point lies on all three planes and the equations have no solution.

Such geometrical ideas can be extended to larger sets of equations, but it becomes necessary to think in terms of intersecting hyperplanes in n-dimensional space: three dimensions are usually enough!

In short,

> A set of n simultaneous linear algebraic equations in n unknowns will have a unique solution if, and only if, the set of n-vectors formed from the coefficients of the l.h.s. are linearly independent. Else, the equations are insufficient and have a family of solutions, or they are contradictory and have no solution.

One particular special case arises when the equations are homogeneous in form: if all of the k_i are zero and the equations are linearly independent then the only possible solution can be seen to be the (trivial) solution where all of the variables are themselves zero. The only way in which a set of homogeneous linear equations can have any nonzero solution is for the equations to form a linearly dependent set, in which case an infinite family of nonzero solutions will be obtained.

Too few or too many equations

So far, only the special case of n equations in n unknowns has been discussed. In a real situation it may be possible to make only a very few measurements on a complex system, leading to a mathematical description which involves n unknown variable parameters (such as voltage levels, temperatures, signal levels, etc.) connected together by m linear equations, where m is rather less than n. If this is this case, then the most that can be done is to represent the solution in a parameterized form, the number of free independent parameters being $(n - m)$. Such a set of **underdetermined** equations is entirely equivalent to the insufficient case described above.

Another possible type of set of linear equations can arise when many measurements

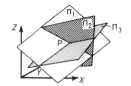

Three linearly independent planes Π_i ($i = 1, 2, 3$) and their unique intersection point P.

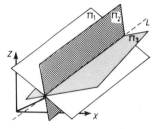

Three planes Π_i ($i = 1, 2, 3$) which correspond to insufficient equations with a one-parameter infinite family of solutions lying along the line L.

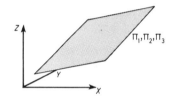

Three planes Π_i ($i = 1, 2, 3$) which correspond to insufficient equations which are pure multiples of each other. The superimposed planes define a two-parameter infinite family of solutions.

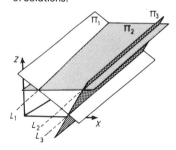

Three planes Π_i ($i = 1, 2, 3$) which correspond to one type of contradictory equations. These intersect in three parallel lines L_i ($i = 1, 2, 3$). Clearly, no point lies on all three planes.

are made over a period of time on a system which involves only a few important physical variables. In this case the number of equations is rather greater than the number of unknown variables and the equations are said to be **overdetermined**. If the system is truly time independent and noise-free the resulting set of equations will be **consistent** – no equation will actually contradict any combination of the others. For a set of consistent overdetermined equations any n equations with a set of linearly independent coefficient vectors can be used to determine a unique solution. The remaining $(n - m)$ equations are **redundant** and do not affect the solution.

More realistically, all circuits, devices, transducers and meters are subject to noise, uncertainties and limited accuracy which ensure that no two measurements on a system under apparently identical circumstances will produce exactly identical results. All of the mathematical tools discussed above implicitly assume that the equations are, in fact, exactly true, so that a set of many equations arising in a practical fashion are, very likely, going to produce contradictory results, simply because there is no allowance for experimental error in the above exact mathematical methods. Ways of dealing with this practical disadvantage and arriving at the closest solution to a set of overdetermined, contradictory equations will be discussed later in this chapter.

Ill-conditioned equations

Ill-conditioned equations arise when a very small change in the coefficients of the original set of equations can produce a very large change in the calculated values of the variables. Ill-conditioning of equations can also be interpreted readily in a geometrical fashion – for simplicity it is best to illustrate it here with intersecting lines, in terms of

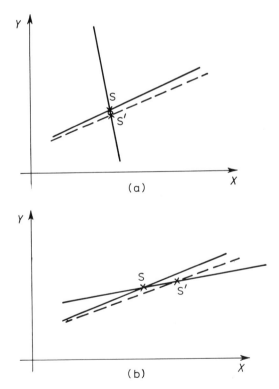

Fig. T3.1 (a) Near-orthogonal lines correspond to well-conditioned equations.
(b) Near parallel lines represent ill-conditioned equations.

only two variables, and imagine that in the more general case the hyperplanes are being viewed edge on. Fig. T3.1a represents two equations as two solid lines, whose intersection defines the solution point, S, of the pair of equations. Because these lines happen to be nearly orthogonal a small change in the parameters of one equation will produce the dotted line, for example, and it can be seen that the new solution point, S', is not very far from the position of S. This represents a pair of well-conditioned equations.

Ill-conditioned equations would produce a diagram rather more like that shown in Fig. T3.1b, where a similar perturbation on only one equation produces a much larger effect on the position of the solution point. In this sense, near-orthogonal planes will tend to produce the most **noise-insensitive** solution while equations which produce planes whose intersection lines are almost parallel (almost linearly dependent) will degrade the **robustness** of the solution to perturbations or noise.

A rapid way to determine whether a set of equations is likely to exhibit ill-conditioning is to evaluate the determinant of the equations.

Determinants

Definition of determinants: Cramer's rule

A determinant of order n is a real (or complex) number (or function) which is characteristic of a square array of $n \times n$ real (or complex) numbers (or functions). It is thus possible to talk about the determinant of:

$$
\begin{vmatrix} 1 & 7 \\ -3 & 13 \end{vmatrix} \quad \text{or} \quad \begin{vmatrix} 1 & j \\ -j & 1 \end{vmatrix} \quad \text{or} \quad \begin{vmatrix} x & x^2 \\ e^x & 1 \end{vmatrix} \quad \text{or} \quad \begin{vmatrix} a_{11} & a_{12} & a_{13} \\ a_{21} & a_{22} & a_{23} \\ a_{31} & a_{32} & a_{33} \end{vmatrix}
$$

where the a_{ij} represents a scalar (or scalar function) in row i and column j of the block. If the block of numbers is represented by **A** it is common to write the determinant as

$$
|\mathbf{A}| = \det(\mathbf{A}) = \begin{vmatrix} a_{11} & a_{12} & a_{13} \\ a_{21} & a_{22} & a_{23} \\ a_{31} & a_{32} & a_{33} \end{vmatrix}
$$

A determinant is a special type of a linear scalar function of n^2 independent scalar variables. It is convenient for the purposes of interpretation and calculation to arrange these variables in a square of side n.

for a 3×3 block of numbers.

The precise definition of determinants arises directly from their original use in the theory of simultaneous linear algebraic equations. Consider the general pair of equations

$$a_{11} x + a_{12} y = k_1$$
$$\text{and } a_{21} x + a_{22} y = k_2$$

Multiplying the first equation by a_{22}, the second by a_{12} and subtracting gives

$$(a_{11} a_{22} - a_{21} a_{12})x = k_1 a_{22} - k_2 a_{12}$$

so that substitution of x into either equation gives a full result

$$x = \frac{k_1 a_{22} - k_2 a_{12}}{a_{11} a_{22} - a_{21} a_{12}} \qquad y = \frac{a_{11} k_2 - a_{21} k_1}{a_{11} a_{22} - a_{21} a_{12}}$$

providing that the denominator is not zero.

Similarly, a page or two of tedious rearrangement shows that the three equations

$$a_{11} x + a_{12} y + a_{13} z = k_1$$
$$a_{21} x + a_{22} y + a_{23} z = k_2$$
$$a_{31} x + a_{32} y + a_{33} z = k_3$$

produce explicit, and cumbersome, solutions

$$x = \frac{k_1 a_{22} a_{33} - k_1 a_{23} a_{32} + a_{12} a_{23} k_3 - a_{12} k_2 a_{33} + a_{13} k_2 a_{32} - a_{13} a_{22} k_3}{a_{11} a_{22} a_{33} - a_{11} a_{23} a_{32} + a_{12} a_{23} a_{31} - a_{12} a_{21} a_{33} + a_{13} a_{21} a_{32} - a_{13} a_{22} a_{31}}$$

$$y = \frac{a_{11} k_2 a_{33} - a_{11} a_{23} k_3 + k_1 a_{23} a_{31} - k_1 a_{21} a_{33} + a_{13} a_{21} k_3 - a_{13} k_2 a_{31}}{a_{11} a_{22} a_{33} - a_{11} a_{23} a_{32} + a_{12} a_{23} a_{31} - a_{12} a_{21} a_{33} + a_{13} a_{21} a_{32} - a_{13} a_{22} a_{31}}$$

$$z = \frac{a_{11} a_{22} k_3 - a_{11} k_2 a_{32} + a_{12} k_2 a_{31} - a_{12} a_{21} k_3 + k_1 a_{21} a_{32} - k_1 a_{22} a_{31}}{a_{11} a_{22} a_{33} - a_{11} a_{23} a_{32} + a_{12} a_{23} a_{31} - a_{12} a_{21} a_{33} + a_{13} a_{21} a_{32} - a_{13} a_{22} a_{31}}$$

assuming that the denominator does not vanish.

If the determinant of a 2×2 block of numbers is defined by

$$\begin{vmatrix} a_{11} & a_{12} \\ a_{21} & a_{22} \end{vmatrix} = a_{11} a_{22} - a_{21} a_{12}$$

and that of a 3×3 block by

$$\begin{vmatrix} a_{11} & a_{12} & a_{13} \\ a_{21} & a_{22} & a_{23} \\ a_{31} & a_{32} & a_{33} \end{vmatrix} = \begin{aligned} & a_{11} a_{22} a_{33} - a_{11} a_{23} a_{32} + a_{12} a_{23} a_{31} \\ & - a_{12} a_{21} a_{33} + a_{13} a_{21} a_{32} - a_{13} a_{22} a_{31} \end{aligned}$$

then it is possible to write the solutions to the above sets of two and three equations as

$$\frac{x}{\begin{vmatrix} k_1 & a_{12} \\ k_2 & a_{22} \end{vmatrix}} = \frac{y}{\begin{vmatrix} a_{11} & k_1 \\ a_{21} & k_2 \end{vmatrix}} = \frac{1}{\begin{vmatrix} a_{11} & a_{12} \\ a_{21} & a_{22} \end{vmatrix}}$$

and

$$\frac{x}{\begin{vmatrix} k_1 & a_{12} & a_{13} \\ k_2 & a_{22} & a_{23} \\ k_3 & a_{32} & a_{33} \end{vmatrix}} = \frac{y}{\begin{vmatrix} a_{11} & k_1 & a_{13} \\ a_{21} & k_2 & a_{23} \\ a_{31} & k_3 & a_{33} \end{vmatrix}} = \frac{z}{\begin{vmatrix} a_{11} & a_{12} & k_1 \\ a_{21} & a_{22} & k_2 \\ a_{31} & a_{32} & k_3 \end{vmatrix}} = \frac{1}{\begin{vmatrix} a_{11} & a_{12} & a_{13} \\ a_{21} & a_{22} & a_{23} \\ a_{31} & a_{32} & a_{33} \end{vmatrix}}$$

respectively. Thus, the solution of a set of two linear equations involves the evaluation of three second-order determinants, while a set of three equations requires the evaluation of four determinants of third order. Similar expressions can be written down for larger sets of equations and these determinantal solutions are known as **Cramer's rule** for the solution of linear algebraic equations.

It may appear at first that not much is gained by Cramer's rule: although the determinantal solutions are rather more compact and systematic than their predecessors, they don't actually seem to involve anything new – the complicated expressions involving sums of products are merely replaced by a box of numbers defined to be the same thing, so that exactly the same expressions must be evaluated to obtain a solution. In fact, there are considerable advantages to using determinants:

1. By extending the definition of determinants beyond order three, Cramer's rule will work for systems of equations of arbitrary size and will remain a compact and neat way of writing the form of the solution – attempting to write out the complete solution of a set of only six equations in its full fractional form would require 720 product terms within each numerator and denominator!

2. There is more to a determinant than we have seen so far – they can be manipulated and simplified, often allowing even determinants of order 5 or 6 to be evaluated readily by hand. Also, larger determinants are presented in a form suitable for direct evaluation by computer.

3. This form of solution separates the unknown variables x, y, z, etc., from the known coefficients in a systematic fashion. As with Gaussian elimination, Cramer's rule is expressed in a form suitable for almost immediate incorporation

142

into a computer program which is capable of evaluating determinants of arbitrary size: the program merely requires $n(n+1)$ data values for the numeric coefficients.

One disadvantage which this form of solution shares with the Gaussian elimination approach is that if the value of even one of the known coefficients is changed then the whole problem must be solved again from the beginning by re-evaluating most of the determinants. Also, problems will arise if the value of any of the determinants happens to be zero.

Expansion of determinants

Having seen the basic definition of a determinant, it must be asked whether there are different (better?) ways of expanding it – are there useful rules which enable simplification?

Consider the third-order determinant defined above

$$|\mathbf{A}| = a_{11}a_{22}a_{33} - a_{11}a_{23}a_{32} + a_{12}a_{23}a_{31} - a_{12}a_{21}a_{33} + a_{13}a_{21}a_{32} - a_{13}a_{22}a_{31}$$

it is possible to gather the terms together to give

$$|\mathbf{A}| = a_{11}(a_{22}a_{33} - a_{23}a_{32}) + a_{12}(a_{23}a_{31} - a_{21}a_{33}) + a_{13}(a_{21}a_{32} - a_{22}a_{31})$$

$$= a_{11}\begin{vmatrix} a_{22} & a_{23} \\ a_{32} & a_{33} \end{vmatrix} - a_{12}\begin{vmatrix} a_{21} & a_{23} \\ a_{31} & a_{33} \end{vmatrix} + a_{13}\begin{vmatrix} a_{21} & a_{22} \\ a_{31} & a_{32} \end{vmatrix}$$

Sarrus's rule is a method for remembering how to expand such a third-order determinant from first principles: simply augment the determinant by writing down its first two columns again:

$$\begin{array}{ccccc} a_{11} & a_{12} & a_{13} & a_{11} & a_{12} \\ a_{21} & a_{22} & a_{23} & a_{21} & a_{22} \\ a_{31} & a_{32} & a_{33} & a_{31} & a_{32} \end{array}$$

then the six arrowed lines define the six terms of the expansion. The upward-pointing arrows lead to the negative terms and the downward-pointing ones give the positive terms. The rule is only valid for third-order determinants.

or $\quad |\mathbf{A}| = a_{11}\begin{vmatrix} a_{22} & a_{23} \\ a_{32} & a_{33} \end{vmatrix} - a_{21}\begin{vmatrix} a_{12} & a_{13} \\ a_{32} & a_{33} \end{vmatrix} + a_{31}\begin{vmatrix} a_{12} & a_{13} \\ a_{22} & a_{23} \end{vmatrix}$

and other, equivalent, expressions. These two expressions are examples of expanding the determinant by the first row and by the first column, respectively. The 2×2 determinant associated with each preceding a_{ij} can be obtained by striking out row i and column j of the original determinant. These 'sub-determinants' are called **minors** and are denoted by M_{ij}.

Therefore, these equations can be written concisely as

$$|\mathbf{A}| = a_{11}M_{11} - a_{12}M_{12} + a_{13}M_{13} = a_{11}M_{11} - a_{21}M_{21} + a_{31}M_{31}$$

To exploit any particular symmetry or structure within the determinant, it is possible to choose to expand by any particular row or column. For instance, for a 3×3 determinant, expanding by the second row would give

$$|\mathbf{A}| = -a_{21}M_{21} + a_{22}M_{22} - a_{23}M_{23}$$

and it is a general result that the sign of the a_{ij} coefficient in the expansion of a determinant of order n is given by $(-1)^{i+j}$: positive if $(i+j)$ is even, and negative if $(i+j)$ is odd. This means that the signs associated with the expansion of a general nth-order determinant follow the rule

$$\begin{vmatrix} + & - & + & - & + & \cdots \cdots \cdots \\ - & + & - & + & \cdots \cdots \cdots \\ + & - & + & \cdots \cdots \cdots \\ - & & & \\ \vdots & \cdots \cdots \cdots \cdots \end{vmatrix}$$

It is common to incorporate the sign variation directly into an object called a **cofactor**, C_{ij}, defined simply by $C_{ij} = (-1)^{i+j}M_{ij}$. In terms of cofactors the expansion of a general nth-order determinant by the ith row takes the form

This can be viewed as a definition of higher-order determinants.

$$|\mathbf{A}| = a_{i1}C_{i1} + a_{i2}C_{i2} + \ldots + a_{in}C_{in} = \sum_{k=1}^{n} a_{ik}C_{ik}$$

A common equivalent definition of a determinant is given by

$$|\mathbf{A}| = \sum_p (-1)^p a_{1i} a_{2j} \ldots a_{nk}$$

where p counts over the $n!$ permutations of the n subscripts $i, j, \ldots, k$ and is ordered so that all even permutations of the subscripts are represented by even values of p and all odd permutations by odd values of p. The theory of permutations and combinations is covered in Chapter T1.

The proofs are given by Jeffrey (1989) and also in many other standard texts on linear algebra.

so that it is possible to define the expansion of arbitrarily large determinants in terms of a summation of a series of lower-order ones – this is known as the **Laplace expansion** of a determinant.

These $2n$ ways (n row expansions and n column expansions) of directly expanding a determinant are very useful if the determinant has several zeros in a particular row or column – the expansion can be chosen that weights as many as possible of the cofactor terms in the above equation with zero values of a_{ik}. This can reduce the workload considerably.

Properties of determinants

The ability to choose how to expand a determinant is very useful, but when the determinant does not actually have many (or any) zero elements little or no advantage may be gained. It is necessary to ask whether there are any other ways to modify or simplify the expansion of the determinant.

Certain basic rules for manipulating determinants can be deduced readily from the general definitions above. The results are:

1. The multiplication of all of the elements of any one row or column of the determinant by a scale factor of λ will merely multiply the overall value of the determinant by λ. For example:

$$\begin{vmatrix} 4 & 5 \\ 3 & 4 \end{vmatrix} = 16 - 15 = 1 \text{ while } \begin{vmatrix} 12 & 5 \\ 9 & 4 \end{vmatrix} = 48 - 45 = 3$$

since the first columns of each are related by a factor of 3.

2. If a row or column contains only zero elements then the determinant is zero.

3. Interchanging all of the elements of any two rows (or any two columns) of a determinant flips the sign of the determinant. For example:

$$\begin{vmatrix} 1 & 3 & 1 \\ 9 & 4 & 1 \\ 12 & 2 & 3 \end{vmatrix} = -65 \text{ (check!) while } \begin{vmatrix} 12 & 2 & 3 \\ 9 & 4 & 1 \\ 1 & 3 & 1 \end{vmatrix} = 65$$

4. The previous result implies that if any two rows (or two columns) of the determinant are identical, then the value of the determinant is zero (since interchanging the identical rows/columns would change the sign but leave the determinant looking the same!).

   As a corollary to this result, it follows that the Laplace expansion of a determinant by the ith row (or column) will give a zero result if the cofactors employed are those appropriate to a different row or column. That is,

$$\sum_{k=1}^{n} a_{ik} C_{lk} = 0$$

if $i \neq l$. This can be combined with the specific Laplace expansion to give the more general expressions

$$\sum_{k=1}^{n} a_{ik} C_{lk} = \delta_{il} |\mathbf{A}|$$

and

$$\sum_{k=1}^{n} a_{kj} C_{kl} = \delta_{jl} |\mathbf{A}|$$

for expansion by the ith row and jth column respectively. These results can be verified easily by writing out the determinants in full. It will be seen that unless the cofactors and their coefficients are synchronized the determinant will contain two rows or columns which are entirely identical.

5. The addition of a multiple of any row (or column) to any other row (or column) leaves the value of the determinant unchanged.
6. Rules 2 and 5 mean that if any row (or column) may be expressed as a linear combination of all of the other rows (or columns), then the determinant must be zero. It is possible to say that if the determinant of n vectors of order n is zero then those vectors form a linearly dependent set (and vice versa).

Rule 6 means that it is possible to test immediately whether a set of equations will have a unique solution, since it has already been stated that a set of n linearly independent equations in n unknowns will produce a single, well-defined solution, while dependent equations will generate either an infinite family of solutions or (if the coefficients on the r.h.s. contradict the form of the dependence on the l.h.s.) no possible solution at all. Therefore, only if

$$|\Delta| = \begin{vmatrix} a_{11} & a_{12} & a_{13} & a_{14} & \cdots & \cdots & \cdots & a_{1n} \\ a_{21} & a_{22} & a_{23} & \cdots & \cdots & \cdots & \cdots & a_{2n} \\ a_{31} & a_{32} & \cdots & \cdots & \cdots & \cdots & \cdots & \cdots \\ \cdots & \cdots & \cdots & \cdots & \cdots & \cdots & \cdots & \cdots \\ a_{n1} & \cdots & \cdots & \cdots & \cdots & \cdots & \cdots & a_{nn} \end{vmatrix}$$

is nonzero can there be a unique solution. If $|\Delta|$ is zero then there are either an infinite number of solutions or no solution at all.

The magnitude of the determinant of coefficients of the equations is a broad measure of the linear independence of the n row vectors of which it is composed. A zero value of the determinant means that at least two of the vectors are dependent and that, correspondingly, the planes which they represent intersect in parallel lines: hence there is either no solution, or an infinity if the lines coincide. A very small value of the determinant means that some of the planes are very nearly dependent and, correspondingly, some of the lines of intersection will meet with very small angles: as discussed above, such equations will be ill-conditioned. A somewhat larger value of the determinant will mean that the vectors are more clearly independent, the intersection lines meet at less acute angles and hence the equations are well-conditioned.

Functional determinants

There is no reason why the elements of a determinant should be restricted to be real numbers, or even to be numbers at all. A determinant may have elements that are functions of some parameter, such as time, and which represent the changing nature of the set of equations associated with the determinant with relation to the parameter. Note that the form of the functional coefficients does not have any effect on the linearity of the equations: the n unknown variables still appear in a linear fashion. Determinants with non-constant elements can be expanded or manipulated in exactly the same fashion as discussed above.

Other situations can arise when the elements of a determinant are not merely numbers. In particular, the solution of many engineering problems requires the evaluation of a determinant dependent on a variable λ, which takes the form

$$\begin{vmatrix} a_{11}-\lambda & a_{12} & a_{13} & a_{14} & \cdots & \cdots & \cdots & a_{1n} \\ a_{21} & a_{22}-\lambda & a_{23} & \cdots & \cdots & \cdots & \cdots & a_{2n} \\ a_{31} & a_{32} & \cdots & \cdots & \cdots & \cdots & \cdots & \cdots \\ \cdots & \cdots & \cdots & \cdots & \cdots & \cdots & \cdots & \cdots \\ a_{n1} & \cdots & \cdots & \cdots & \cdots & \cdots & \cdots & a_{nn}-\lambda \end{vmatrix}$$

Indeed, it is true that addition of a general linear combination of any set of rows $\{\mathbf{r}_k\}$ to row $\mathbf{r}_i$ $(i \neq k)$ produces a new row $\mathbf{r}_i'$ given by

$$\mathbf{r}_i' = \mathbf{r}_i + \sum_{k \neq i} c_k \mathbf{r}_k$$

which still leaves the value of the determinant unchanged. A similar result holds for the columns.

When referring to the 'magnitude' of the determinant it must be realized that the determinant can be scaled to any desired figure by multiplying each equation by a constant: it is the size of the determinant relative to the range of values of the coefficients that is important. As a broad rule, if the equations are scaled so that the largest coefficient in each is unity, then a determinant that is also near unity means that the equations are well-conditioned, while a very much smaller determinant is a sign of ill-conditioning.

This is a special case of a one-parameter functional determinant. If, as here, all of the elements of a determinant are composed of linear functions of a single variable or constant coefficients then, when expanded, a polynomial of order n (at most) will result.

145

which is sometimes called a **characteristic determinant**. Such a determinant arises in the theory of eigenvalue analysis, discussed briefly below.

Matrices

Definition of a matrix

The usual definition of a matrix is as an $m \times n$ block of numbers or functions written as a rectangular array:

$$\mathbf{A} = \begin{bmatrix} a_{11} & a_{12} & a_{13} & a_{14} & \cdots & \cdots & \cdots & a_{1n} \\ a_{21} & a_{22} & a_{23} & \cdots & \cdots & \cdots & \cdots & a_{2n} \\ a_{31} & a_{32} & \cdots & \cdots & \cdots & \cdots & \cdots & \cdots \\ \cdots & \cdots & \cdots & \cdots & \cdots & \cdots & \cdots & \cdots \\ a_{m1} & \cdots & \cdots & \cdots & \cdots & \cdots & \cdots & a_{mn} \end{bmatrix} = (a_{ij})$$

with m rows and n columns, the element in the ith row and jth column being a_{ij} and the notation (a_{ij}) often being used as a shorthand notation for the whole matrix, as indicated above. At first, this definition may look rather like that given for a determinant, but there are two important differences: firstly, a determinant was only defined for a square block of $n \times n$ numbers while a matrix can be any size of rectangle; and secondly, a determinant is a single number/function which is calculated from the given block of numbers/functions while a matrix is the ordered block of numbers/functions in its entirety.

Matrices, linear equations and vectors: matrix algebra

The definition of a set of operations for manipulating sets of abstract objects such as matrices creates what mathematicians call an **algebra**. The combination of the definition of the internal structure of a matrix as a block of numbers/functions together with a set of rules for combining matrices with each other, or with other objects such as vectors and scalars, creates the topic of **matrix algebra**.

If one accepts that a 1×1 matrix is merely an ordinary number, then this definition is sensible in that it is consistent with ordinary arithmetic. Likewise, matrix addition and vector addition are consistent if a $1 \times n$ matrix is identified with a row vector and an $n \times 1$ matrix with a column vector.

The theory of matrices dates back to the mid-nineteenth century and developed originally from the study of systems of linear equations.

Generally, the rules for operating on any mathematical object are determined by the uses to which that operation is going to be put: they must reflect the desired properties of the particular method and yet also be internally consistent and mathematically reasonable.

With regard to a definition for addition of matrices, an obvious and sensible formula is used and the sum of two matrices (a_{ij}) and (b_{ij}) is given by

$$(a_{ij}) + (b_{ij}) = \begin{bmatrix} a_{11} & a_{12} & \cdots \\ a_{21} & a_{22} & \cdots \\ \cdots & \cdots & \cdots \end{bmatrix} + \begin{bmatrix} b_{11} & b_{12} & \cdots \\ b_{21} & b_{22} & \cdots \\ \cdots & \cdots & \cdots \end{bmatrix}$$

$$= \begin{bmatrix} a_{11}+b_{11} & a_{12}+b_{12} & \cdots \\ a_{21}+b_{21} & a_{22}+b_{22} & \cdots \\ \cdots & \cdots & \cdots \end{bmatrix} = (a_{ij} + b_{ij})$$

providing that (a_{ij}) and (b_{ij}) are both $m \times n$ matrices, in which case they are said to be **conformable for addition** (else they are **inconformable**). It is thus meaningless to attempt to add a 3×3 matrix to a 4×2 one.

Just as with the definitions of the expansion of a determinant, the multiplication rules for matrices are based on their application within the field of linear equations. As discussed above, it is possible to view any set of linear equations:

$$a_{11} x_1 + a_{12} x_2 + \ldots + a_{1n} x_n = k_1$$
$$a_{21} x_1 + a_{22} x_2 + \ldots + a_{2n} x_n = k_2$$
$$\vdots \qquad \vdots \qquad \vdots \qquad \vdots$$
$$a_{m1} x_1 + a_{m2} x_2 + \ldots + a_{mn} x_n = k_m$$

146

as the equations of planes which can expressed more compactly in vector form as

More correctly, these are the equations of hyperplanes in *n*-dimensional space.

$$\mathbf{a}_1^T \mathbf{v} = k_1$$
$$\mathbf{a}_2^T \mathbf{v} = k_2$$
$$. \quad . \quad . \quad .$$
$$. \quad . \quad . \quad .$$
$$\mathbf{a}_m^T \mathbf{v} = k_m$$

where the coefficients are gathered into m row vectors of order n,

$$\mathbf{a}_i^T = (a_{i1}, a_{i2}, ..., a_{in})$$

and $\mathbf{v}$ is a column vector of the n variables. Matrices were originally designed to improve further on this, fairly compact, way of expressing the equations by gathering the m row vectors into an object which operated on a single column vector of variables and produced a column vector of the r.h.s. coefficients k_i:

$$\begin{bmatrix} \mathbf{a}_1^T \\ \mathbf{a}_2^T \\ ... \\ \mathbf{a}_m^T \end{bmatrix} \mathbf{v} = \begin{bmatrix} k_1 \\ k_2 \\ .. \\ k_m \end{bmatrix}$$

The bracketed object on the l.h.s. contains m row vectors of order n which, when written in full, is merely the $m \times n$ block of coefficients of the original equations:

$$\begin{bmatrix} a_{11} & a_{12} & a_{13} & a_{14} & ... & ... & ... & a_{1n} \\ a_{21} & a_{22} & a_{23} & ... & ... & ... & ... & a_{2n} \\ a_{31} & a_{32} & ... & ... & ... & ... & ... & ... \\ ... & ... & ... & ... & ... & ... & ... & ... \\ a_{m1} & ... & ... & ... & ... & ... & ... & a_{mn} \end{bmatrix} \begin{bmatrix} x_1 \\ x_2 \\ x_3 \\ .. \\ x_n \end{bmatrix} = \begin{bmatrix} k_1 \\ k_2 \\ k_3 \\ .. \\ k_m \end{bmatrix}$$

The requirement that this product of the **matrix of coefficients** and the **vector of unknown variables** should produce a column vector of the coefficients from the r.h.s. of the equations acts as a definition of the usual form of **premultiplication of a column vector by a matrix**. Such premultiplication by an $m \times n$ matrix is only possible if the column vector is of order n; if this is so a new column vector of order m is the result of the operation:

A matrix with $n \times n$ elements is a square matrix order n.

$$\begin{bmatrix} a_{11} & a_{12} & ... & a_{1n} \\ a_{21} & a_{22} & ... & a_{2n} \\ ... & ... & ... & ... \\ a_{m1} & ... & ... & a_{mn} \end{bmatrix} \begin{bmatrix} b_1 \\ b_2 \\ .. \\ b_n \end{bmatrix} = \begin{bmatrix} a_{11}b_1 + a_{12}b_2 + ... + a_{1n}b_n \\ a_{21}b_1 + a_{22}b_2 + ... + a_{2n}b_n \\ ... & ... & ... & ... \\ a_{m1}b_1 + a_{m2}b_2 + ... + a_{mn}b_n \end{bmatrix}$$

Thus, if $\mathbf{b}$ and $\mathbf{c}$ are column vectors of order n and m respectively, and $\mathbf{A}$ is an $m \times n$ matrix, then we can summarize all of this equation as

$$\mathbf{A}\,\mathbf{b} = \mathbf{c}$$

where the m elements of $\mathbf{c}$ are given by

$$c_i = \sum_{j=1}^{n} a_{ij} b_j \qquad i = 1,2,...,m$$

As already discussed, it is also possible to think of the matrix as being composed of m, n-dimensional row vectors $\mathbf{a}_i^T$ ($i = 1,2,...,m$) arranged in a column

$$\mathbf{A} = \begin{bmatrix} \mathbf{a}_1^T \\ \mathbf{a}_2^T \\ ... \\ \mathbf{a}_m^T \end{bmatrix}$$

It is also possible to partition a matrix into columns or subsidiary blocks of numbers. Such partitioning is a useful approach for exploiting any internal structure of a matrix (such as a block of zeros) or for examining the transfer characteristics of a particular subsystem within a circuit, for example.

This is known as **partitioning** of the matrix into rows. With this partitioning the definition of matrix multiplication can be written compactly as

$$\mathbf{A}\,\mathbf{b} = \begin{bmatrix} \mathbf{a}_1^{\mathrm{T}} \\ \mathbf{a}_2^{\mathrm{T}} \\ \ldots \\ \mathbf{a}_m^{\mathrm{T}} \end{bmatrix} \mathbf{b} = \begin{bmatrix} \mathbf{a}_1^{\mathrm{T}}\mathbf{b} \\ \mathbf{a}_2^{\mathrm{T}}\mathbf{b} \\ \ldots \\ \mathbf{a}_m^{\mathrm{T}}\mathbf{b} \end{bmatrix}$$

so that the elements of the $\mathbf{c}$ vector can be interpreted as ordinary vector dot products.

Multiplication of a matrix by another matrix follows as a natural extension of the previous rules by considering the second matrix as being partitioned into column vectors:

$$\mathbf{A}\,\mathbf{B} = \begin{bmatrix} \mathbf{a}_1^{\mathrm{T}} \\ \mathbf{a}_2^{\mathrm{T}} \\ \ldots \\ \mathbf{a}_m^{\mathrm{T}} \end{bmatrix} (\mathbf{b}_1, \mathbf{b}_2, \ldots, \mathbf{b}_p) = \begin{bmatrix} \mathbf{a}_1^{\mathrm{T}}\mathbf{b}_1 & \mathbf{a}_1^{\mathrm{T}}\mathbf{b}_2 & \ldots & \mathbf{a}_1^{\mathrm{T}}\mathbf{b}_p \\ \mathbf{a}_2^{\mathrm{T}}\mathbf{b}_1 & \mathbf{a}_2^{\mathrm{T}}\mathbf{b}_2 & \ldots & \ldots \\ \ldots & \ldots & \ldots & \ldots \\ \mathbf{a}_m^{\mathrm{T}}\mathbf{b}_1 & \ldots & \ldots & \mathbf{a}_m^{\mathrm{T}}\mathbf{b}_p \end{bmatrix}$$

so that if $\mathbf{A}\,\mathbf{B} = \mathbf{C}$, or $(a_{ij})(b_{ij}) = (c_{ij})$, then

$$c_{ij} = \mathbf{a}_i^{\mathrm{T}}\mathbf{b}_j = \sum_{k=1}^{n} a_{ik}\,b_{kj}$$

These statements are sensible only if the first matrix is $m \times n$ in form and the second matrix is $n \times p$ – the second matrix must have the same number of rows as the first has columns. If this is so then the matrices are said to be **conformable for multiplication** and the resulting matrix will possess m rows and p columns. It is important to note that, in general, matrix multiplication is **non-commutative**:

$$\mathbf{A}\,\mathbf{B} \neq \mathbf{B}\,\mathbf{A}$$

In fact, if $\mathbf{A}$ is $m \times n$ and $\mathbf{B}$ is $n \times p$ the product on the l.h.s. can be evaluated without difficulty, while the product on the r.h.s. does not exist at all.

Matrix definitions and properties

Having defined how to add and multiply two matrices or multiply a matrix and a vector, it is necessary to list some common special types of matrix that can occur.

Firstly, the $n \times n$ matrix

$$\Lambda = \begin{bmatrix} \lambda_1 & 0 & 0 & 0 & 0 & . & . & 0 \\ 0 & \lambda_2 & 0 & 0 & . & . & . & . \\ 0 & 0 & \lambda_3 & . & . & . & . & . \\ . & . & . & . & . & . & . & . \\ 0 & . & . & . & . & . & . & \lambda_n \end{bmatrix}$$

is known as a **diagonal** matrix. When all of the diagonal elements λ_i are unity, this matrix is known as the **unit matrix** of order n and is usually denoted by I. When an $m \times n$ matrix is premultiplied by an order m unit matrix or is postmultiplied by an order n unit matrix the original matrix is left unchanged. I is the matrix equivalent of the number 1 as regards the operation of multiplication. Similarly, the **zero matrix** (or **null matrix**) has all of its elements identically equal to zero and is the matrix equivalent to the number 0 as regards addition.

The diagonal matrix with all of the λ_i equal to the same constant value, λ, has the effect of multiplying every individual element of the matrix by λ, so that, for example,

$$\begin{bmatrix} 3 & 0 \\ 0 & 3 \end{bmatrix} \begin{bmatrix} 1 & 3 \\ 2 & 1 \end{bmatrix} = \begin{bmatrix} 3 & 9 \\ 6 & 3 \end{bmatrix}$$

This is the matrix analogue of multiplication by a scalar and is often written as $\lambda \mathbf{A}$. Note that in this particular case it does not matter whether the diagonal matrix premultiplies or postmultiplies the other matrix – the effect is exactly the same.

Premultiplying any matrix $\mathbf{A}$ by the above general diagonal matrix $\mathbf{\Lambda}$ will have the effect of multiplying all of the elements of row i of $\mathbf{A}$ by the factor λ_i. Postmultiplication multiplies all elements of column j by λ_j.

A $1 \times n$ matrix can be thought of as equivalent to a row vector and likewise an $n \times 1$ matrix as a column vector. It is thus possible to consider the product of a $1 \times n$ matrix and an $n \times 1$ matrix as being an analogue of the vector dot (or inner) product (see Chapter 2). It follows that it is now possible to define the product of a column vector ($n \times 1$ matrix) and a row vector ($1 \times n$ matrix) as producing an $n \times n$ matrix. For example,

$$\begin{bmatrix} 1 \\ 2 \\ 3 \end{bmatrix} (1 \quad 1 \quad 2) = \begin{bmatrix} 1 & 1 & 2 \\ 2 & 2 & 4 \\ 3 & 3 & 6 \end{bmatrix}$$

whereas $(1 \quad 1 \quad 2) \begin{bmatrix} 1 \\ 2 \\ 3 \end{bmatrix} = 1 + 2 + 6 = 9$

This makes it clear that matrix algebra includes as special cases the entire algebra of ordinary numbers, vector addition and the vector dot product. Matrix algebra is more general, and more powerful, than each of these methods in isolation.

It is also possible to premultiply an $m \times n$ matrix by an mth-order row vector and produce an nth-order row vector.

Matrix transposition

Another concept that transfers directly from vectors into matrices is the transposition of column vectors into row vectors as discussed in Chapter T2. The **transpose** of a matrix $\mathbf{A} = (a_{ij})$ is defined by $\mathbf{A}^T = (a_{ji})$, or in full

$$\mathbf{A} = \begin{bmatrix} a_{11} & a_{12} & \cdots & a_{1n} \\ a_{21} & a_{22} & \cdots & a_{2n} \\ \cdots & \cdots & \cdots & \cdots \\ a_{m1} & \cdots & \cdots & a_{mn} \end{bmatrix} \Rightarrow \mathbf{A}^T = \begin{bmatrix} a_{11} & a_{21} & \cdots & a_{m1} \\ a_{12} & a_{22} & \cdots & a_{m2} \\ \cdots & \cdots & \cdots & \cdots \\ a_{1n} & a_{2n} & \cdots & a_{mn} \end{bmatrix}$$

Clearly, an $m \times n$ matrix transposes into an $n \times m$ one, and a second transposition returns the matrix to its original form:

$$(\mathbf{A}^T)^T = \mathbf{A}$$

A less obvious, but important, result is

$$(\mathbf{A}\,\mathbf{B})^T = \mathbf{B}^T \mathbf{A}^T$$

Jeffrey (1989), amongst others, gives a short proof.

The structure of the matrix as regards transposition also often merits some special definitions. A **symmetric matrix** is one which satisfies $\mathbf{A}^T = \mathbf{A}$ (or $a_{ij} = a_{ji}$ for all i, j). Similarly an **antisymmetric** (or **skewsymmetric**) **matrix** satisfies $\mathbf{A}^T = -\mathbf{A}$ (or $a_{ij} = -a_{ji}$) For example,

A skewsymmetric matrix must have zero elements along the diagonal.

$$\begin{bmatrix} 1 & 2 & 7 & 4 \\ 2 & 0 & 3 & 2 \\ 7 & 3 & -1 & -2 \\ 4 & 2 & -2 & 4 \end{bmatrix} \quad \text{and} \quad \begin{bmatrix} 0 & 9 & 4 \\ -9 & 0 & 7 \\ -4 & -7 & 0 \end{bmatrix}$$

are symmetric and antisymmetric respectively.

As has already been discussed briefly in Chapter 2, complex variables are useful for describing the behaviour of simple circuits involving time-varying sinusoidal currents. Similarly, complex matrices prove helpful in the description of circuit networks involving time-dependent sources.

Other special types of matrix

A **complex matrix**, naturally enough, contains complex numbers or functions as its elements and, in particular, an **imaginary matrix** contains only purely imaginary elements. With a complex matrix it is sensible to talk about a **complex conjugate matrix A***, just as with complex numbers, where every element of $\mathbf{A}^*$ is the complex conjugate of the corresponding element of $\mathbf{A}$. Thus,

$$\text{If} \quad \mathbf{A} = \begin{bmatrix} 1 & j \\ 2+j & 3 \end{bmatrix} \quad \text{then} \quad \mathbf{A}^* = \begin{bmatrix} 1 & -j \\ 2-j & 3 \end{bmatrix}$$

The **Hermitian transpose** of a complex matrix is defined by taking both the operations of complex conjugation and transposition:

$$\mathbf{A}^H = (\mathbf{A}^*)^T = (\mathbf{A}^T)^*$$

As for real matrices, certain forms of complex matrices are given special names, and all of the most important types are summarized below:

A **real matrix** satisfies $\mathbf{A}^* = \mathbf{A}$.
A **real symmetric matrix** satisfies $\mathbf{A}^T = \mathbf{A}$.
A **real antisymmetric (skewsymmetric) matrix** satisfies $\mathbf{A}^T = -\mathbf{A}$.
A **Hermitian matrix** satisfies $\mathbf{A}^H = \mathbf{A}$.
An **antihermitian (skewhermitian) matrix** satisfies $\mathbf{A}^H = -\mathbf{A}$.
An **imaginary matrix** satisfies $\mathbf{A}^* = -\mathbf{A}$.
An **orthogonal matrix** satisfies $\mathbf{A}^T \mathbf{A} = \mathbf{A}\mathbf{A}^T = I$.
An **unitary matrix** satisfies $\mathbf{A}^H \mathbf{A} = \mathbf{A}\mathbf{A}^H = I$.

Some other special structures that can arise include triangular matrices and banded matrices. An **upper triangular matrix** contains only zero elements below its main diagonal; a **lower triangular matrix** contains only zero elements above its main diagonal; and a **banded matrix** contains zero elements everywhere except along a diagonal strip centred around the main diagonal.

Determinant and trace of a matrix

This is why the notation |**A**| was used earlier for determinants, the vertical lines signifying the determinant of the $n \times n$ block of numbers associated with the matrix **A**.

Determinants have been shown to have utility value in their own right. But when square matrices are being used it is also sensible to refer to the **determinant of the matrix** – the determinant being defined exactly as before for the square array of numbers or functions from which the matrix is formed. Certain useful results are straightforward to prove:

1. The determinant of Λ, the diagonal matrix defined above is $\prod_{i=1}^{n} \lambda_i$
2. $|I| = 1$
3. $|\mathbf{A}\mathbf{B}| = |\mathbf{A}||\mathbf{B}| = |\mathbf{B}\mathbf{A}|$

A further property of square matrices that will crop up in several applications is the **trace** of a matrix – defined simply as the sum of the diagonal elements:

$$\text{Tr}(\mathbf{A}) = \sum_{i=1}^{n} a_{ii}$$

It can be shown that:
1. $\text{Tr}(\mathbf{A} + \mathbf{B}) = \text{Tr}(\mathbf{A}) + \text{Tr}(\mathbf{B})$
2. $\text{Tr}(\mathbf{A}\mathbf{B}) = \text{Tr}(\mathbf{B}\mathbf{A})$
3. $\text{Tr}(\mathbf{A}\mathbf{B}) \neq \text{Tr}(\mathbf{A})\text{Tr}(\mathbf{B})$

Adjoint and inverse matrices

The last few pages have done little more than list nomenclature which will be found in many texts and research papers, but when it comes to actually using matrices one major topic is yet to be covered – how can the equation $\mathbf{A}\,\mathbf{x} = \mathbf{b}$ generally be solved for the unknown vector $\mathbf{x}$ if $\mathbf{A}$ and $\mathbf{b}$ are given? Is it valid to attempt to divide by $\mathbf{A}$?

It turns out that matrix division as such is not feasible, but for a square matrix $\mathbf{A}$ it is usually possible to define a unique **inverse matrix** $\mathbf{A}^{-1}$ that satisfies the relationship $\mathbf{A}\,\mathbf{A}^{-1} = \mathbf{A}^{-1}\,\mathbf{A} = I$ so that

$$\mathbf{A}\,\mathbf{x} = \mathbf{b} \quad \Rightarrow \quad I\,x = \mathbf{A}^{-1}\,\mathbf{b} \quad \Rightarrow \quad \mathbf{x} = \mathbf{A}^{-1}\,\mathbf{b}$$

by premultiplying both sides by the inverse matrix. It is possible to calculate systematically the inverse matrix using determinants alone. The Laplace expansion of a determinant, defined earlier in this chapter, means that if we construct the **adjoint matrix**, defined by

$$\text{adj}(\mathbf{A}) = \begin{bmatrix} C_{11} & C_{12} & C_{13} & C_{14} & \cdots & \cdots & \cdots & C_{1n} \\ C_{21} & C_{22} & C_{23} & \cdots & \cdots & \cdots & \cdots & C_{2n} \\ C_{31} & C_{32} & \cdots & \cdots & \cdots & \cdots & \cdots & \cdots \\ \cdots & \cdots & \cdots & \cdots & \cdots & \cdots & \cdots & \cdots \\ C_{n1} & \cdots & \cdots & \cdots & \cdots & \cdots & \cdots & C_{nn} \end{bmatrix}^{\mathrm{T}}$$

whose elements are the cofactors of the corresponding elements of $\mathbf{A}$, then it has the property that

$$\mathbf{A}\,\text{adj}(\mathbf{A}) = \text{adj}(\mathbf{A})\,\mathbf{A} = |\mathbf{A}|\,I$$

a result which follows from the earlier statement that

$$\sum_{k=1}^{n} a_{ik}\,C_{lk} = \delta_{il}\,|\mathbf{A}|$$

From this it is clear that the inverse matrix to $\mathbf{A}$ can be defined uniquely by

$$\mathbf{A}^{-1} = \text{adj}(\mathbf{A})/|\mathbf{A}|$$

providing that $|\mathbf{A}|$ is not equal to zero.

Note that the inverse of a product of two matrices is given by the expression

$$(\mathbf{A}\,\mathbf{B})^{-1} = \mathbf{B}^{-1}\,\mathbf{A}^{-1}$$

This follows from the observation that

$$(\mathbf{A}\,\mathbf{B})(\mathbf{B}^{-1}\,\mathbf{A}^{-1}) = \mathbf{A}\,(\mathbf{B}\,\mathbf{B}^{-1})\,\mathbf{A}^{-1} = \mathbf{A}\,I\,\mathbf{A}^{-1} = \mathbf{A}\,\mathbf{A}^{-1} = I$$

Direct evaluation of the cofactors and the determinant is one way of calculating inverse matrices. An alternative approach which involves rather less computational effort is to perform a series of elementary operations on the matrix.

If $|\mathbf{A}| = 0$ then the inverse is not defined. In such a case the matrix has no inverse and the set of linear equations which the matrix represents has no unique solution.

Equivalent matrices and elementary operations

Above, an inverse matrix has been defined directly in terms of an adjoint matrix whose elements are sub-determinants of the original matrix. For matrices of order two or three this definition is enough to allow the hand calculation of an inverse matrix. For larger systems, however, the evaluation of many determinants is an extremely time-consuming and error-prone process, and renders such an approach practically unfeasible. Fortunately, a useful and rapid approach is available, based on a sequence of elementary transformations.

A and **B** are **equivalent** matrices if **B** can be obtained from **A** by a series of elementary transformations:
1. Interchange two rows or columns.
2. Multiply a row or column by a nonzero scalar.
3. Add a multiple of one row (or column) to another row (or column).

Equivalence is denoted by the symbol $\sim$. For example

$$\begin{bmatrix} 1 & 2 & -1 & 4 \\ 2 & 4 & 3 & 5 \\ -1 & -2 & 6 & -7 \end{bmatrix} \sim \begin{bmatrix} 1 & 2 & -1 & 4 \\ 0 & 0 & 5 & -3 \\ -1 & -2 & 6 & -7 \end{bmatrix} \sim \begin{bmatrix} 1 & 2 & -1 & 4 \\ 0 & 0 & 5 & -3 \\ 0 & 0 & 5 & -3 \end{bmatrix}$$

For example, the elementary matrix

$$\begin{bmatrix} 0 & 1 & 0 \\ 1 & 0 & 0 \\ 0 & 0 & 1 \end{bmatrix}$$

interchanges the first and second rows when it pre-multiplies any given $3 \times n$ matrix.

The elementary transformations 1–3 listed above can all be produced by multiplying the matrix of interest by a simple **elementary matrix** which has the desired effect. This provides yet another way of solving systematically sets of linear equations and inverting matrices.

Suppose that the problem is to solve the matrix equation $\mathbf{A}\,\mathbf{x} = \mathbf{b}$; where **A** is $n \times n$, then write down in full the **augmented matrix** $(\mathbf{A}\,|\,\mathbf{b}\,|\,\mathbf{I})$, which is of order $n \times (2n + 1)$. If this new matrix is operated on with a series of elementary transformations that reduce the first submatrix, **A**, to the identity matrix, then the overall effect is to produce

$$\mathbf{A}^{-1}(\mathbf{A}\,|\,\mathbf{b}\,|\,I) = (I\,|\,\mathbf{x}\,|\,\mathbf{A}^{-1})$$

so that this new matrix contains the solution to the set of equations and the matrix inverse. In application the method is similar to Gaussian elimination, but expressed in a matrix form. It is usually a more suitable approach for rapid and error-free hand calculations. A worked example appears in Chapter 3, p. 52.

Rank and linear dependence

A common definition of the **rank** of a matrix is the order of the largest nonzero determinant that can be obtained by deleting rows and columns from the matrix. This is not necessarily enlightening at first glance, but basically, rank is a measure of the degree of dependence of the vectors that build up the matrix. It is equally valid to define rank as a number of linearly independent row vectors (or, equivalently, column vectors) within the matrix.

For an $m \times n$ matrix **A**, rank(**A**) $\leqslant$ minimum(m, n), since the rank cannot be greater than the lesser dimension of the matrix.

For square matrices, the matrix is called **singular** if rank(**A**) $< n$, while if rank(**A**) $= n$ the matrix is **nonsingular**. It follows that, for an $n \times n$ matrix **A** the following statements are all equivalent:
1. The n row vectors are linearly independent.
2. The n column vectors are linearly independent.
3. $|\mathbf{A}| \neq 0$.
4. **A** is nonsingular.
5. rank(**A**) $= n$.
6. The n in homogeneous linear equations which produce **A** have a unique solution.

Least squares solution of linear equations

The equation $\mathbf{A}\,\mathbf{x} = \mathbf{b}$, with **A** an $m \times n$ matrix does not usually have an exact solution if $m > n$. The equations are overdetermined, and will very likely be inconsistent with each other. However, it is possible to define a 'best' solution of this set of equations by demanding the answer which minimizes the quantity

$$S = \sum_{i=1}^{m} \left[\sum_{j=1}^{n} a_{ij} x_j - b_i \right]^2$$

The expression in the square brackets gives, row by row, the amount by which the proposed solution fails to satisfy the equation corresponding to that row. S thus gives the sum of the squares of all such errors. It is possible to determine analytically the optimum solution which minimizes S and show that the **least squares solution** is given by

$$\mathbf{x}_{ls} = (\mathbf{A}^T \mathbf{A})^{-1} \mathbf{A}^T \mathbf{b}$$

This expression is based on one particular definition of what is the 'best' type of approximate solution. Other, more exotic, definitions do exist, but nearly all are based on minimizing some norm or cost function which defines a consistent criteria for 'distance' from the correct solution. Chapter 3 contains an example of this useful formula in action in a practical application.

Linear transformations

When the vectors upon which square matrices act represent points in two- or three-dimensional Cartesian space, it is common to refer to the matrix operation as representing a **linear transformation**. These transformations can rotate, reflect, stretch, shear and distort objects or curves visualized in the appropriate coordinate system. The important property of these linear transformations is that a straight line will always be transformed into another straight line.

This statement can be proved by noting that the vector equation of a line is given by

$$\begin{bmatrix} x \\ y \end{bmatrix} = \mathbf{r} = \mathbf{p} + \lambda \mathbf{q}$$

in a plane, so that operation with a 2×2 matrix $\mathbf{A}$ will produce a new equation

$$\mathbf{r}' = \mathbf{A}\,\mathbf{r} = \mathbf{p}' + \lambda \mathbf{q}'$$

with new vectors $\mathbf{p}' = \mathbf{A}\,\mathbf{p}$ and $\mathbf{q}' = \mathbf{A}\,\mathbf{q}$. This is simply the equation of a new line.

Some useful types of transformation matrices include

$\begin{bmatrix} a & 0 \\ 0 & d \end{bmatrix}$ scale by a in the X-direction and d in the Y.

$\begin{bmatrix} \cos \alpha & -\sin \alpha \\ \sin \alpha & \cos \alpha \end{bmatrix}$ rotate object by an angle α.

$\begin{bmatrix} 1 & b \\ 0 & 1 \end{bmatrix}$ shear along the X-axis by a factor b.

$\begin{bmatrix} 1 & 0 \\ 0 & -1 \end{bmatrix}$ reflection in the X-axis.

$\begin{bmatrix} 0 & 1 \\ 1 & 0 \end{bmatrix}$ reflection in the line $y = x$.

These matrices can be combined to produce more complicated effects. For example, a reflection in the line making an angle θ with the X-axis can be achieved by the steps:
1. Rotate the entire plane through an angle $-\theta$ to make the line coincide with the X-axis.
2. Carry out a reflection in the X-axis.
3. Rotate the entire plane through an angle θ to replace the reflection line in its original position.

Norm may be thought of as a mathematical generalization of length. It is usual to think of the length of a vector (x, y, z) as being $(x^2 + y^2 + z^2)^{1/2}$. This concept can be extended to n dimensions by defining the norm of the vector as being the square root of the sum of the squares of all n elements – giving a consistent measure of n-dimensional 'length'.

Mathematically, these transformations are **mappings**: they map one object in the plane into another.

Consider the consecutive effects of these operations on the vector of a general point in the plane:

$$\begin{bmatrix} x_{\text{new}} \\ y_{\text{new}} \end{bmatrix} = \begin{bmatrix} \cos\theta & -\sin\theta \\ \sin\theta & \cos\theta \end{bmatrix} \begin{bmatrix} 1 & 0 \\ 0 & -1 \end{bmatrix} \begin{bmatrix} \cos(-\theta) & -\sin(-\theta) \\ \sin(-\theta) & \cos(-\theta) \end{bmatrix} \begin{bmatrix} x \\ y \end{bmatrix}$$

$$\qquad\qquad \uparrow \qquad\qquad\qquad \uparrow \qquad\qquad\qquad\qquad \uparrow$$

$$\text{second rotation} \quad \text{reflection} \qquad\quad \text{first rotation}$$

Note that the matrices are written in reverse order to that in which the operations are carried out: it is the matrix which is nearest to the vector to be transformed which is first in the sequence of operation. These three matrices can be multiplied together to show that a single 2×2 matrix which reflects objects in the plane in the line which makes an angle of θ with the X-axis is:

$$\begin{bmatrix} \cos(2\theta) & \sin(2\theta) \\ \sin(2\theta) & -\cos(2\theta) \end{bmatrix} \qquad \text{reflection in the line } y = x\tan\theta.$$

Any linear transformation will map a pair of parallel lines into another pair of parallel lines. Hence, a rectangle will generally be transformed into a parallelogram. Also, it can be shown that a circle will become an ellipse. When a 2×2 matrix transforms any closed object such as these, the determinant of the matrix will govern the relative areas of the original and transformed objects. In particular, the determinant of any rotation matrix, which leaves areas unaltered, is unity, while the determinant of any reflection matrix, which reverses the areas of objects, is minus one.

Similar matrices exist for three-dimensional cases, and in particular the matrix which rotates an object through an angle θ around the axis defined by the unit vector (l, m, n) is

$$\begin{bmatrix} ll(1-\cos\theta) + \cos\theta & ml(1-\cos\theta) - n\sin\theta & nl(1-\cos\theta) + m\sin\theta \\ lm(1-\cos\theta) + n\sin\theta & mm(1-\cos\theta) + \cos\theta & nm(1-\cos\theta) - l\sin\theta \\ ln(1-\cos\theta) - m\sin\theta & mn(1-\cos\theta) + l\sin\theta & nn(1-\cos\theta) + \cos\theta \end{bmatrix}$$

This expression simplifies somewhat for rotations around the coordinate axes!

Eigenvalues and eigenvectors

It has been shown that in general a matrix will operate on a line with a given vector direction and produce another line with a different vector direction. For any square matrix, however, there are a number of special vectors which will remain unchanged, except for a scale factor, when operated on by the matrix. The vectors which define these **invariant directions** are known as the **eigenvectors** of the matrix and the associated scale factors are the corresponding **eigenvalues**. The theory of eigenvalues and eigenvectors is very important in determining the properties of coupled dynamic systems, which occur frequently in a wide range of applications within electronic engineering.

As a brief example of how to derive eigenvalues and eigenvectors, consider the 2×2 matrix

$$\begin{bmatrix} 1 & -1 \\ 2 & 4 \end{bmatrix}$$

which produces a linear tranformation of the plane. We are looking for scalars λ_1 and λ_2 and associated vectors

$$\mathbf{v}_1 = \begin{bmatrix} a_1 \\ b_1 \end{bmatrix} \qquad \text{and} \qquad \mathbf{v}_2 = \begin{bmatrix} a_2 \\ b_2 \end{bmatrix}$$

For example, the matrix

$$\begin{bmatrix} 2 & 0 \\ 0 & -2 \end{bmatrix}$$

will reflect an object in the X-axis and simultaneously enlarge to an area four times that of the original.

With some algebraic effort, it can be shown that the determinant of this matrix is unity for all values of l, m, n and θ. Hence this rotation matrix will not change the volume of any three-dimensional object that it is applied to.

It is easy to see that eigenvalues are defined only to within an arbitrary multiplying constant: if the vector $\mathbf{v}_1$, is an eigenvector of the matrix **A** with eigenvalue λ_1, then so is the vector $\alpha\mathbf{v}_1$ for any scalar α.

154

which satisfy

$$\begin{bmatrix} 1 & -1 \\ 2 & 4 \end{bmatrix} \begin{bmatrix} a_i \\ b_i \end{bmatrix} = \lambda_i \begin{bmatrix} a_i \\ b_i \end{bmatrix} \qquad i = 1,2$$

or, equivalently,

$$\begin{bmatrix} 1-\lambda_i & -1 \\ 2 & 4-\lambda_i \end{bmatrix} \begin{bmatrix} a_i \\ b_i \end{bmatrix} = 0 \qquad i = 1,2$$

This is a matrix version of a pair of homogeneous equations. The criterion for such a set of equations to have a nonzero solution is that the equations should form a linearly dependent set or equivalently, that the determinant of the matrix should vanish. Applying this criterion to the expanded determinant requires that

$$
\begin{aligned}
(1 - \lambda_i)(4 - \lambda_i) + 2 &= 0 \\
\Rightarrow \qquad \lambda_i^2 - 5\lambda_i + 6 &= 0 \\
\Rightarrow \qquad (\lambda_i - 2)(\lambda_i - 3) &= 0
\end{aligned}
$$

The determinant of this matrix is the **characteristic determinant**, described briefly above. For an $n \times n$ matrix it will, in general, produce an nth-order polynomial, n eigenvalues and n corresponding eigenvectors.

Therefore, the eigenvalues of this matrix are $\lambda_1 = 2$ and $\lambda_2 = 3$. The corresponding eigenvectors are obtained by substituting these eigenvalues into the original matrix equations, one at a time.

Putting the eigenvalue of 2 into the matrix requires that

$$\begin{bmatrix} -1 & -1 \\ 2 & 2 \end{bmatrix} \begin{bmatrix} a_1 \\ b_1 \end{bmatrix} = 0 \quad \Rightarrow \quad a_1 = -b_1$$

which only fixes one of the two parameters within the vector: but the eigenvector is arbitrary to within a constant, and so it is possible to set $a_{11} = -b_1$, ignore the multiplying factor of b_1, and conclude that an eigenvector which corresponds to the eigenvalue of 2 is

$$\mathbf{v}_1 = \begin{bmatrix} -1 \\ 1 \end{bmatrix}$$

Similarly, an eigenvector corresponding to $\lambda_2 = 3$ is

$$\mathbf{v}_2 = \begin{bmatrix} -1 \\ 2 \end{bmatrix}$$

Similar methods can be applied to find the eigenvalues and eigenvectors or larger matrices, but sets of order 3 or 4 are a practical limit for hand calculation. Beyond this, without resorting to a computer program, it becomes difficult to find the roots of the polynomial which arises from the requirement that the determinant should vanish, and then to fix the corresponding eigenvectors.

T4 Differential Equations

A very wide range of engineering systems can be described readily in terms of an assortment of differential equations. Fortunately, similar dynamic effects occur in very different practical systems and it is possible, and useful, to classify differential equations into types (and group them as sets of related types) whose properties can be studied independently of the specific application. Because of this, much work has been performed on studying and classifying differential equations – leading to an impressive set of jargon which it is useful to understand.

General jargon

The word 'ordinary' is used merely to distinguish these types of differential equation from **partial differential equations**, which involve a number of independent variables and are much harder to handle. It is common to omit the word 'ordinary' and simply take it for granted that the equation has only one independent variable unless otherwise specified. Some applications of partial differentiation are discussed in Chapter 5.

Often, in practical systems, the independent variable will be time and the dependent variable some important system output. The differential equation can be thought of as a model for the internal dynamics of the system of interest and the solution of the equation as representing the dynamic response or time response – the behaviour of the output as a function of time.

An **ordinary differential equation** is a relationship between a function $y(x)$ and its derivatives with respect to a single variable x, such as:

$$\left[\frac{dy}{dx}\right]^3 + \tan y + y^{11} = \sin x$$

y is known as the **dependent variable** and x as the **independent variable**.

A differential equation is said to be **inhomogeneous** or **nonhomogeneous** if a term appears that is independent of y. If such a term does not appear the equation is **homogeneous**.

The **order** of a differential equation refers to the highest derivative that appears:

$$\left[\frac{d^4y}{dx^4}\right]^3 + y^5 \sin x = 0$$

is homogeneous and order 4.

The **degree** is the power of the highest derivative that appears in the equation. For example:

$$\left[\frac{d^2y}{dx^2}\right]^3 + \frac{dy}{dx} + \sin y = x$$

is an inhomogeneous differential equation of order 2 and degree 3. Similarly,

$$\frac{dy}{dx} + y = 1$$

is inhomogeneous, order 1 and degree 1.

A **linear** differential equation is one in which all derivatives of y, and y itself, that appear in the equation have power one:

$$\frac{d^2y}{dx^2} + \sin x \frac{dy}{dx} + y = 0$$

is a linear, second-order, first-degree, homogeneous differential equation. Likewise

$$\frac{d^3y}{dx^3} + y = \cos x$$

is inhomogeneous, linear, third-order and first degree, while

$$\frac{d^3y}{dx^3} + y^2 = 0$$

is homogeneous, nonlinear, third-order and first degree. Note that a linear equation must always be of degree one, while a first degree equation is not necessarily linear.

A differential equation of the form

$$a_n \frac{d^n y}{dx^n} + a_{n-1} \frac{d^{n-1} y}{dx^{n-1}} + \dots + a_2 \frac{d^2 y}{dx^2} + a_1 \frac{dy}{dx} + a_0 y = f(x)$$

where the a_i are pure numbers, is a linear, nth-order differential equation with **constant coefficients**.

Linearity and differential equations

Ideally, the solution of an nth-order differential equation would involve n integrations – each systematically removing one derivative. Unfortunately the equation couples the function to its derivatives in a highly complicated fashion and generally such a procedure is not possible. In fact, because of the extreme complexity of differential equations of general order and degree it is common to find most engineering systems being modelled by linear differential equations. This is usually adequate to provide a realistic representation of the properties of practical systems over a wide range of operating conditions. When the system is too complex to be represented well by a linear approximation it is usually necessary to resort to computational methods. The important point about the use of linear equations is that it is possible to exploit the linearity of the equation to apply the **principle of superposition** to the solution of the equation – if several simple solutions to the equation can be found they can be added together as a linear combination (superposition) to build up the complete solution.

For differential equations of order higher than one it is also usual to simplify the analysis by working with constant coefficients within the equation where at all possible. Equations with variable coefficients are much harder to handle and the general theory is beyond the scope of this text. An nth-order, linear differential equation with constant coefficients is capable of being solved fairly readily (for values of n that are not too large), and is still able to simulate the most important dynamic effects within many practical systems.

A specific application example is given in Chapter 4.

The solution of a linear differential equation with constant coefficients will contain, as indicated above, a linear combination of simpler functions. In particular, for an nth-order equation part (or all) of the solution will always be composed of a linear combination of n functions (one for each integration, effectively) and the coefficients (relative weightings) of these solutions are referred to as **arbitrary constants**. It can be shown that when a function is found that satisfies the complete differential equation and contains n arbitrary constants, then it is as full a solution as can be obtained – it is called the **general solution** of the linear differential equation. It is always true to say that the general solution of an nth-order linear differential equation will contain n arbitrary constants, and conversely any solution with n arbitrary constants must be the general solution.

The arbitrary constants provide a family of solutions of the differential equation, just as the arbitrary constant in an indefinite integral allows the value of the solution of the integral to be shifted up or down by a constant. As for an integral, if a **particular solution** is required, it is necessary to give some extra information which fixes a set of specific values for the arbitrary constants. This information is usually given as **initial**

In fact, an indefinite integral is totally equivalent to a specific type of first-order differential equation:
$y = \int f(x)\,dx + C \equiv dy/dx = f(x).$

conditions or **boundary conditions** – a set of specified values of the dependent variable and/or its derivatives at a given value (or set of values) of the independent variable. To fix all of the arbitrary constants within the general solution, n such independent conditions are needed.

First-order differential equations

The most general form of a first-order differential equation is

$$\frac{dy}{dx} = f(y, x)$$

where f can be any function of x and/or y. Because only one integration is involved in the solution of this equation a wide range of types, including nonlinear, can be readily solved. Not all forms of $f(x, y)$ can be handled, however, and the main types of use or interest are listed below. The 'type' numbers are merely for convenience of reference. A series of application examples are given in Chapter 4.

Before reading the suggested approaches to each type of equation, it should be borne in mind that, in general, there are usually a number of ways of solving any given differential equation. The ability to recognize which approach is likely to be the simplest is a skill which can only be obtained by working through a variety of examples and comparing the relative suitability and strengths/weaknesses of the methods under a range of different circumstances.

Type I: $f(x, y)$ = a function of x alone

In the special case when the function is y-independent both sides of the equation can be integrated directly (providing that the integral can be evaluated!):

$$\frac{dy}{dx} = f(x) \quad \Rightarrow \quad y = \int f(x)\, dx + C$$

where C is an arbitrary constant. For example,

$$\frac{dy}{dx} = 4x^3 + 2x \quad \Rightarrow \quad y = x^4 + x^2 + C$$

Type II: $f(x, y)$ = a function of y alone

This type of equation can also be integrated directly, after a slight rearrangement:

$$\frac{dy}{dx} = f(y) \quad \Rightarrow \quad \frac{1}{f(y)} \frac{dy}{dx} = 1 \quad \Rightarrow \quad \int \frac{dy}{f(y)} = x + C$$

For example,

$$\frac{dy}{dx} = -y \quad \Rightarrow \quad \frac{1}{y} \frac{dy}{dx} = -1 \quad \Rightarrow \quad \ln|y| = -x + C \quad \Rightarrow \quad y = A \exp(-x)$$

where A and C are arbitrary constants related by $A = \exp(C)$.

Type III: $f(x, y)$ = u(x) v(y): variables separable

When f can be written as the product of two expressions which are each functions of x and y alone the equation is said to be **variables separable**. It is possible to divide both sides of the equation by $v(y)$ to obtain a form suitable for direct integration of both sides:

$$\frac{dy}{dx} = u(x) \; v(y) \; \Rightarrow \; \frac{1}{v(y)} \frac{dy}{dx} = u(x) \; \Rightarrow \; \int \frac{dy}{v(y)} = \int u(x) \, dx + C$$

Types I and II are just special cases of this type. For example,

$$\frac{dy}{dx} = \frac{\cos x}{y} \; \Rightarrow \; y \frac{dy}{dx} = \cos x \; \Rightarrow \; \tfrac{1}{2} y^2 = \sin x + C$$

Type IV: $f(x, y)$ linear in y

This type covers a large number of equations which arise in practical examples. If f is linear in y the differential equation can be written:

$$\frac{dy}{dx} = Q(x) - P(x) \, y \qquad \text{or} \qquad \frac{dy}{dx} + P(x) \, y = Q(x)$$

where $Q(x)$ and $P(x)$ are any functions of x. The approach with this type of equation is to exploit the fact that the derivative of a product of two functions uv has the form

$$\frac{d}{dx} (uv) = \frac{du}{dx} v + u \frac{dv}{dx}$$

In the special case when $v = y$ this looks rather like the y-dependent portion of the original differential equation. Therefore, the appropriate trick is to find a function $u(x)$ which can be multiplied throughout the differential equation and which leaves the l.h.s. in such a form that it is merely the derivative of the product $[u(x) \; y(x)]$. Effectively, we are requiring that the expressions:

$$\frac{d}{dx} (uy) = u \frac{dy}{dx} + \frac{du}{dx} y$$

and

$$u \frac{dy}{dx} + u P y = u Q$$

should match. This will occur if $du/dx = u \, P$. This is itself a first-order differential equation of type III for the function u and has solution

$$u(x) = A \; \exp[\textstyle\int P(x) \, dx]$$

The idea is to multiply this expression throughout the equation, so that the arbitrary constant A is irrelevant and can be set to unity. The quantity $u = \exp[\int P \, dx]$ which reduces the l.h.s. to product form is known as the **integrating factor**. After multiplication by the integrating factor, both sides of the equation are ready for direct integration. The approach is best illustrated by an example. Consider

$$\tan x \, \frac{dy}{dx} - y = x \sin x \tan x \; \Rightarrow \; \frac{dy}{dx} - (\cot x) \, y = x \sin x$$

so that $P(x) = -\cot x$, and the integrating factor is given by

$$u = \exp\left[- \int \frac{\cos x}{\sin x} \, dx \right] = \exp[- \ln(\sin x)]$$
$$= \exp[\ln|\mathrm{cosec} \, x|] = \mathrm{cosec} \, x$$

It should now be possible to write the original differential equation as

$$\operatorname{cosec} x \ \frac{dy}{dx} - (\operatorname{cosec} x)(\cot x) \, y = x$$

where the difficult-looking l.h.s. is merely the sum of functions obtained by differentiating the product $[(\operatorname{cosec} x)(y)]$ using the ordinary product rule of differentiation. Therefore, integrating both sides of the equation gives

$$(\operatorname{cosec} x) \, y = \tfrac{1}{2} x^2 + C \ \Rightarrow \ y = [\tfrac{1}{2} x^2 + C] \sin x$$

Many of the exotic forms of 'standard' integrals considered earlier arise as integrals within the integrating factor when trying to solve this type of differential equation for practical systems.

Type V: f homogeneous in x and y

This is a different (and totally confusing!) use of the word 'homogeneous' from its meaning in 'nth-order homogeneous differential equations' (as defined in the introductory 'jargon'), which will be covered in detail below.

A first-order equation is said to be **homogeneous** if f can be expressed in the form $f(y/x)$. For example,

$$\frac{x^2}{y^2}, \quad \frac{x+y}{x-y}, \quad \text{and} \quad \frac{x^3 + x^2 y + y^3}{8 \, x \, y^2 - 5 \, y^3}$$

are all expressions for $f(x, y)$ which are homogeneous in form (simply divide through by x^2, x and x^3 respectively in the three expressions).

The approach with first-order homogeneous differential equations is to make the substitution

$$y = x \, z \ \Rightarrow \ \frac{dy}{dx} = x \frac{dz}{dx} + z$$

which reduces the differential equation to the form

$$x \frac{dz}{dx} + z = f(z) \equiv x \ \frac{dz}{dx} = f(z) - z$$

which is now a variables separable (type III) differential equation for the new dependent variable z in terms of x. This equation can now be solved to obtain the solution, relating z and x, as discussed above, and then finally put back in terms of the original variables by replacing every occurrence of z with y/x. For example, the equation

$$\frac{dy}{dx} = \frac{x^2 + y^2}{x \, y} \quad \text{becomes} \ x \frac{dz}{dx} + z = \frac{1 + z^2}{z}$$

after the transformation of variables $y = x \, z$. This simplifies to give:

$$x \frac{dz}{dx} = \frac{1}{z} \ \Rightarrow \ \int z \, dz = \int \frac{dx}{x} + C$$

$$\Rightarrow \ \tfrac{1}{2} z^2 = \ln|x| + C \ \Rightarrow \ y^2 = 2 \, x^2 \ln|x| + 2 \, C x^2$$

as the solution of the differential equation in terms of the original variables y and x.

It is worth stressing that it is not actually necessary to make the substitution $y = xz$ to solve this type of differential equation – very often it is quite possible to use an integrating factor, for example, as an alternative approach. The point is that, if the equation is recognized as being homogeneous in x and y, it will almost certainly be simpler in form and easier to solve using the suggested change of dependent variable.

Type VI: Linear fractional equations

A first-order equation is **linear fractional** in form when it can be written as

$$\frac{\mathrm{d}y}{\mathrm{d}x} = \frac{a\,x + b\,y + c}{A\,x + B\,y + C}$$

for any constants a, b, c, A, B and C. The solution of this differential equation exploits the fact that if c and C were zero it would merely be a homogeneous (type V) equation and could be solved using the usual transformation of variables. The approach is to define new dependent and independent variables which are related to the old variables by a change of origin:

$$X = x - h, \quad Y = y - k$$

In terms of these shifted variables the original equation becomes

$$\frac{\mathrm{d}Y}{\mathrm{d}X} = \frac{a\,X + b\,Y + (a\,h + b\,k + c)}{A\,X + B\,Y + (A\,h + B\,k + C)}$$

so that it is possible to choose the shift factors h and k to satisfy

$$a\,h + b\,k = -c$$
$$A\,h + B\,k = -C$$

which are a pair of linear equations for h and k in terms of the specified constants. These will have a unique solution provided that $a\,B \neq A\,b$. With such a choice for the change of origin, the new equation will now be homogeneous and can be solved as an ordinary type V equation. It is worth pointing out that after progressing through these various transformations of the equation from one form to another and solving the final equation, it is still necessary to put the solution back in terms of the original variables – which are presumably those of practical interest.

If it so happens that $a\,B = A\,b$, then this approach fails, but in such a case the equation can instead be solved by defining a new variable $z = a\,x + b\,y$.

As in this case, it is quite possible for an equation to pass through a number of intermediate stages before taking on a readily manageable form. There should be no problem with relating the final transformed dependent variable to the initial one, however.

Arbitrary constants and initial conditions

All of these types of first-order equation can be solved to give the general solution – a relationship (implicit or explicit) between y and x which involves a single arbitrary constant. The fact that this constant can take on any value means that the general solution is actually a family of possible solutions – corresponding to a range of possible behaviours of the system being modelled under a variety of different circumstances, such as initial current, maximum amplitude of output voltage, etc. Any one piece of such information about the first-order system is enough to fix the value of the arbitrary constant and specify one particular solution as the appropriate one for the given circumstances.

One important application arises, for example, when a system is subject to switching or a sudden change in its internal parameters. In such a case the system dynamics, and hence the nature of the differential equation itself, will change between two operational regions and it is necessary to solve the two equations entirely separately for the different ranges of independent variable for which the equations hold.

Switching and parameter changes in first- and second-order systems are discussed in Chapter 4.

Each solution will contain an arbitrary constant, but the real system will only be specified with one initial condition. Thus, to fix all of the arbitrary constants in a switched system the procedure is to solve the separate differential equations (to obtain a series of general solutions) for all ranges of the independent variable and then 'feed in' the initial condition to the first equation. This fixes the behaviour of the system in the first range and, in particular, gives a unique value for the output at the end of that range of the independent variable. This final condition for the first range can then be used as the initial condition for the next range – since the value of a variable of physical interest (such as position, current, temperature) is not expected to leap suddenly to a different value.

Physically, this is sensible in that a unique and consistent output would be expected from a circuit whatever switching or modifications are performed while the circuit is in operation – all that matters is the conditions under which the circuit is started.

The progress can be repeated at the next interface between operational regions, so that the overall approach is to 'daisy-chain' the value of the dependent variable together throughout all of the different regions of system operation, so that only one initial condition is required to fix any number of arbitrary constants in a switched first-order system.

Second and higher-order differential equations

Broadly, all of the approaches listed above for first-order equations are ways of reorganizing the equation to allow straightforward integration with respect to the independent variable. For general higher-order equations such an approach is nearly always impossible because more than one integration is required and the variables are mixed together in a way that makes reorganization impractical. Because of the increased complexity of higher-order equations, the types used most commonly are linear with constant coefficients.

Homogeneous, second-order linear equations with constant coefficients

These second-order equations form the springboard for the study of more complex cases. The general form of such an equation is

$$\frac{d^2y}{dx^2} + a\,\frac{dy}{dx} + b\,y = 0$$

where a and b are constants. This is the simplest form of second-order equation and is a direct extension of the first-order equation

$$\frac{dy}{dx} + b\,y = 0$$

which has general solution $y = C\exp(-bx)$. Working by analogy, it may be worth while to try a solution of the form $y = C\exp(mx)$ in the second-order equation and see what happens. With this suggested form of trial solution,

$$y = C\exp(mx),\quad \frac{dy}{dx} = m\,C\exp(mx),\ \text{and}\ \frac{d^2y}{dx^2} = m^2\,C\exp(mx)$$

so that substitution of these into the second-order equation gives

$$C\exp(mx)[m^2 + a\,m + b] = 0$$

The characteristic equation is also known in various texts as the characteristic polynomial, the associated equation/polynomial, the auxiliary equation/polynomial, and even the indical equation/polynomial. Likewise, the characteristic roots are also described as associated roots, auxiliary roots, or indical roots. Beware the various conventions and jargon in different texts!

Now, if this form of $y(x)$ is to be a solution of the original second-order differential equation, this expression must be valid for all x. Since $C \neq 0$ (else the solution is the trivial solution: $y = 0$) and $\exp(mx) \neq 0$ for finite values of x, it can be said that:

$y = C\exp(mx)$, for any constant C will be a solution of the second-order homogeneous equation if (and only if) m satisfies the equation: $m^2 + am + b = 0$.

This quadratic equation is called the **characteristic equation**, and the two (real or complex) values of m which satisfy it are called the **characteristic roots** of the differential equation.

The characteristic equation will have two roots, say p and q, generally distinct,

162

which means that it is possible to specify two different (independent) expressions which will each be solutions of the second-order homogeneous differential equation, But, since the equation is linear, if these two independent functions are solutions of the equation, then so is a general linear combination (superposition) of the functions. This means that

$$y = A \exp(px) + B \exp(qx)$$

where A and B are any constants, is a solution of the differential equation. Since this expression contains two arbitrary constants and we are dealing with a second-order equation this must be the general solution of the homogeneous differential equation.

The only way in which the above statements can be invalid is if the roots of the characteristic equation are repeated: if $p = q$. In this case the two solutions derived above are dependent – they differ only by a constant multiplier. It turns out that the solution in this special case is given by

$$y = A \exp(px) + B x \exp(px)$$

where the second function has been modified by the introduction of a multiplying x factor: $\exp(px)$ and $x \exp(px)$ are independent functions of x.

The general procedure for writing down the general solution of a second-order homogeneous equation thus reduces to the steps:

1. Write down the characteristic equation.
2. Solve the equation for the characteristic roots p and q.
3. Write down the general solution as a linear combination of exponential factors:

$$y = A \exp(px) + B \exp(qx) \quad \text{if } p \neq q$$
$$\text{or} \quad y = A \exp(px) + B x \exp(px) \quad \text{if } p = q$$

In the case where the characteristic roots are complex (and thus distinct!) they will appear as a complex conjugate pair: $p = u + jv$ and $q = u - jv$ for some real numbers u and v. This means that it is possible to write the general solution for complex roots in the alternative forms:

$$y = A \exp[(u+jv)x] + B \exp[(u-jv)x]$$
$$\text{or} \quad y = \exp(ux) [C \cos(vx) + D \sin(vx)]$$
$$\text{or} \quad y = E \exp(ux) \cos(vx - \alpha)$$

These solutions are totally equivalent, and each can be readily expressed in terms of another – the only real difference is in the particular role that the pairs of arbitrary constants (A and B, C and D, E and α) play in each case. The third form of the solution is one that is often convenient in electronic applications, since the amplitude, E, and the phase, α, of the solution (which are usually those quantities which are measured experimentally in a practical dynamic system) appear quite naturally.

See Jeffrey (1989) for a proof of this statement and a fuller description of repeated roots with regard to the construction of general solutions by superposition of independent functions.

Examples

The differential equation

$$\frac{d^2y}{dx^2} + 3 \frac{dy}{dx} + 2y = 0$$

has characteristic equation

$$m^2 + 3m + 2 = 0 \quad \Rightarrow \quad (m + 1)(m + 2) = 0$$

The characteristic roots are therefore $m = -1$ and $m = -2$, and the general solution is given by

$$y = A \exp(-x) + B \exp(-2x)$$

Similarly, the equation

$$\frac{d^2y}{dx^2} + 4\frac{dy}{dx} + 5y = 0$$

has characteristic equation

$$m^2 + 4m + 5 = 0 \quad \Rightarrow \quad m = -2 \pm j$$

so that the general solution may be written as

$$y = A \exp[(-2+j)x] + B \exp[(-2-j)x]$$
$$y = \exp(-2x)[C \cos(x) + D \sin(x)]$$
$$\text{or} \quad y = E \exp(-2x) \cos(x - \alpha)$$

Finally, the equation

$$\frac{d^2y}{dx^2} + 2\frac{dy}{dx} + y = 0$$

has characteristic equation

$$m^2 + 2m + 1 = 0 \quad \Rightarrow \quad m = -1 \quad \text{(twice – repeated root)}$$

and the general solution is given by

$$y = A \exp(-x) + B x \exp(-x)$$

Higher-order homogeneous equations

Differential equations of order two are amazingly effective at describing the important properties of a wide range of systems. Very high-order equations are used relatively infrequently.

Homogeneous, nth-order linear differential equations with constant coefficients can be treated in a very similar fashion. The general differential equation

$$a_n \frac{d^ny}{dx^n} + a_{n-1}\frac{d^{n-1}y}{dx^{n-1}} + \ldots + a_2 \frac{d^2y}{dx^2} + a_1 \frac{dy}{dx} + a_0 y = 0$$

corresponds to a characteristic polynomial

$$a_n m^n + a_{n-1} m^{n-1} + \ldots + a_2 m^2 + a_1 m + a_0 = 0$$

which has n characteristic roots. The general solution of the differential equation will be a superposition (linear combination) of n independent functions determined by the form of the characteristic roots. As before, n distinct roots will produce n independent solutions of the form $C \exp(px)$, while repeated roots will require the introduction of modified, independent functions in a similar fashion to that outlined above.

Higher-order equations are harder to handle generally, and at some stage it is necessary to evaluate the n roots of a polynomial – which is going to require computational assistance!

Arbitrary constants and initial conditions

Examples of physical systems involving different sets of initial conditions are given in Chapter 4.

For second- or higher-order systems the general solutions outlined above contain a number of arbitrary constants. Just as before, these constants generate families of solution types depending on the particular values assigned to them. To fix n arbitrary constants it is necessary to specify n additional pieces of information about the system, so that it is not enough just to specify the starting value of y, but also dy/dx and perhaps higher derivatives. Alternatively, the measured values of y at a series of n values of x could be specified. Provided that n independent values are given, the constants will be specified and the particular solution for that set of conditions will have been obtained.

Inhomogeneous, second-order linear equations with constant coefficients

These form the more general class of second-order equations which are of practical utility. The general form of the equation is

$$\frac{d^2y}{dx^2} + a\,\frac{dy}{dx} + b\,y = f(x)$$

where a and b are constants and f is any function of x alone. The general solution of this type of equation partitions into two components:

$y(x) = $ complementary function $+$ particular integral

where the **complementary function** (CF) is the general solution of the **associated homogeneous equation** (i.e. this differential equation with f set to zero) and the **particular integral** (PI) is any single function that satisfies the original inhomogeneous equation. Finding the complementary function is not usually a difficulty, the problem being identical to the homogeneous case discussed above. The awkward part is finding the particular integral – an exact solution of the full inhomogeneous differential equation. One approach is the method of **undetermined coefficients**, which takes a trial form of particular integral containing a number of free constants, which can then be chosen to ensure that the expression satisfies the inhomogeneous differential equation. The undetermined coefficients in the particular integral must not be confused with the arbitrary constants in the complementary function. Several lists of suitable trial functions are given below, and the whole technique is best illustrated by an example.

Function $f(x)$	Suggested trial particular integral
k (constant)	C
$k\,x$	$C\,x + D$
$k\,x^2$	$C\,x^2 + D\,x + E$
nth-degree polynomial	nth-degree polynomial ($n+1$ coefficients)
$k\cos(mx)$ or $k\sin(mx)$	$C\cos(mx) + D\sin(mx)$ or $E\cos(mx-\alpha)$
$k\cosh(mx)$ or $k\sinh(mx)$	$C\cosh(mx) + D\sinh(mx)$
$\exp(kx)$	$C\exp(kx)$

The trial function will be inadequate if a term is omitted that can possibly contribute to the solution or if the trial function (or part of it) already appears in the complementary function. The particular integral must be independent of the complementary function – it is performing a separate task. The usual way around this is to try the simplest form of function which is independent of those appearing in the complementary function. For example, if the characteristic roots are p and q:

Function $f(x)$	Suggested trial particular integral
$k\exp(px)$ $(p \neq q)$	$C\,x\exp(px)$
$k\exp(px)$ $(p = q)$	$C\,x^2\exp(px)$
$k\cos(mx)$ or $k\sin(mx)$	$x\,[C\sin(mx) + D\cos(mx)]$
$(p = jm, q = -jm)$	or $E\,x\cos(mx-\alpha)$

It is easy to see that the sum $y(x) =$ CF $+$ PI is a solution of the inhomogeneous equation. Just differentiate y twice and substitute into the l.h.s. of the equation – only the PI will produce a nonzero contribution, and it has been chosen to produce the desired $f(x)$. Since this solution contains two arbitrary constants (in the CF) it must be the general solution. Jeffrey (1989) gives a very detailed discussion.

This whole range of differential equations, homogeneous and inhomogeneous, with and without initial conditions, can be solved readily using Laplace transform techniques. Laplace methods are used heavily in control theory, communication theory and circuit theory but are beyond the scope of this text. Jeffrey (1989) discusses the approach with regard to differential equations.

The arbitrary constants are fixed by extra conditions imposed upon the solution, while the undetermined coefficients are fixed by the internal structure of the differential equation – they have nothing to do with the initial conditions.

So there can certainly be some difficulty in choosing a suitable form of particular integral to try out. Fortunately, when the function, $f(x)$, is composed of a sum or product of the functions listed above, it is also possible to construct suitable composite trial functions by constructing similarly structured combinations of the suggestions given above. For example:

Function $f(x)$	Suggested trial particular integral
$x + \exp x$	$C x + D + E \exp x$
$\exp(2x) \cos(3x)$	$\exp(2x) [C \cos(3x) + D \sin(3x)]$

Bear in mind that any of these suggested forms may need to be modified to ensure that they are not already included within the complementary function.

Examples

The differential equation

$$\frac{d^2y}{dx^2} - 2 \frac{dy}{dx} - 3 y = \exp(2x)$$

has characteristic equation

$$m^2 - 2m - 3 = 0 \quad \Rightarrow \quad (m-3)(m+1) = 0$$

The characteristic roots are therefore $m = 3$ and $m = -1$, so that the complementary function is given by

$$CF = A \exp(3x) + B \exp(-x)$$

Here, $f(x) = \exp(2x)$, which does not appear elsewhere in the solution so that PI $= C \exp(2x)$ is a suitable trial form. Insertion of this expression into the original (inhomogeneous) differential equation gives

$$4 C \exp(2x) - 4 C \exp(2x) - 3 C \exp(2x) = \exp(2x)$$

so that $C = -1/3$ will give a particular integral for the equation. The general solution is

$$y = A \exp(3x) + B \exp(-x) - \frac{1}{3} \exp(2x)$$

As another example, consider the differential equation

$$\frac{d^2y}{dx^2} + \frac{dy}{dx} = 1$$

which has characteristic equation

$$m^2 + m = 0 \quad \Rightarrow \quad m(m + 1) = 0$$

therefore the complementary function is given by

$$CF = A + B \exp(-x)$$

In this example $f(x) = 1$, so that a suitable particular integral would normally be PI $= C$, but a constant term already appears in the complementary function, therefore it is necessary to try PI $= C x$, which is a form which does not appear elsewhere in the solution. Substitution of this form of PI into the original differential equation gives:

$$0 + C = 1$$

so that the trial function will be a suitable form of particular integral if the undetermined coefficient C is set to unity. The general solution is the sum of the complementary function and the particular integral:

$$y = A + B \exp(-x) + x$$

The point to note about these examples is that the coefficients of the particular integral should be completely determined by 'fitting' it to the differential equation. If it is impossible to obtain a fit, then some component has been omitted from the particular integral, or it has a component in common with the complementary function.

Higher-order inhomogeneous equations

For higher-order inhomogeneous equations the procedure is very similar to that described immediately above for second-order equations. The CF is obtained as the general solution of the associated nth-order homogeneous differential equation, and the PI can be obtained by the undetermined coefficient method as the simplest function which satisfies the full inhomogeneous differential equation and is independent of the components of the CF. For an inhomogeneous nth-order differential equation the general solution should be composed of a CF involving n arbitrary constants and a PI which involves no unknown constants.

Linear differential equations with non-constant coefficients

The many basic types of differential equation discussed above are the ones which are most commonly used for the mathematical simulation of dynamic systems – because of their ease of solution. But their simple structure can act as a limit on the complexity of the system to be modelled. For example, if one or more components of a system gradually change their properties while the system is in operation, the differential equation might take on the form

$$a(x) \frac{\cdot d^2 y}{dx^2} + b(x) \frac{dy}{dx} + c(x)\, y = f(x)$$

where the coefficients of this linear equation are now no longer constant. Even such a simple modification to the equation means that all of the approaches listed above are now useless. However, there is always some way to examine the solution of a differential equation – the methods discussed here have concentrated only on the simplest types.

For example, for this non-constant coefficient differential equation it is possible to use two tools of basic calculus, Leibnitz's theorem for arbitrary orders of differentiation of a product, and Taylor's theorem for the expansion of a function as a Taylor series around a given point, to build up a power series solution to the equation, given only information such as the initial conditions of the system to remove the arbitrary constants. The method hinges on using the differential equation, differentiated n times, to act as a **recurrence relation**, linking the derivatives of the solution in a systematic fashion. It is then possible to evaluate increasingly higher-order derivatives of the function and insert the sequence of derivative values into an (increasingly accurate) Taylor expansion.

A realistic application of this recurrence relation/Taylor expansion procedure is discussed in Chapter 4, p. 86

More complex (and more powerful) analytic, graphical and numerical methods for the solution of more complicated differential equations, and sets of coupled differential equations, are beyond the scope of this text, but in all likelihood they will be encountered in some advanced field of electrical and electronic engineering!

T5 Multivariable Calculus

Generally a function can depend on any number of independent variables: $z = f(u,v, \ldots, x,y)$. Much of the time it is convenient to illustrate ideas with a function of only two or three variables, which can be interpreted easily in three-dimensional space.

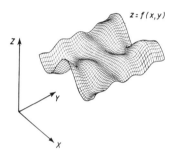

A typical plot of the value of $z = f(x,y)$. As x and y are varied independently a surface is scanned out above the XY-plane. The height of a point on the surface above the point (x_0,y_0) is $f(x_0,y_0)$.

As opposed to an ordinary derivative, which is appropriate to functions of a single variable.

Where $u,v, \ldots x,y$ are independent variables.

The $\partial z/\partial u$ notation is used to distinguish this partial derivative from the ordinary derivative dz/du. As with functions of a single variable, there is no need to retain the bracket describing the explicit functional dependence: but remember that no matter how many times a multivariable function is differentiated, or with respect to what variable, in general the result will still be another function of all of the variables.

Functions and variables

The function $y = f(x)$ relates a dependent variable, y, to the value of a single independent variable, x, by some specific functional relationship. As an extension of this idea a function is said to be **multivariable** if it involves more than one independent variable: $z = f(x,y)$, for example, where z is a dependent variable which is specified by inserting specific values of the two independent variables x and y into the function. Just as it is possible to plot y as a curve above the X-axis in the case of a single-variable function, it is possible to plot z as a **surface** above the XY-plane in the case of a function of two variables.

Just as with functions of a single variable, in practical applications the situation will arise where it is desired to evaluate the rate of change of the function with respect to some variable which has physical meaning, such as time. But the definitions of differentiation given previously are only valid for functions of a single variable: the definitions and methods must be extended.

The full theory of multivariable methods involves the simultaneous use of the tools of calculus, vectors and matrices: only a brief summary is given in this text, although an attempt has been made to derive the less obvious results. Jeffrey (1989) covers most of the topics in more detail. A range of illustrative examples is given in Chapter 5.

Basics of partial differentiation

The **partial derivative** of a multivariable function

$$z = f(u, v, \ldots, x, y)$$

with respect to any one of the variables, say u, is denoted by

$$\frac{\partial z}{\partial u}(u, v, \ldots, x, y) \quad \text{or} \quad \frac{\partial z}{\partial u} \quad \text{or} \quad \frac{\partial f}{\partial u} \quad \text{or} \quad f_u$$

It is defined as the function which is obtained by carrying out an ordinary differentiation of f with respect to u and treating all other variables except u as constants. For a function of n variables there are thus n different first-order partial derivatives: each obtained by differentiation with respect to each one of the variables independently of the others.

Higher-order partial derivatives of a function can be obtained by repeated application of these definitions but, unlike ordinary differentiation, it is possible to obtain **cross-derivatives** of the form

$$\frac{\partial}{\partial u}\left[\frac{\partial f}{\partial v}\right] \equiv \frac{\partial^2 f}{\partial u\, \partial v} \quad \text{or} \quad \frac{\partial^3 f}{\partial u\, \partial v\, \partial x} \quad \text{or} \quad \frac{\partial^3 f}{\partial u^2\, \partial v}$$

as well as higher-order derivatives with respect to just one variable:

$$\frac{\partial^2 f}{\partial u^2} \quad \text{or} \quad \frac{\partial^2 f}{\partial v^2} \quad \text{or} \quad \frac{\partial^3 f}{\partial v^3}$$

Other notations are commonly used: sometimes it is necessary to be explicit about the fact that differentiation is being carried out while other variables are held constant. The notation

$$\left[\frac{\partial f}{\partial u}\right]_{v,x}$$

is used to indicate that the function has three independent variables and that v and x are being held constant while the differentiation with respect to u is being carried out. A more compact notation is

$$f_{xy} \equiv \frac{\partial^2 f}{\partial x\,\partial y} \equiv \frac{\partial}{\partial x}\left[\frac{\partial f}{\partial y}\right]$$

where the function is first differentiated with respect to y, with x being kept constant, and then again with respect to x, while y is kept constant. For most 'well-behaved' functions (it is sufficient that they are continuous) the order of the respective differentiations is irrelevant.

For example, for the function $f(x,y,z) = x^3 \sin y + y/z$,

$$f_x = 3x^2 \sin y \qquad f_y = x^3 \cos y + \frac{1}{z} \qquad f_z = -\frac{y}{z^2}$$

$$f_{xx} = 6x \sin y \qquad f_{yy} = -x^3 \sin y \qquad f_{zz} = \frac{2y}{z^3}$$

$$f_{xy} = f_{yx} = 3x^2 \cos y$$

$$f_{yz} = f_{zy} = -\frac{1}{z^2}$$

and

$$f_{zx} = f_{xz} = 0$$

Geometrically, for the two-variable function $z = f(x,y)$, the partial derivatives can be viewed as the gradients of the tangents to the surface in the directions of the X- and Y-axes. They correspond to standing on a hillside and measuring the slope of the ground on which you are standing in two orthogonal directions. For functions of more than two variables the picture is still valid, but it is necessary to try and imagine measuring n orthogonal gradients on an n-dimensional surface in $(n+1)$-dimensional space!

Total differential: the chain rule

For a function $f(x)$, if x is itself a function of some other variable, t, the chain rule of ordinary differentiation can be rearranged so that the gradient, df/dx, can be viewed as a function which gives the differential df in terms of the differential dx:

$$\frac{df}{dt} = \frac{df}{dx}\frac{dx}{dt} \equiv df = \frac{df}{dx}dx$$

For a function of several variables $z = f(u,v,\ldots,x,y)$ this expression must be extended to the form:

$$dz = \frac{\partial f}{\partial u}du + \frac{\partial f}{\partial v}dv + \ldots + \frac{\partial f}{\partial x}dx + \frac{\partial f}{\partial y}dy$$

where dz is the **total differential** of the function. If each of the variables are themselves functions of a single parameter, say t, this is equivalent to

$$\frac{dz}{dt} = \frac{\partial f}{\partial u}\frac{du}{dt} + \frac{\partial f}{\partial v}\frac{dv}{dt} + \ldots + \frac{\partial f}{\partial x}\frac{dx}{dt} + \frac{\partial f}{\partial y}\frac{dy}{dt}$$

which is known as the **chain rule** of partial differentiation. This expression means that if the independent variables within such a function are themselves functions of a single variable, t, the overall function can be viewed as a single-variable function of t. This equation then provides the tool for evaluating the ordinary derivative dz/dt.

If you are worried about splitting up the numerator and denominator of df/dx it is also possible to think of this as the limit of the expression

$$\Delta f \approx \frac{df}{dx}\Delta x$$

which gives the approximate change in a function produced by a small disturbance in x. With this view it is nearly always mathematically safe to work with individual differentials and think of them as arbitrarily small disturbances.

In this form the expression is very useful for the theory of the effect of a number of small simultaneous changes in the parameters of a system.

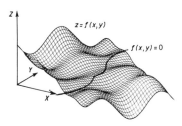

In other words, x and y are no longer able to vary independently; they are connected by the constraint equation.

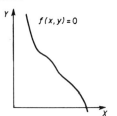

Ignoring the three-dimensional nature of the surface, the curve $f(x,y) = 0$ can be plotted in the XY-plane alone and the tools of ordinary differentiation can be applied to obtain dy/dx.

Note that it is not possible to cancel the differentials within a ratio of partial derivatives as it is with ordinary derivatives: the numerator and denominator of this ratio are gradient measurements taken with different variables held constant, and are already in their simplest general form.

One particularly confusing special case arises when a functional relationship is prescribed in the implicit form $f(x,y) = 0$. This expression has already been considered as a single-variable function and quantities such as dy/dx can be evaluated for such functions by implicit differentiation. It is now possible to think of it as a two-variable function $z = f(x,y)$ combined with a **constraint** equation $z = 0$. In general, a function of two variables will have two degrees of freedom and will generate a surface when plotted in three-dimensional space. When any constraint is added to the function, one of the degrees of freedom is removed: in this case only one will remain and the total effect will be to choose a particular curve within the surface. This curve can be plotted in a plane and subjected to the tools of ordinary differentiation, or it can be viewed as one curve within a larger surface, in which case it is possible to calculate the partial derivatives of the function: the two approaches should be compatible!

If for this two-variable constraint case, x and y are considered to be related by any parameter t, the chain rule would give

$$\frac{dz}{dt} = \frac{\partial f}{\partial x}\frac{dx}{dt} + \frac{\partial f}{\partial y}\frac{dy}{dt}$$

but to satisfy the constraint, z must be kept at zero, so that dz/dt is also zero for all values of t:

$$0 = \frac{\partial f}{\partial x}\frac{dx}{dt} + \frac{\partial f}{\partial y}\frac{dy}{dt}$$

$$\Rightarrow \quad \frac{dy}{dx} = \frac{dy}{dt} \bigg/ \frac{dx}{dt} = -\frac{\partial f}{\partial x} \bigg/ \frac{\partial f}{\partial y} = -\frac{f_x}{f_y}$$

provided that f_y is nonzero. This final equation looks contradictory: an ordinary derivative appears on the l.h.s. while only partial derivatives appear on the r.h.s. The explanation is that this equation relates the value of a gradient measurement made on a curve within the XY-plane to gradient measurements made on a surface which extends out of that plane but contains the curve within it.

Coordinate systems

Multivariable problems arise in a very wide variety of applications, but the commonest are perhaps those involving the position or properties of some object or function in three-dimensional space. The Cartesian coordinate system is suitable for the description of many three-dimensional problems, but many cases arise where other coordinate systems are more suitable. Besides the Cartesian system, the most common three-dimensional coordinate systems are cylindrical polar and spherical polar coordinates.

Cylindrical polar coordinates

These are an extension of the two-dimensional polar coordinate system. In terms of some pre-defined set of Cartesian axes the position of a point (x,y,z) is given by the point (r,θ,z) in the cylindrical system, where the equations

$$\left.\begin{array}{l} x = r\cos\theta \\ y = r\sin\theta \\ z = z \end{array}\right\} \Leftrightarrow \left\{\begin{array}{l} r = \sqrt{(x^2 + y^2)} \\ \theta = \tan^{-1}[y/x] \\ z = z \end{array}\right.$$

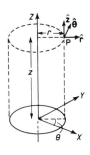

The cylindrical polar coordinate system.

define the geometrical relationships between the two coordinate systems. The angle θ lies in the interval $[0, 2\pi]$. Clearly, cylindrical polar coordinates are merely the planar polar coordinate system augmented by a Z-axis. In this coordinate system the distance of a point from the origin is given by $(r^2 + z^2)^{1/2}$.

Notice that, just as it is possible to define a right-handed triad of fixed unit vectors **i**, **j** and **k** in the directions of the increasing independent variables for the Cartesian system, it is possible to define a right-handed triad $\hat{\mathbf{r}}$, $\hat{\boldsymbol{\theta}}$, and $\hat{\mathbf{z}}$ for this coordinate system which play a similar role. However, in this case, unlike Cartesian coordinates, the triad of vectors changes its position and orientation with the point at which it is positioned. The above coordinate conversion formulae are equivalent to the vector equations

$$\begin{aligned}\hat{\mathbf{r}} &= \cos\theta\,\mathbf{i} + \sin\theta\,\mathbf{j} \\ \hat{\boldsymbol{\theta}} &= -\sin\theta\,\mathbf{i} + \cos\theta\,\mathbf{j} \\ \hat{\mathbf{z}} &= \mathbf{k}\end{aligned}$$

which describe the position-dependent relationship between these two particular sets of basis vectors for three-dimensional space.

Spherical polar coordinates

This coordinate system is designed to be suitable for problems involving spherical symmetry. Three parameters (r, θ, ϕ) are used to specify a point in space, where r is the distance of the point from the origin, θ is the angle between the vector to the point from the origin and the Z-axis, and ϕ is the angle which the projection of that vector onto the XY-plane makes with the X-axis. The Cartesian and spherical polar coordinate systems are related by the equations

$$\left.\begin{aligned}x &= r\sin\theta\cos\phi \\ y &= r\sin\theta\sin\phi \\ z &= r\cos\theta\end{aligned}\right\} \Leftrightarrow \left\{\begin{aligned}r &= \sqrt{(x^2 + y^2 + z^2)} \\ \phi &= \tan^{-1}[y/x] \\ \theta &= \tan^{-1}\left[\frac{\sqrt{(x^2 + y^2)}}{z}\right]\end{aligned}\right.$$

Where $r \geqslant 0$, $\theta \in [0, \pi]$ and $\phi \in [0, 2\pi]$.

If a right-handed triad of mobile basis vectors is defined at each point in space, pointing in the directions in which each coordinate increases, an equivalent set of conversion formulae for vectors in the two coordinate systems is

$$\begin{aligned}\hat{\mathbf{r}} &= \sin\theta\cos\varphi\,\mathbf{i} + \sin\theta\sin\varphi\,\mathbf{j} + \cos\theta\,\mathbf{k} \\ \hat{\boldsymbol{\theta}} &= \cos\theta\cos\varphi\,\mathbf{i} + \cos\theta\sin\varphi\,\mathbf{j} - \sin\theta\,\mathbf{k} \\ \hat{\boldsymbol{\varphi}} &= -\sin\varphi\,\mathbf{i} + \cos\varphi\,\mathbf{j}\end{aligned}$$

These are by no means the only three-dimensional coordinate systems in use, but they are certainly the most common. A conversion between two general multivariable coordinate systems $(p, q, r....)$ and $(u, v, w, ...)$ can be expressed in the form

$$\begin{aligned}u &= f_1(p, q, r, ...) \\ v &= f_2(p, q, r, ...) \\ w &= f_3(p, q, r, ...) \\ &\text{etc.}\end{aligned}$$

for a series of functions f_i. The relevance of the inclusion of the definition of these coordinate systems with the material on multivariable calculus is that whereas the above expressions enable the conversion of coordinates and vectors from one coordinate system to another, they do not allow the transformation of gradient information from one system to another.

These equations can be expressed neatly in a matrix form where the θ-dependent matrix represents the linear transformation between the two coordinate systems. The Cartesian basis vectors are given in terms of the cylindrical vectors by the inverse of this matrix.

The cylindrical coordinate system is most useful for problems involving some axis of symmetry, which can be chosen as the Z-axis.

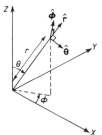

The r and θ in spherical polar coordinates are not the same as those in cylindrical polar coordinates.

As with cylindrical coordinates, the linear transformation between the fixed Cartesian basis and the mobile spherical basis can be expressed compactly as a matrix equation.

Many other coordinate systems exist: a three-dimensional set of ellipsoidal coordinates are used in the theory of molecular structure, for example.

Change of variables

Note that it is the coordinate system that is changed: the object described by the function does not change its nature, but is represented by a different function in each coordinate system. For example, a unit sphere centred at the origin has functional form $x^2 + y^2 + z^2 = 1$ in a Cartesian coordinate system and $r = 1$ in a spherical polar system.

If often occurs that it is desired to relate the differential properties of some multi-dimensional object described by a multivariable function $z = f(u, v, w, ...)$ to those that would be measured in some other coordinate system in which the same object is represented by the function $F(p, q, r, ...)$. It can be shown that (see Jeffrey, 1989)

$$\frac{\partial F}{\partial p} = \frac{\partial u}{\partial p}\frac{\partial f}{\partial u} + \frac{\partial v}{\partial p}\frac{\partial f}{\partial v} + \frac{\partial w}{\partial p}\frac{\partial f}{\partial w} + \dots$$

$$\frac{\partial F}{\partial q} = \frac{\partial u}{\partial q}\frac{\partial f}{\partial u} + \frac{\partial v}{\partial q}\frac{\partial f}{\partial v} + \frac{\partial w}{\partial q}\frac{\partial f}{\partial w} + \dots$$

$$\frac{\partial F}{\partial r} = \frac{\partial u}{\partial r}\frac{\partial f}{\partial u} + \frac{\partial v}{\partial r}\frac{\partial f}{\partial v} + \frac{\partial w}{\partial r}\frac{\partial f}{\partial w} + \dots$$

etc.

are the appropriate transformation equations. All of the derivatives of the form $\partial u/\partial p$ can be obtained directly from the specified relationships between the basis variables in each coordinate system.

These equations can be put into a compact matrix form:

$$\begin{bmatrix} \dfrac{\partial F}{\partial p} \\[2mm] \dfrac{\partial F}{\partial q} \\[2mm] \dfrac{\partial F}{\partial r} \\[2mm] \vdots \end{bmatrix} = \begin{bmatrix} \dfrac{\partial u}{\partial p} & \dfrac{\partial v}{\partial p} & \dfrac{\partial w}{\partial p} & \cdots & \cdot \\[2mm] \dfrac{\partial u}{\partial q} & \dfrac{\partial v}{\partial q} & \dfrac{\partial w}{\partial q} & \cdots & \cdot \\[2mm] \dfrac{\partial u}{\partial r} & \dfrac{\partial v}{\partial r} & \dfrac{\partial w}{\partial r} & \cdots & \cdot \\[2mm] \vdots & \vdots & \vdots & \vdots & \vdots \end{bmatrix} \begin{bmatrix} \dfrac{\partial f}{\partial u} \\[2mm] \dfrac{\partial f}{\partial v} \\[2mm] \dfrac{\partial f}{\partial w} \\[2mm] \vdots \end{bmatrix}$$

where the two vectors of derivative measurements in the two coordinate systems are related by a gradient transformation matrix which is totally independent of the properties of the function being differentiated: it is formed only from the functions which relate the coordinate system $(u, v, w, ...)$ to $(p, q, r, ...)$. This matrix is known as the **Jacobian matrix** of the coordinate transformation and is often written in the shorthand notation

$$\frac{\partial(u, v, w, ...)}{\partial(p, q, r, ...)}$$

A similar set of equations can be written for the conversion from derivatives in the $(p, q, r, ...)$ coordinate system to those in the $(u, v, w, ...)$ system:

$$\frac{\partial f}{\partial u} = \frac{\partial p}{\partial u}\frac{\partial F}{\partial p} + \frac{\partial q}{\partial u}\frac{\partial F}{\partial q} + \frac{\partial r}{\partial u}\frac{\partial F}{\partial r} + \dots$$

$$\frac{\partial f}{\partial v} = \frac{\partial p}{\partial v}\frac{\partial F}{\partial p} + \frac{\partial q}{\partial v}\frac{\partial F}{\partial q} + \frac{\partial r}{\partial v}\frac{\partial F}{\partial r} + \dots$$

$$\frac{\partial f}{\partial w} = \frac{\partial p}{\partial w}\frac{\partial F}{\partial p} + \frac{\partial q}{\partial w}\frac{\partial F}{\partial q} + \frac{\partial r}{\partial w}\frac{\partial F}{\partial r} + \dots$$

etc.

or in matrix form

$$\begin{bmatrix} \dfrac{\partial f}{\partial u} \\[2mm] \dfrac{\partial f}{\partial v} \\[2mm] \dfrac{\partial f}{\partial w} \\[2mm] \vdots \end{bmatrix} = \begin{bmatrix} \dfrac{\partial p}{\partial u} & \dfrac{\partial q}{\partial u} & \dfrac{\partial r}{\partial u} & \cdot & \cdot & \cdot \\[2mm] \dfrac{\partial p}{\partial v} & \dfrac{\partial q}{\partial v} & \dfrac{\partial r}{\partial v} & \cdot & \cdot & \cdot \\[2mm] \dfrac{\partial p}{\partial w} & \dfrac{\partial q}{\partial w} & \dfrac{\partial r}{\partial w} & \cdot & \cdot & \cdot \\[2mm] \vdots & \vdots & \vdots & \vdots & \vdots & \vdots \end{bmatrix} \begin{bmatrix} \dfrac{\partial F}{\partial p} \\[2mm] \dfrac{\partial F}{\partial q} \\[2mm] \dfrac{\partial F}{\partial r} \\[2mm] \vdots \end{bmatrix}$$

For n-variable functions both of the Jacobian matrices involved in these two transformations are $\acute{n} \times n$ and, in fact, they must be a pair of inverse matrices since the effects of their consecutive applications must cancel. It often happens that the partial derivatives of a particular desired coordinate transformation are rather harder to calculate than those for the reverse transformation: it can be convenient to evaluate the easier set of partial derivatives and then calculate the inverse Jacobian matrix if necessary.

For example, if $x = r \cos \theta$ and $y = r \sin \theta$ it is far easier to calculate $\partial x / \partial \theta = -r \sin \theta$ than it is to show that $\partial \theta / \partial x = -\sin \theta / r$. Note in particular that in general

$$\frac{\partial \theta}{\partial x} \neq 1 \bigg/ \frac{\partial x}{\partial \theta}$$

because these two partial derivatives have been evaluated while holding different variables constant in each case.

Linear operators

One concept which eases the manipulation of partial derivative expressions is the idea of an **operator**. Broadly, an operator is any mathematical device that operates on some argument/function and returns a resultant value or function. In this sense multiplication by any number, differentiation and integration are all **operations** on some following function. An operator, L, is said to be **linear** if it satisfies the criterion that

$$L[\alpha f(x) + \beta g(x)] = \alpha L[f(x)] + \beta L[g(x)]$$

when it is applied to any two functions $f(x)$ and $g(x)$ for any constants α and β. With this requirement it is easy to see that multiplication by any function, differentiation, integration and partial differentiation are all linear operators. The key point about operators is that their properties can be studied independently of the functions that they will later be operated on. This means that operators can be written and manipulated without any following function: the manipulation will be valid without it. Examples of valid linear operators are

$$x(\ ) \qquad \frac{\mathrm{d}}{\mathrm{d}x}(\ ) \qquad x^3(\ ) \qquad \frac{\partial}{\partial u}(\ ) \qquad \text{and} \qquad \int_0^1 (\ )\, \mathrm{d}x$$

where the brackets indicate that a suitable function placed in this position can be operated on by the specific operator.

The uses of operators, and of the previous partial derivative formulae, are illustrated by example in Chapter 5. Here it is sufficient to illustrate their use in the derivation of the multivariable Taylor expansion.

As an example of a nonlinear operator consider the operation of raising an input function to any power other than unity:

$$[\alpha f(x) + \beta g(x)]^n \neq \alpha f^n(x) + \beta g^n(x)$$

in general.

The operator $\mathrm{d}/\mathrm{d}x$ is often written as the **D operator** of differentiation and treated as an algebraic quantity. This can be used to simplify the solution of linear differential equations.

Except in the case of integrals, there is usually no need to write such brackets in practice: it is conventional to arrange that the function should appear at the extreme right of most expressions. In cases of ambiguity use the brackets!

Taylor's theorem for two variables

The basic Taylor expansion (Chapter 1) allows the expansion of a single-variable function in terms of a number of measurements of the higher derivatives at a single point. Likewise, for a multivariable function it is possible to build up a picture of the local properties of the function with a multivariable Taylor series, but all partial

The total differentiation operator is often usefully expressed in the more specific form

$$\frac{d}{dx} = \frac{\partial}{\partial x} + \frac{dy}{dx}\frac{\partial}{\partial y}$$

Two points to beware when using operators are that: the order of operations must be maintained at all times, unless the operators are known to commute; and an operator must be treated as a multivariable function for the purposes of differentiation: for example,

$$\frac{\partial}{\partial x}\left[x^2\frac{\partial}{\partial y}\right]$$

$$= 2x\frac{\partial}{\partial y} + x^2\frac{\partial^2}{\partial x\,\partial y}$$

by the product rule. This is because the operator will, in practice, operate on some function and produce a new multivariable function: this must be taken into account when carrying out a differentiation.

If all of the partial derivatives can be calculated analytically it is possible to expand a multivariable function in an infinite n-dimensional polynomial series expansion which is an exact representation of the function.

This series can be truncated after any number of terms to obtain a local approximation to the detailed form of the function in the region of the point (a,b). If the series is truncated after the first-order terms the tangent plane to the surface at that point is obtained: this linearizes every variable of the function. By substituting $h = (x - a)$ and $k = (y - b)$ the expansion can be written in the alternative form

$$f(x,y) = f + (x-a)\,f_x + (y-b)\,f_y + \ldots$$

where all terms on the r.h.s. are evaluated at (a,b).

derivative information up to a given order must be included. This approach will be illustrated for a function of two variables, but can easily be extended to any number.

For a two-variable function $z = f(x,y)$, where x and y are themselves functions of t, the chain rule is

$$\frac{dz}{dt} = \frac{dx}{dt}\frac{\partial f}{\partial x} + \frac{dy}{dt}\frac{\partial f}{\partial y}$$

which can be written in operator form as

$$\frac{dz}{dt} = \left[\frac{dx}{dt}\frac{\partial}{\partial x} + \frac{dy}{dt}\frac{\partial}{\partial y}\right]f$$

where the bracketed term is known as the **total differentiation operator** and is equivalent, in effect, to the operator d/dt. Therefore to calculate higher derivatives of the function z it is necessary to apply the total differentiation operator a number of times to the function f. For example,

$$\frac{d^2z}{dt^2} = \frac{d}{dt}\left[\frac{dz}{dt}\right] = \left[\frac{dx}{dt}\frac{\partial}{\partial x} + \frac{dy}{dt}\frac{\partial}{\partial y}\right]\left[\frac{dx}{dt}\frac{\partial}{\partial x} + \frac{dy}{dt}\frac{\partial}{\partial y}\right]f$$

Now, concentrate on a particular point (a,b) in the XY-plane and consider deviations away from that point of the form $(a + ht, b + kt)$ for some constants h, k and a variable t. Then for this special case

$$z(t) = f(x(t), y(t)) \text{ where } x = a + ht \text{ and } y = b + kt$$

so that $dx/dt = h$ and $dy/dt = k$ and the total differentiation operator is

$$\frac{d}{dt} = h\frac{\partial}{\partial x} + k\frac{\partial}{\partial y} = D_t, \quad \text{say}$$

For d^2/dt^2 since the ordinary derivatives dx/dt and dy/dt are constants as far as the partial differentiation operators are concerned it is possible to expand the **operator product** to give

$$\frac{d^2z}{dt^2} = \left[h^2\frac{\partial^2}{\partial x^2} + 2hk\frac{\partial^2}{\partial x\,\partial y} + k^2\frac{\partial^2}{\partial y^2}\right]f$$

In operator form the single-variable Maclaurin expansion for the function $z(t)$ is

$$z(t) = \left[1 + t\frac{d}{dt} + \frac{t^2}{2!}\frac{d^2}{dt^2} + \ldots + \frac{t^r}{r!}\frac{d^r}{dt^r} + \ldots\right]z(0)$$

so that replacing the occurrences of $z(t)$ by $f(a + ht, b + kt)$, and d/dt by the total differentiation operator D_t leads to

$$f(a+h, b+k) = \left[1 + D_t + \frac{1}{2!}D_t^2 + \ldots + \frac{1}{r!}D_t^r + \ldots\right]f(a,b)$$

for the particular case of $t = 1$.

Using the techniques for expansion of operator products discussed above, this leads in full to the **Taylor series expansion in two variables**:

$$f(a+h, b+k) = f + hf_x + kf_y + \frac{h^2 f_{xx} + 2hk\,f_{xy} + k^2 f_{yy}}{2!} + \ldots$$

where f and all its derivatives in the r.h.s. are evaluated at the particular point (a, b).

As with the single-variable Taylor expansion this formula is extremely useful in a truncated form for the purposes of constructing an approximate function by extrapolation from a limited knowledge of the function properties at a point. It also enables the study of the maxima and minima of multivariable functions.

Multivariable maxima and minima

·When considering the stationary points of a continuous differentiable function of a single variable it is conventional to obtain those points at which the function has a zero derivative and consider the second derivative at those points to determine the nature of the stationary point. If df/dx is zero at a point x_0 then it is generally true that

$$\frac{d^2f}{dx^2} > 0 \;\Rightarrow\; \text{a minimum}$$

$$\frac{d^2f}{dx^2} = 0 \;\Rightarrow\; \text{a point of inflexion}$$

$$\frac{d^2f}{dx^2} < 0 \;\Rightarrow\; \text{a maximum}$$

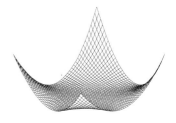

The function $z = x^2y^2$ has a minimum point on the surface above the origin, but is totally flat in the directions of the X- and Y-axes.

although exceptional cases exist. These broad criteria can be extended to the case of multivariable functions, although the number of types of stationary point that can occur is considerably increased.

For a general two-variable function $z = f(x,y)$ the ideas can be extended and stationary points can be viewed as all points on the surface which are locally 'flat': the two partial derivatives f_x and f_y are both zero. The main difficulty lies in identifying the local nature of the stationary point: when viewed along each orthogonal direction it can appear to be a maximum, minimum, a point of inflexion, or completely flat. Clearly, a stationary point can be a maximum/minimum only if it is a maximum/-minimum in both directions: but even this is not necessarily sufficient! It is also necessary to ensure that the function does not behave unexpectedly in between the two orthogonal directions: in general this requires the use of the cross-derivative f_{xy} in addition to f_{xx} and f_{yy}.

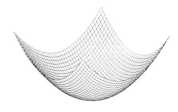

The function $z = x^2 + y^2$ has a single minimum at the origin.

To examine the stationary properties of a function consider its Taylor expansion around a point (a,b), as given above. At a stationary point the first-order terms will vanish and in general it is the quadratic terms of the expansion that will determine the nature of the stationary point for small deviations away from the point:

$$f(a+h, b+k) - f(a,b) \approx \frac{h^2 f_{xx}(a,b) + 2hk\, f_{xy}(a,b) + k^2 f_{yy}(a,b)}{2!}$$

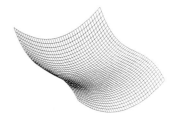

The function $z = x^2 + y^3$ appears to be a minimum at the origin when viewed in some directions, and a point of inflexion when examined along others.

For a true minimum/maximum the term on the r.h.s. must be negative/positive for all sets of small deviations h and k. Fortunately, multiplying that term by $(f_{xx} + f_{yy})$ shows that it can be rearranged:

$$(f_{xx} + f_{yy})(h^2 f_{xx} + 2hk\, f_{xy} + k^2 f_{yy})$$
$$= h^2 f_{xx}^2 + 2hk\, f_{xx}f_{xy} + h^2 f_{xx}f_{yy} + k^2 f_{yy}^2 + 2hk\, f_{xy}f_{yy} + k^2 f_{xx}f_{yy}$$
$$= (hf_{xx} + kf_{xy})^2 + (hf_{xy} + kf_{yy})^2 + (h^2 + k^2)(f_{xx}f_{yy} - f_{xy}^2)$$

where the derivatives are evaluated at (a,b). In this last expression all of the terms are guaranteed to be positive except for the final bracketed term. If this term is positive, then the sign of the quadratic terms of the Taylor expansion will be determined solely by the sign of the sum $(f_{xx} + f_{yy})$. Therefore a true maximum is guaranteed if

$$f_{xx} < 0 \qquad f_{yy} < 0 \qquad \text{and} \qquad f_{xx}f_{yy} - f_{xy}^2 > 0$$

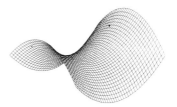

The function $f = x^2 - y^2$ has a saddle point at the origin: when viewed in orthogonal directions the point appears to be a maximum and a minimum.

while a true minimum will have

$$f_{xx} > 0 \qquad f_{yy} > 0 \qquad \text{and} \qquad f_{xx}f_{yy} - f_{xy}^2 > 0$$

while any other combination of signs for these second derivatives will mean that the stationary point has one of the other assorted structures: a saddle point, or any point which is not a true maximum or minimum. In general, a complicated function may exhibit a considerable number of assorted types of stationary points: finding a global minimum or maximum out of potentially many local minima and maxima can be a very difficult process indeed and is the basis of the theory of nonlinear multivariable optimization.

Line integrals

The theory of single-variable integration was used in Chapter 2 to express the arc length of a given curve in three-dimensional space as the integral

$$\text{arc length} = \int_{t_0}^{t_1} \left[\left[\frac{dx}{dt} \right]^2 + \left[\frac{dy}{dt} \right]^2 + \left[\frac{dz}{dt} \right]^2 \right]^{1/2} dt$$

where the coordinates of the curve are expressed in parametric form: $(x(t), y(t), z(t))$. This is, in fact, a special case of a **line integral**:

$$\int_{t_0}^{t_1} f[x(t), y(t), z(t), t] \, dt$$

which is the integral along some particular parameterized curve of the values of a general three-dimensional function along the curve. In general, the value of this integral will change if a different curve of integration is chosen, even when the end points of the curves are the same: the value will be **path-dependent**.

It is possible to split line integrals up into a sum of simpler integrals along only sections of the path: the integral from A to C along a curve is the sum of the integrals from A to B and from B to C along the same curve. It is also sometimes possible to use one of the Cartesian coordinates, say x, as the integration parameter, in which case the integral will collapse to the familiar form of an integral of a function of x.

Line integrals often arise with respect to the total component of some position-dependent vector **F** which acts along some curve in space:

$$\int_{s_0}^{s_1} \mathbf{F}[x(s), y(s), z(s)] . \frac{d\mathbf{r}}{ds} \, ds$$

since the vector $d\mathbf{r}/ds$ is a unit tangent vector to the curve scanned out by the position vector $\mathbf{r}(s)$. Since the ds factors effectively cancel, this is equivalent to the integral

$$\int_{t_0}^{t_1} \mathbf{F}[x(t), y(t), z(t)] . \frac{d\mathbf{r}}{dt} \, dt$$

for any parameter, t, and is usually written in the shorthand form

$$\int_A^B \mathbf{F}.d\mathbf{r}$$

for two points A and B on the curve.

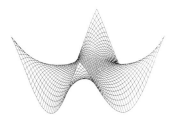

A more complicated function can appear to be a minimum when viewed along two orthogonal directions and seem to be a maximum when viewed in two other orthogonal directions!

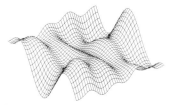

A more realistic representation of a multivariable surface showing that a range of local maxima, minima and other stationary points can combine together in a complicated fashion.

In cases where the integral value is path independent it is then possible to choose a path which goes from A to B in three orthogonal steps and evaluate integrals along three lines which point in the direction of the coordinate axes. The advantage of this is that along these sections of lines only one variable is free: the other two must remain constant and do not affect the integral along that section of the path.

Where s is the arc length measured along the curve (see Chapter T2). The position-dependent component of the vector field is **F** . (d**r**/ds), which can be integrated with respect to s.

If the integration is to be carried out around a closed path it is usually written as

$$\oint_C \mathbf{F} \cdot d\mathbf{r}$$

for some specified closed curve C. Such an integral is said to give the **circulation** of the vector field $\mathbf{F}$.

Some applications require the evaluation of a different form of line integral:

$$\int_A^B \mathbf{F} \wedge d\mathbf{r}$$

which can be treated in a very similar fashion.

Multiple integrals

Another set of important types of integral arise not with regard to the integration of a single-variable function or the integration of a multivariable function along a curve, but from the problem of integration of functions of two or three variables across associated areas or volumes.

Given an arbitrary area in the XY-plane defined by some boundary curve C it is possible to think of extending the ideas of single-variable integration to calculate the integral of some function $f(x, y)$ over the area: the area can be divided up into a set of infinitesimal areas $dx\,dy$ and the integral defined as

$$\iint_{\text{area within } C} f(x, y)\, dx\, dy$$

which is a **double integral**. Likewise, a **triple integral**

$$\iiint_{\substack{\text{volume within a} \\ \text{boundary surface}}} f(x, y, z)\, dx\, dy\, dz$$

can be defined in a similar fashion. The specification of the boundary can take a number of forms: the integral

$$\int_{-a}^{a} dx \int_{-b}^{b} dy \int_{-c}^{c} dz\, f(x, y, z)$$

is particularly simple in form and represents the integral of the function within a rectangular box with sides $2a$, $2b$ and $2c$. In Cartesian coordinates the area of a unit circle centred on the origin is given by the integrals

$$\int_{-1}^{1} dx \int_{-\sqrt{1-x^2}}^{\sqrt{1-x^2}} dy \qquad \text{or} \qquad \int_{-1}^{1} dy \int_{-\sqrt{1-y^2}}^{\sqrt{1-y^2}} dx$$

where, in the first integral, the double integration can be carried out by allowing x to vary throughout its allowed range of $[-1, 1]$ and associating a y integral of 'width' dx with every value of x: the second integral has the order of integration reversed. In the first integral the integration is carried out first along a vertical strip as a function of y alone: along that strip x is a constant and is unchanged by the integration. This is a

$\mathbf{F}$ is known as a **vector field**. The electric and magnetic fields are vector fields. A function which produces a pure number which depends on x, y and z is called a **scalar field**.

The $d\mathbf{r}$ can be thought of as a **vector differential**: it can be broken up into component form as $d\mathbf{r} = \mathbf{i}\, dx + \mathbf{j}\, dy + \mathbf{k}\, dz$, or $d\mathbf{r} + \mathbf{i}\,(dx/dt)dt + \mathbf{j}\,(dy/dt)dt + \mathbf{k}\,(dz/dt)\,dt$.

The ideas can be applied to the integration of an n-dimensional function over some 'volume' of n-dimensional space: two or three variables are enough for current purposes!

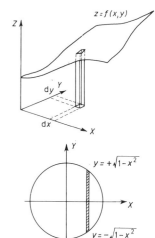

The double integral can be interpreted, for example, as giving the total mass associated with a given shape of a substance with a variable density. Alternatively, it can be seen to represent the volume contained under a section of surface a height $f(x, y)$ above the XY-plane. The triple integral is best viewed as giving the total mass of some volume of gas of a variable density.

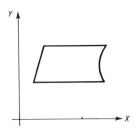

Certain shapes may be easier to handle when viewed from different directions: the illustrated shape would require partitioning into several sub-integrals if integrated first with respect to y, whereas by integrating with respect to x first it can be expressed as one integral with variable upper and lower limits.

Generally, the boundary can be expressed as some constraint equation between x and y: $g(x,y) = 0$. This equation will define (at least) a double function whose lower and upper branches specify the limits of the y integration as a function of x.

In cases where the boundary curves in on itself the integral can be expressed as the difference of two integrals which have simpler boundary structures.

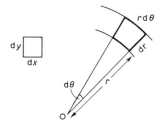

In Cartesian coordinates the infinitesimal area element is $dA = dx\,dy$. In polar coordinates it is $dA = r\,d\theta\,dr$. This relationship follows from the Jacobian of the transformation, as illustrated shortly.

definite integration with respect to y, but the limits are themselves a function of x: the height of the strip depends on its x position across the circle. Hence the overall procedure is to carry out the integration with respect to y, treating x as a constant, and then substitute the (x-dependent) limit for the appearances of y: the result will be an integral which now involves x alone. The second double integral views the area in an orthogonal fashion, which is practically no different in this simple case.

If the integrand involves only a separable function which can be expressed as a product of functions of a single variable, the multiple integral can be split up into a product of single-variable integrals and normal techniques of integration can be used: even though some limits are functions and not numbers. More generally, the integrand will couple the variables together in a complicated fashion and the inclusion of the function limits produces integrals that are beyond normal analytic techniques: it is usually necessary to try to exploit any features of the integral that can lead to simplification of the boundary structure.

The considerable art associated with the evaluation of such integrals arises because of the fact that in realistic applications it often occurs that the boundary of the region is not simple in form. Many techniques are available to attack difficult forms of integrand, and numerical methods can also be employed if necessary, but no methods have been given for coping with a problematic boundary.

Two main techniques prove particularly useful: one is to reverse the order of integration, as mentioned a few lines above; the second is to change the coordinate system in which the integration is to be carried out. For example, the circular area which appears so complicated in Cartesian form is

$$\int_0^1 dr \int_0^{2\pi} d\theta \; r$$

when expressed in polar coordinates. This has a slightly more complicated overall integrand (r as opposed to unity) but a considerably simpler set of boundary conditions. The polar coordinate system is a more natural coordinate system in which to perform integration over a circle: it is almost certainly easier to evaluate such integrals in a polar form.

To convert multiple integrals between coordinate systems it is necessary to take account of
1. the change in form of the boundary (limits)
2. the change in the functional form of the original integrand
3. the change in the form of the infinitesimal area/volume element.

For example, for the area of a circle:

	Cartesian	Polar
Limits:	variable	constant
Integrand:	1	1
Area element:	$dx\,dy$	$r\,dr\,d\theta$

so that the r that appears in the polar integrand can be seen to be associated with a non-uniformity in the area element in polar coordinates, not from the original integrand.

More generally, it is possible to change a multiple integral into a more suitable form by using a coordinate transformation which is contrived to simplify the boundary of the integral. A set of functional relationships can be designed to convert the boundary structure and the functional form of the integrand: to relate the infinitesimal area/volume element it is necessary to use the **Jacobian determinant**:

$$\left|\ \frac{\partial(p,q,r,\ldots)}{\partial(u,v,w,\ldots)}\ \right| = \begin{vmatrix} \dfrac{\partial p}{\partial u} & \dfrac{\partial q}{\partial u} & \dfrac{\partial r}{\partial u} & \cdot & \cdot & \cdot & \cdot \\[2mm] \dfrac{\partial p}{\partial v} & \dfrac{\partial q}{\partial v} & \dfrac{\partial r}{\partial v} & \cdot & \cdot & \cdot & \cdot \\[2mm] \dfrac{\partial p}{\partial w} & \dfrac{\partial q}{\partial w} & \dfrac{\partial r}{\partial w} & \cdot & \cdot & \cdot & \cdot \\[2mm] \cdot & \cdot & \cdot & \cdot & \cdot & \cdot & \cdot \end{vmatrix}$$

The Jacobian matrix was introduced earlier as representing the detailed multivariable geometrical relationship between the gradient measurements made in two coordinate systems $(p,q,r,\ldots)$ and $(u,v,w,\ldots)$. The determinant of the matrix governs the relationship between the n-dimensional infinitesimal 'volumes' in the two coordinate systems.

For example, for conversion from the XY-plane to the polar plane:

$$x = r\cos\theta \qquad \text{and} \qquad y = r\sin\theta$$

$$\left|\ \frac{\partial(x,y)}{\partial(r,\theta)}\ \right| = \begin{vmatrix} \cos\theta & \sin\theta \\ -r\sin\theta & r\cos\theta \end{vmatrix}$$

so that $\quad \mathrm{d}x\,\mathrm{d}y = r(\cos^2\theta + \sin^2\theta)\,\mathrm{d}\theta\,\mathrm{d}r = r\,\mathrm{d}\theta\,\mathrm{d}r$

which shows how the result used above can be obtained. Likewise, using the definitions for the spherical polar coordinate system:

$$x = r\sin\theta\cos\phi \qquad y = r\sin\theta\sin\phi \qquad z = r\cos\theta$$

$$\Rightarrow \quad \mathrm{d}x\,\mathrm{d}y\,\mathrm{d}z = \begin{vmatrix} \sin\theta\cos\phi & \sin\theta\sin\phi & \cos\theta \\ r\cos\theta\cos\phi & r\cos\theta\sin\phi & -r\sin\theta \\ -r\sin\theta\sin\phi & r\sin\theta\cos\phi & 0 \end{vmatrix} \mathrm{d}r\,\mathrm{d}\theta\,\mathrm{d}\phi$$

$$\Rightarrow \quad \mathrm{d}x\,\mathrm{d}y\,\mathrm{d}z = r^2\sin\theta\,\mathrm{d}r\,\mathrm{d}\theta\,\mathrm{d}\phi$$

is the correct weighting to attach to the coordinate transformation.

In summary, to convert a triple integral (for example):

$$\int_{\substack{\text{boundary in } XYZ \\ \text{coordinate system}}} \mathrm{d}x \int \mathrm{d}y \int \mathrm{d}z\ f(x,y,z) = \int_{\substack{\text{boundary in } PQR \\ \text{coordinate system}}} \mathrm{d}p \int \mathrm{d}q \int \mathrm{d}r\ g(p,q,r)\ \frac{\partial(x,y,z)}{\partial(p,q,r)}$$

where $g(p,q,r)$ is the function $f(x,y,r)$ expressed in the new coordinate system.

The application of these techniques is best illustrated by example, and a range of cases are covered in Chapter 5.

Volume integrals can be represented in Cartesian, cylindrical polar, spherical polar coordinates, or a specially designed coordinate system.

For example, the function $f = x^2 + y^2$ takes the form $g = r^2\sin^2\theta$ in spherical polar coordinates.

References

Boctor, S.A., *Electric Circuit Analysis*, Prentice-Hall (1987).

Carter, R.G., *Electromagnetism for Electronic Engineers*, Van Nostrand Reinhold (1986).

Compton, A.J., *Basic Electromagnetism*, Van Nostrand Reinhold (1986).

Desoer, C.A. and Kuh, E.S., *Basic Circuit Theory*, McGraw-Hill (1969).

Dwight, H.B., *Table of Integrals and Other Mathematical Data* (4th edn), Macmillan (1961).

Franklin, G.F., Powell, J.D. and Emami-Naeini, A., *Feedback Control of Dynamic Systems*, Addison-Wesley (1986).

Glenn, J.A. and Littler, G.H., *A Dictionary of Mathematics*, Harper & Row (1984).

Gradshteyn, I.S. and Ryzhik, I.M., *Table of Integrals, Series, and Products*, Academic Press (1980).

Horrocks, D.H., *Feedback Circuits and Op. Amps.* (2nd edn), Van Nostrand Reinhold (1989).

Jeffrey, A., *Mathematics for Engineers and Scientists* (4th edn), Van Nostrand Reinhold (1989).

Lindsay, P.A., *Introduction to Quantum Mechanics for Electrical Engineers*, McGraw-Hill (1967).

Lorrain, P. and Corson, D.R., *Electromagnetism, Principles and Applications*, Freeman (1978).

Meade, M.L. and Dillon, C.R., *Signals and Systems*, Van Nostrand Reinhold (1986).

Nilsson, J.W., *Electric Circuits* (2nd edn), Addison-Wesley (1986).

O'Reilly, J.J., *Telecommunication Principles* (2nd edn), Van Nostrand Reinhold (1989).

Ritchie, G.J., *Transistor Circuit Techniques* (2nd edn), Van Nostrand Reinhold (1987).

Sangwine, S.J., *Electronic Components and Technology*, Van Nostrand Reinhold (1987).

Smol, G. Hamer, M.P.R. and Hills, M.T., *Telecommunications: A Systems Approach*, George Allen & Unwin (1981).

Sparkes, J.J., *Semiconductor Devices*, Van Nostrand Reinhold (1987).

Stephenson, G., *Mathematical Methods for Science Students*, Longman (1961).

Stroud, K.A., *Engineering Mathematics* (2nd edn), Macmillan (1982).

Stroud, K.A., *Further Engineering Mathematics*, Macmillan (1986).

Williams, I.P., *Matrices for Scientists*, Hutchinson (1972).

Answers to Exercises

1.1 $\left. \dfrac{d^2F}{dx^2} \right|_{x=0} = -\dfrac{e\,A\,k^3}{8}$ *(i.e. a maximum)*

1.2 $\left. \dfrac{d^2p}{dR_1^2} \right|_{R_1=R_s} = -\dfrac{E^2}{8\,R_s^3}$ *(i.e. a maximum)*

1.4 $V_C(t) \approx 2.270 + 0.751(t-1) - 1.969(t-1)^2 + 0.184(t-1)^3 + 1.382(t-1)^4$
   $V_C(1.5) \approx 2.263$ V $-\ 0.94\%$ above the current value.

1.5 $\cos(t)\exp(-t) \approx 1 - t + t^3/3 - t^4/6 + t^5/30$

1.7 $\alpha t = \ln \left| \dfrac{2(1-x)}{2-x} \right| + \dfrac{x}{1-x}$ (assuming $x=0$ when $t=0$)

   This solution cannot be expressed in explicit form as $x=f(t)$.

1.8 $\dfrac{dP}{dt} = \dfrac{E^2}{R}\dfrac{\sin(\omega t)}{(1+\alpha t)^2}[2\omega(1+\alpha t)\cos(\omega t) - \alpha\sin(\omega t)]$

1.9 (a) $\sin(t)\exp(-t) \approx t - t^2 + t^3/3 - t^5/30$
   (b) $\sin(3t)\exp(-t) \approx 3t - 3t^2 - 3t^3 + 4t^4 - t^5/10$
   At $t = 0.5$ s the first equation leads to an error of -0.06% and the second to an error of 2.79%.
   At $t = 1$ s the first equation leads to an error of -3.08% and the second to an error of 1664%.

   The second function varies more rapidly than the first [$\sin(3t)$ oscillates at a higher frequency than $\sin(t)$] and hence in general will require a rather higher order polynomial expansion to give a valid approximation over any specified range.

1.10 0.021 J.

2.1 $\overrightarrow{OC} = \begin{bmatrix} 3.30 \\ 0.78 \\ 2.25 \end{bmatrix}$ units

2.2 Control signal (i) is the closest to the received signal.

2.3 The separation is 4031 feet.

2.4 admittance magnitude $= |A| = \left[\dfrac{1}{R^2} + \left[\omega C - \dfrac{1}{\omega L}\right]^2 \right]^{1/2}$

   admittance phase $= \phi$ where $\cos\phi = \dfrac{1}{R|A|}$ $\sin\phi = \dfrac{\omega C - 1/\omega L}{|A|}$

2.5 Closest approach is 1.79 miles at $t = 0.6$ hours (36 minutes). At this time ship one is at coordinates (5, 8.4) and ship two is at (3.4, 9.6).

2.6 The volume of the crystal decreases by 0.033%.
   The three sides are distorted by $8.21°$, $3.85°$ and $4.33°$ respectively.

2.7 (9, 4, 4)

2.8 $Z = R - \dfrac{j}{\omega C - 1/\omega L}$

2.9 $13\exp(-1.18j)\exp(2jt)$

3.1 $I_1 = 4\,\text{A}, I_2 = 2\,\text{A}, I_3 = 5\,\text{A}$.

The $5\,\Omega$ resistor dissipates the most power: 80W.

3.4 $I_1 = \dfrac{850}{356}$ $I_2 = \dfrac{935}{356}$ $I_3 = \dfrac{710}{356}$

3.5 $I_1 = \dfrac{1250}{1107}$ $I_2 = \dfrac{1300}{1107}$ $I_3 = \dfrac{1005}{1107}$

3.6 The equations of Exercise 3.5 are better conditioned.

3.7 $A^{-1} = \dfrac{1}{712} \begin{bmatrix} 132 & 74 & 60 \\ 74 & 117 & 66 \\ 60 & 66 & 92 \end{bmatrix}$ is the inverse matrix of coefficients for Exercise 3.4

and the loop currents for the modified circuit are

$I_1 = \dfrac{231}{89}$ $I_2 = \dfrac{263}{89}$ $I_3 = \dfrac{194}{89}$

$A^{-1} = \dfrac{1}{2214} \begin{bmatrix} 253 & 86 & 75 \\ 86 & 178 & 78 \\ 75 & 78 & 171 \end{bmatrix}$ is the inverse matrix of coefficients for Exercise 3.5

and the loop currents for the modified circuit are

$I_1 = \dfrac{1336}{1107}$ $I_2 = \dfrac{1478}{1107}$ $I_3 = \dfrac{1083}{1107}$

3.8 12.54 W.

4.2 $\dfrac{B^2}{A^2} = \dfrac{V_0^2 \sinh^2\left[\left[2m(V_0 - E)\right]^{1/2} \dfrac{2\pi a}{h}\right]}{V_0^2 \sinh^2\left[\left[2m(V_0 - E)\right]^{1/2} \dfrac{2\pi a}{h}\right] + 4E(V_0 - E)^2}$

$\underset{a \to 0}{\text{Lim}} \left|\dfrac{C^2}{A^2}\right| = 1$ $\qquad$ $\underset{V_0 \to \infty}{\text{Lim}} \left|\dfrac{C^2}{A^2}\right| = 0$

4.3 $V_C(t=0) = -\dfrac{1}{10}\,\text{V}$ $\qquad$ $\dfrac{dV_C}{dt}(t=0) = \dfrac{3}{5}\,\text{Vs}^{-1}$

4.4 $V_C \approx 1 + 2t - \dfrac{6}{2!}t^2 + \dfrac{14}{3!}t^3 - \dfrac{38}{4!}t^4 + \dfrac{86}{5!}t^5 + \dfrac{150}{6!}t^6$

$I = \underbrace{\dfrac{E_0[R\sin(\omega t) - \omega L\cos(\omega t)]}{R^2 + \omega^2 L^2}}_{\text{steady state}} + \underbrace{\dfrac{\omega L E_0}{R^2 + \omega^2 L}\exp\left[-\dfrac{Rt}{L}\right]}_{\text{transient}}$

4.7 $I = -3.2\exp(-2t) - 25.6\exp(-8t) + 1.6\sin(5t) + 8.96\cos(5t)$

4.8 $\omega_n = 4\,\text{rad s}^{-1}$ The circuit is overdamped and resonance cannot occur.

4.9 $L\dfrac{d^2q}{dt^2} + R\dfrac{dq}{dt} + \dfrac{1}{C}q = E_0\cos(\omega t)$

$m\dfrac{d^2x}{dt^2} + r\dfrac{dx}{dt} + k\,x = F_0\cos(\omega t)$

Charge can be compared to displacement.
Inductance can be compared to mass.
Resistance can be compared to viscous retardation.
Inverse capacitance can be compared to the spring strength.
Electromotive force can be compared with mechanical force.

5.1 $\dfrac{d^2y}{dx^2} = -\dfrac{a^2}{y^3}$

5.2　$\displaystyle \frac{\partial^2 p}{\partial R_1^2}\bigg|_{\substack{R_1 = R_s \\ X_1 = -X_s}} = -\frac{|E|^2}{8R_s^3}$

$\displaystyle \frac{\partial^2 p}{\partial X_1^2}\bigg|_{\substack{R_1 = R_s \\ X_1 = -X_s}} = -\frac{|E|^2}{8R_s^3}$

$\displaystyle \frac{\partial^2 p}{\partial R_1\,\partial X_1}\bigg|_{\substack{R_1 = R_{ss} \\ X_1 = -X_s}} = 0$

5.3　It is easiest to minimize the square of the distance. The closest approach of the trajectories is 1462 feet.

5.5　$\displaystyle \mathbf{E} = \frac{p}{4\pi\epsilon_0}\ \frac{1}{[x^2 + y^2 + z^2]^{5/2}}\begin{bmatrix} 3xz \\ 3yz \\ 2z^2 - x^2 - y^2 \end{bmatrix}$

5.6　$\displaystyle \Delta V(1+\Delta x,\ 4+\Delta y,\ 8+\Delta z) \approx -\frac{p}{4\pi\epsilon_0}\ \frac{1}{19683}\,(8\,\Delta x + 32\,\Delta y + 37\,\Delta z)$

5.8　5.625 C

5.9　0.00296 A

Index

In general, the page references given in this index refer to first or main appearance of a particular topic in the mathematical toolkit section of the book. References to mathematical topics which are introduced or discussed in the main chapters are also included but no attempt has been made to index the many specific applied subjects such as 'circuit analysis' which appear with such frequency in the application examples.

191